Essays
in the
History
of
Embryology
and
Biology

ESSAYS
IN THE
HISTORY
OF
EMBRYOLOGY
AND
BIOLOGY

JANE M. OPPENHEIMER

THE M.I.T. PRESS

MASSACHUSETTS INSTITUTE OF TECHNOLOGY
CAMBRIDGE, MASSACHUSETTS,
AND LONDON, ENGLAND

Preface

THE Western view would have it that the essential contribution that one can make to history is by doing, or by
thinking or expressing thoughts that lead to doing. Some of
us who cannot aspire to the making of history may still enjoy
thinking or reading about those who are making or who have
created it.

There are various methods of encouraging such interest.
For embryologists, indubitably the best is that followed twice
by Howard Adelmann: once, in 1942, in what then seemed
a long book on Fabricius; more recently, in 1966, in a five-
volume treatise on Malpighi and his predecessors and followers that dwarfs the one on Fabricius. What distinguishes
the studies by Adelmann is not size but motive. He has returned to recently unread original sources; he has made them
accessible to us, and has made them intelligible in the light
of their own and our past and present.

It is not given to us all to produce works of the accuracy
and magnitude of Adelmann's. Nonetheless, a number of us
who are working embryologists feel that our life in our laboratories is made more meaningful to us when we know something about our intellectual forebears, albeit at a more
superficial level than Adelmann's. It is to such workers in
developmental biology that the essays to follow are addressed.

The order in which they appear here deserves a word of comment. They are presented more or less in reverse chronological order with respect to their content, since it is my belief that we understand our contemporaries more clearly than our earlier predecessors, and our near-contemporaries better than those from whom time separates us farther. The design of the volume is thus intended to conduct us from what we know best toward what we see only more dimly.

The great majority of the articles have been written in response to invitations by colleagues to lecture or to contribute to compendium volumes. I am grateful for their encouragement; without it the essays would not have been written. They are reprinted almost exactly as originally published elsewhere, except for minor changes in the format of the acknowledgments. They have been variously written at Bryn Mawr College, at Yale University, the University of Rochester, Brown University, and the Stazione Zoologica, Naples. I am in debt to all of these institutions, not least to those that have had no formal obligation to support my work yet have given me space and leisure to think and write.

During the course of preparing a number of these articles, and other writings too, Professor Ernst Berliner of Bryn Mawr College has been unfailingly kind in helping me with translations from the German. The original editors and publishers of the articles (the latter named in the acknowledgments that accompany each essay) have been generous in granting permission to reprint them.

I repay my greatest debts by dedicating this collection of thoughts to the memory of my father, Dr. James H. Oppenheimer, who first led me into the ways of the mind and of science, and to that of Professor John S. Nicholas, who finally focused my interests on embryology and its history.

JANE M. OPPENHEIMER

Bryn Mawr, Pennsylvania
August, 1966

Contents

vii

CONTENTS

CONTENTS

Embryological Concepts in the Twentieth Century[1]

I. INTRODUCTION

IT was an embryologist who wrote that "Die Madonna della Sedia nimmt sich auf 1 cm Entfernung mit der Lupe betrachtet auch anders aus, als auf 5 m Distanz. Das erste Mal sehen wir nur Klexe," and who then raised the question: "Ist denn das Studium von Klexen wirklich die einzige Aufgabe des Biologen?"[2] (Driesch, 1894, p. 163). An intellectual historian concerned with the history of biology might well ask himself a similar question with respect to the subject or object of his studies, substituting the parameter of time for that of space, and he might justifiably regard as formidable the difficulties of establishing the interrelationships of ideas evolving during the period which includes his own development. If, however, there is any truth in the so frequently repeated truism that the ideas of the present can properly be understood only in the light of their precursors, in the same manner that an event in the development of an embryo can be fully com-

[1] An expansion of an address by the same title delivered as part of the Presidential Symposium of the American Society of Zoologists at the meetings of the American Institute of Biological Sciences in East Lansing, Michigan, in September, 1955. Reprinted from *Survey of Biological Progress*, Vol. III, 1957, pp. 1–46. Academic Press Inc., New York, N.Y.

[2] The *Madonna of the Chair* examined with a lens at a distance of 1 cm shows up quite differently than at 5 m away. The first time we see only blotches. Is then the study of blotches really the only task of the biologist?

prehended only in terms of the previous events which have led up to it, there is no period to which it is more desirable for the practicing scientist to apply the techniques of intellectual history than the stage immediately preceding his own.

For embryology, at least, there has been no dearth of preliminary attempts to trace sequences of ideas from the time of antiquity towards the 1900's (Bilikiewicz, 1932; Needham, 1934; Meyer, 1939; Oppenheimer, 1955a). The development of specific concepts of morphogenesis within the 20th century has also recently been treated most thoughtfully by Seidel (1955) and by Bautzmann (1955) in lectures presented at a 1954 meeting of the Gesellschaft Deutscher Naturforscher und Ärzte. The task at hand therefore might seem to simplify itself to the further pursuit into the middle of the 20th century of the same concepts that have been followed into the 19th.

While the difficulties of acquiring perspective on contemporary ideas are obvious — in fact, perhaps because they are obvious — they are not insuperable. One need only remember, to pass for a moment into other fields, Einstein and Freud, the impact of whose ideas can at midcentury surely be estimated with considerable accuracy. Now these are extreme examples, to be sure. Embryology has never bred any counterparts of Einstein and Freud, and questions concerning the sphere of influence of ideas originating from particular embryologists can be framed only with reference to lesser luminaries than these. But if the skies of embryology have lacked such suns, they have been decorated by a number of stars of the first magnitude. For the sake of attempting to estimate how their successors a half century later may have reacted to their contributions, let us return for a moment to some of the investigators who shone in embryology towards the beginning and the end of the 19th century.

Pander was almost certainly appreciated 50 years after his prime in quite the same way in which we value him now: witness Kölliker, who wrote in 1861 (pp. 8–9):

PANDER'S . . . Untersuchungen . . . geben nicht nur eine genauere Geschichte der allerersten Entwicklung des Hühnchens, als man sie bisher besass, sondern waren vor Allem dadurch von grösster Tragweite, dass durch dieselben zum ersten Male die ursprünglichen, von WOLFF geahnten Primitivorgane, die der Entwicklung der Organe und Systeme zu Grunde liegen, durch die Beobachtung nachgewiesen wurden. PANDER unterscheidet an der Keimhaut des Hühnereies schon in der zwölften Stunde der Bebrütung zwei Schichten, eine äussere . . . und eine innere . . . zwischen welchen dann später noch eine dritte Lage . . . sich entwickelt. Obschon nun PANDER diese Blätter als den Ausgangspunct aller spätern Organe betrachtet, so hat er sich doch über ihre Umwandlungen und ihre Bedeutung im Ganzen genommen nur sehr kurz ausgesprochen und wären wegen des Aphoristischen seiner Darstellung seine Angaben wohl nicht so bald zu einer grösseren Bedeutung gelangt, wenn dieselben nicht in v. BAER einen Förderer und theilweise auch einen Vertreter gefunden hätten, der es verstand, der Blättertheorie in den weitesten Kreisen Eingang zu verschaffen.[3]

Haeckel, in contrast, fifty years after his moment in history was certainly evaluated quite differently than we interpret him today; Kerr in a brief history of the germ layer theory published in 1919 could write (p. 506) of the *Gastraea* theory quite factually and uncritically that:

Haeckel . . . about the same time as Lankester also developed the idea that the diploblastic stage of ontogeny was to be interpreted as the repetition of an ancestral form: Haeckel called this ancestral form *Gastraea*. The main difference between Haeckel's view and Lankester's was that the former regarded the endoderm as having arisen by a

---

[3] Pander's investigations not only present a more exact history of the earliest development of the chick than was previously available; but they were of the greatest importance since it was through these studies that the primitive organs, foreseen by Wolff, which lie at the basis of the development of later organs and tissues, were for the first time authenticated by observation. Pander distinguished two layers in the blastoderm of the chick, an outer . . . and an inner . . . between which a third layer . . . later develops. Although Pander considered these layers as the point of origin of all later organs, yet he expressed himself only very briefly concerning their transformations and general significance; and because of the aphoristic manner of his presentation his statements would not so soon have attained their great significance had they not found in von Baer a promoter and partly an advocate who understood how to bring the layer theory into fashion in the widest circles.

process of invagination — as it actually does arise in ontogeny in the great majority of cases — while Lankester regarded it as having arisen by a process of delamination from the outer layer.

He terminated his historical discussion of the establishment of the germ layer theory (published, it may be noticed, the year after Spemann's first exhaustive communication on the relationships of the layers during gastrulation) with only a single and rather insignificant reservation: "The author regards as the chief qualification of the germ layer theory indicated by modern work . . . that the boundary between two layers where they are continued into one another must be regarded not as a sharply marked line but as a more or less broad debatable zone" (Kerr, 1919). It is an interesting and perhaps meaningful fact that the view expressed a half century later concerning the contribution of Pander, who flourished early in the 19th century, has changed less during the ensuing years than the evaluation, after an approximate half century, of Haeckel who worked closer to our own time; clearly the passage of time as measured in years is not the only factor involved in the acquisition of historical perspective.

The choice of Pander and Haeckel for examples has not been haphazard. These investigators are appropriate as illustrations since they can be said, in a qualified simplification, to have represented in a way the beginning and the end of the development of the germ layer theory that dominated the embryology of the 19th century: Pander the beginning, since he first put on a sound observational basis what Wolff had extracted from natural philosophy; Haeckel the end, since he stretched what had been observed by his time into a theoretical framework so taut that whatever tenuous relations might otherwise have been maintained between the germ layer concept and biological reality were severed as a result of its artificial overextension.

If maintaining an attitude of reverence for the germ layers seems to us from our vantage point to represent a prevailing

4

intellectual habit of a majority of 19th century embryologists, what often appears to us to exemplify the equivalent frame of mind at the turn of the century is the outlook which characterized the investigators who followed soon after Haeckel — Roux, Driesch, Herbst, Boveri, O. Hertwig, Spemann, and Harrison; and we often say glibly of these, that they modernized embryology by making it experimental. The implication is thus very frequently drawn that the embryology characteristic of the 19th century was static, as contrasted with the more dynamic developmental physiology of the 20th. There is a strong fallacy in this argument which ignores the very evident facts that Pander and von Baer were just as profoundly concerned with change as we are today, and that those later 19th century investigators who patiently developed the germ layer theory had themselves a broad general background and a consequent wide variety of embryological interests. The customary and frequent opposition of 19th century embryology as morphological to that of the 20th century as experimental is further misleading in that it accentuates the use of the experimental method as an end in itself rather than as an adjunct to the descriptive method which deals with the more obvious embryonic features. It confuses the content of what was studied with the manner of its studying, and quite obscures what may well prove to be a much more incisive distinction between the exertions of this science as carried out before and after the turn of the century.

First to concentrate briefly on method, it might to some persons seem a closer approximation to accuracy to generalize that the methods of the 19th century were descriptive, while those of the 20th are analytical, and that a difference between the 19th century and the 20th may be that the latter has penetrated beyond the horizons of the former through the elaboration of special techniques. This contention may well hold true for many fields of biology, but it is not adequate for the case of embryology.

In the first place, the application of the new experimental method to embryology was initiated considerably earlier in the 19th century than is commonly admitted. It is no secret (Schleip, 1929), though it is not commonly bruited about, that in 1869 Haeckel himself, with whom Roux was to start studying the following year, published the results of experimental division of siphonophore larvae, demonstrating that half-larvae were able to form whole organisms. But if initiation of the experimental method, so often said to be the special contribution of the innovators of the changed embryology, was both possible and actual a third of the way back into the 19th century, this is not the only example where the specific chronology of events distorts our perspective. A further complication is that the methods used by experimental embryologists well into the 20th century in their stark and beautiful simplicity were essentially 19th century methods. Roux killed the frog's blastomere by a cautery needle in fact as brutal as the amputation iron of Paré; and what were the first tools of Spemann but a lens, a dish, and a loop of hair?

If a clear division between the methods of 19th century and 20th century embryology seems blurred by such considerations, it is possible that a sharper line can be drawn between the two periods by considering the nature of the problems investigated during the two periods. It might be held that the 19th century was more single-minded; and viewed retrospectively this may be a greater significance of the 19th century germ layer theory than that it was established by morphological techniques. The investigators in the 19th century, sprung as they were from *Naturphilosophie,* were inspirited with an idea which became the germ layer theory, a concept recognizable as such even to those who have difficulty in defining concepts in biology; and this doctrine, subject as it became through the efforts of Haeckel to the unifying control of the evolutionary concept of Unity of Descent, was a centralized and centralizing concept for the whole century, losing

6

little of its sovereignty in 19th century embryology even after the general acceptance of the cell theory and even though much other embryological work of varied nature was completed.

The investigators at the turn into the 20th century, in contrast, no longer centered their efforts on one focus. It is the essence of 20th century embryology that it has not limited itself, until fairly recently, to concentration on a single specific idea. Its earliest workers were astonishing at the first for their widening curiosity. True, at the backs of their minds lay the problem of progressive differentiation, but here they differed little from their predecessors of the 19th century or of all the centuries since Aristotle. The great difference became that their questions were more eclectic and thus provided a strong revitalizing impulse towards the production of new ideas, for the solution of which they invented transitory not permanent technical approaches. What does a blastomere do in the absence of its sisters? How does an embryo develop when you cut off its tail? What happens when you shake an egg to pieces? or if you cut away some of its protoplasm? or if you whirl it around or turn it upside down? or if you put it into a solution as improbable of developmental significance as lithium? It was a hallmark of the work of the turn of the century that when the new experimental method was turned toward devising a crucial experiment, the question to be answered was one that had been framed earlier by older and other methods (e.g. Harrison's introduction in 1907 of the tissue culture technique to verify a former hypothesis that the neuroblast is the source of the outgrowing axone); otherwise the inquiries were at the start to a considerable degree undirected.

Roux himself, to be sure, might not have concurred with this interpretation, and it is not to be denied that he and others of his time were men of ideas. Great volumes of theoretical discussion poured from his own pen and from that of Driesch, and Roux as well as Driesch eventually abandoned

7

actual experimentation in favor of theorizing. But while the Roux-Weismann theory, for instance, stimulated considerable attention to the possibilities of its experimental confirmation or invalidation, this theory never matched the intellectual dominance attained by the germ layer theory before it, and it remained a proclivity of a majority of the early experimentalists that they were men of many ideas and not just a single one. And even when the contemporaries and immediate followers of Roux and Driesch started their experiments out of theoretical considerations, it is quite possible that they often forgot their ideas in their joy at being able at last to play with the embryo as they would. No one who has ever operated on a living embryo can ever believe but that when the early experimentalists carried out their manipulations they did so in large part because of their sheer pleasure in doing so. Whatever their motivation, it can hardly have worked to the detriment of embryology that they diversified their interests instead of concentrating them, since thereby they opened the many new avenues of investigation whose divergence characterizes the entrance to the modern scene.

The fact remains, however, that the generalization of the early experimental results on a profound theoretical level had to await the passage of approximately a third of the 20th century. Spemann's (1936, 1938) Silliman Lectures at Yale, which looked somewhat in the direction of the past, and Harrison's (1945) address at the Harvard Tercentenary, which faced squarely into the future, were not delivered until the 1930's (in 1933 and 1936, respectively; Harrison's Silliman Lectures, delivered in 1949, have not yet appeared in print).[4] Pantin (1955) has recently set 1918 as the date for biology's breaking of tradition with its morphological past. For em-

4 Harrison's Silliman Lectures were entitled "Organization and Development of the Embryo." The titles of the six individual lectures were: Introduction; The Egg and Early Stages of Development; Autonomy and Mutual Dependence of Cells; The Nervous System; The Symmetry of Organisms; and Development and Growth in Complex Systems.

bryology, the change was a gradual one, from 1869 through to the 1930's, and it may or may not be significant that the midpoint of the transition was passed close to the turn of the century.

It is quite often said, by those who try to outline the methods by which science operates, that a first phase in its development consists of the observation of data, a second, of their classification, and that there finally follows an inquiry into their relationships. If there is any single generalization that can be safely formulated concerning the history of embryology as a whole, it is probably that this science has carried out all these procedures simultaneously at all phases of its development, from the time of Aristotle through to our own.

It can be argued, on the other hand, that embryos were first studied as whole organisms (Aristotle, Fabricius, Harvey, Malpighi, Wolff), then in terms of their constituent layers (Wolff, Pander, von Baer, His, Haeckel, Spemann), next in relationship to their constituent cells (Roux, Driesch, all the students of cell lineage, Spemann, Harrison), and finally with reference to the components of cells, through the 19th century largely nuclear (O. Hertwig, Boveri) though in some cases visible cytoplasmic inclusions were also investigated (Boveri, E. B. Wilson, Conklin). It is hardly necessary to point out that the 20th century continues the process by describing and analyzing both the visible and invisible nuclear and cytoplasmic elements of the cell in terms of their constituent molecules.

The integrative powers of the embryo, at all of its levels, are however so pervasive that they never permit themselves to be overlooked by those who avail themselves of the privilege of looking at the embryo at all. The result has been that when each of the practices just enumerated became fashionable, the previous one was never completely outmoded; and when, at each stage of its development, embryology has added a new dimension to its studies, it has never wholly discarded the old ones. Spemann, for instance, who analyzed the relations

9

between layers in terms of cellular interactions, never lost sight of the whole embryo. These effects have, as a matter of clear cold fact, been cumulative throughout the centuries, with the result that even in the 20th century the embryo is still being actively investigated at all of its levels: as a whole, in terms of its layers, of its cells, and of their microscopic and submicroscopic constituents. Selected aspects of studies carried out at all of these levels will be taken up briefly in the main text to follow.

II. THE WHOLE EMBRYO

While the contributions of Roux and Driesch possess too many virtues for individual commendation, it may be pointed out here that one of the principal merits of both investigators was that when they considered the action of a particular part of the embryo, they both referred that action, different though this was construed to be according to the interpretation of each, to the whole embryo. The fact that both of them remembered the embryo in its entirety remained eminently influential on subsequent workers during the first two or three decades of the 20th century; and it was in terms of the whole embryo that the two principal overt attempts of the early part of the century towards the formulation of generalizing concepts were expressed. I refer to the concepts of the axial gradient, as developed by Child and his adherents; and of the organizer, as developed by Spemann and his followers (see Bautzmann, 1955, for an extended statement of the history and the present status of the organizer concept).

These two concepts were in many ways, as expressed by their originators, highly disparate. The organizer concept was designed as an interpretation of phenomena peculiar to rather specific stages of embryonic development; the axial gradient concept, which originally grew out of studies of regeneration, was extended later to cover phenomena characteristic of many phases not only of morphogenesis but of the whole life cycle. The organizer concept, though transcending in implication the limits of any particular taxonomic category, was developed almost exclusively as a result of experimentation on a specific group, the vertebrates; the data adduced in support of the axial gradient concept were drawn from observations on a far greater range of biological forms. The organizer concept, at least as developed by Spemann, tended on the whole to account for regional differences, at least within the medullary plate, on a qualitative basis, though to be sure some later devotees of the organizer concept, for whom Dalcq (Dalcq and Pasteels, 1937) might be considered as spokesman, modified this view to consider that the vertebrate axis produces its diversity as a result of quantitative variation in the distribution of a single substance. The axial gradient concept, from its birth to its demise, never deviated from its conviction that axial differences in an organism are to be explained exclusively on a quantitative basis.

The patrons of these concepts were well aware of the discrepancies between their rival interpretations, and were in fact rather strongly critical of each other, Spemann (1938, Chapter XVI) somewhat philosophically, Child (1946) in fairly tart polemics. Yet though both workers might have hesitated to admit it, their concepts shared in many respects both heritage and effect, and some of their common features may well be considered as illustrative of the mode in which these theories of the beginning third of the century intermediated between the concepts of the 19th century and the problems that are being experimentally investigated today.

The concepts both of Spemann and Child stemmed ultimately from the same roots in the concept of polarity. It is astonishing that the early history of ideas concerning polarity has never been comprehensively treated for the animal egg (see Harrison, 1945, for a brief summary and some key references). Unfortunately the background for this concept is too broad to be adequately covered here. The nature of polarity was an enigma which fascinated the romantic biologists of the 18th and 19th centuries, and polar differentiation seems first to have been discussed with respect to the animal egg by von Baer, who was himself often strongly influenced by romanticism. Driesch too was vastly concerned with polarity, and he considered it, almost certainly under the influence of electromagnetic field theory, first in terms of the orientation of the blastomeres themselves ["Man denke sich jede Blastomere als Magneten oder auch mit zweifacher Elektrizität geladen, so hat man ein Bild der Sache"[5] (Driesch, 1894, p. 22)], finally in terms of a directed polar orientation of the smallest components of the plasma ["Den Richtungsbau hat man als blosse Polarität, meinetwegen im Bilde als elektrische Polarität der kleinsten Teile, zu denken,"[6] (Driesch, 1894, p. 100)]. Boveri, always one of the profoundest of his contemporaries in embryological wisdom, went beyond Driesch; while he also referred the polar qualities of the egg to the properties of its minute constituents, he drew attention to a visible stratification of demonstrable elements in the egg (Boveri, 1901), and he introduced as its explanation the concept of the gradient, "Gefälle" (Boveri, 1910), evoking at least on the basis of qualitative evidence the possibility of a quantitative distribution of some entity or entities as appertaining to the structural and functional differences in the egg along the axis joining its two poles.

The question of the extent to which Child and Spemann were individually obligated to Boveri is an interesting and a puzzling one. Child in his fullest treatment of his interpretations freely acknowledges Boveri's priority in postulating the idea of a gradient (Child, 1941, p. 700):

[5] One might think of each blastomere as a magnet or as provided with opposite electrical charges, then one would have a picture of the state of affairs.

[6] One has to consider orientation-structure as plain polarity, in my opinion as an image of electrical polarity of the smallest parts.

The frequency with which the suggestion that physiological polarity is a gradation or gradient pattern of some sort or a stratification of substances has appeared in biological literature is both interesting and significant. A polar pattern of this sort was suggested for the sea-urchin egg and later for the egg of Ascaris by Boveri. . . . In many papers on regeneration Morgan postulated gradations of formative substances and also suggested gradation of tension.

Child himself first used the term axial gradient, to the best of my knowledge, in the title of a paper, published in April, 1911, which included no reference to Boveri. Boveri's 1910 paper was published not in a regular periodical but in the "Festschrift" for Richard Hertwig's sixtieth birthday; it was already cited by Child in The Process of Reproduction in Organisms, published in June, 1912. In a rather general paper on the physiological gradients Child (1928) refers not only to Boveri, but also to Morgan, in 1904 and 1905, and to Sachs in 1880 as having conceived of polarity "in terms of the flow or gradation of formative substances" (Child, 1928, p. 448).

It is one of the obstacles to an approach to certainty in intellectual history that the influence of one idea or pattern of ideas on the development of another is not always accurately indicated by references either in texts or bibliographies, a fact which Spemann himself well recognized; and he discussed it specifically with reference to the influence of Boveri on the concepts forming the basis of the present disquisition. Spemann was quite cognizant of the kinship of some of Child's notions to Boveri's ideas, and commented that Child's "conception of a 'dominant region' corresponds very nearly to Boveri's 'region of preference'," (Spemann, 1938, p. 321), a region of predilection at the vegetal pole of the egg postulated as influencing the development of the rest.[7] But

[7] The common philosophical background leading to concepts of dominance in both embryology and genetics at this time has not to the best of my knowledge been investigated, nor have the relationships between the concepts of dominance in biology and in the political field, except insofar as both may be related to the struggle for existence implied by 19th century Darwinism.

he was not certain (Spemann, 1938, p. 142) as to the degree to which he himself, Spemann, was beholden to Boveri's *Vorzugsbereich* for his own conception of a

". . . center of differentiation" as the starting point of this determination. A similar interpretation had been considered by Boveri (1901), many years earlier, for the development of the sea-urchin egg and its fragments. The relatively most vegetative point of the normal germ or a fragment of it might be a "privileged region" ("*Vorzugsbereich*") from which everything else would be determined. I could myself (Spemann and Hilde Mangold, 1924, p. 636) point out the likeness of the two conceptions when, many years later, I again came across this interpretation of Boveri. It may have been working subconsciously after I had encountered it in the publication just mentioned, or even in oral communication, or it may have been part of our common stock of ideas in those invaluable years of daily intercourse with that great investigator.

It is not only with respect to their twin origins in the parent concept of polarity and their duplicate postulates of the particular importance of an especially influential part of the egg or organism that Child's and Spemann's concepts bore some similarity to each other. They also derived their intellectual descent from the same philosophical confusion regarding the dichotomy between qualitative and quantitative explanation. Boveri's quantitative conceptions, as noted above, grew out of qualitative observations. The same was true for Child, a major significance of whose contribution rested on his ability to postulate a quantitative basis for qualitative differences which had been observed along an axis. Granted that Child *counted* his results, the results which he counted remained qualitatively distinct from one another. While Spemann in contrast eschewed the quantitative as a basis of explanation, his own most important interpretations were intimately related in their origins to theories which also, although founded on qualitative observations, were strongly quantitative in their implication, as their later elaboration was to bear out (J. Loeb, 1905). I refer here to the theories of tropisms, whose

14

historical relationship to the earliest concepts of induction through Roux and Herbst and Driesch has already been pointed out (Oppenheimer, 1955a, p. 19; p. 162, this volume).

What Child and Spemann and their various successors have failed to take into account — or at least have not sufficiently emphasized in their technical publications — is that attempted reference of the qualitative to the quantitative is not a concern unique to morphogenetic study alone. The whole history not only of biological but also of physical science has exhibited a steadily mounting practice of attempting to derive the supposedly qualitative from the supposedly quantitative. Yet in the last analysis, the relation of quality to quantity remains now, as it has been during the whole development of human thought, one of the thorniest problems to vex the complacency of philosophy, and even today some of the keener of the modern philosophers of science consider the whole dualism postulated between the qualitative and the quantitative to rest only very insecurely on fallacious logical grounds (see for instance the illuminating essay, Malicious Philosophies of Science, by Nagel, 1954).

Perhaps, however, the ultimate demonstration of the complementariness of the axial gradient and the organizer concepts is that at least one subsequent concept is of such a nature as to be able to encompass them both, namely, the field concept. Priority for this, so far as ideas rather than name is concerned, is due to Harrison (1918), though Spemann (1921) considered the organizer to produce what he called a field of organization. It is rather a singular fact, however, that this concept has never acquired quite the general popularity and prestige of the other two under discussion, perhaps partly because its validity is so completely taken for granted by working embryologists, perhaps partly because no writing embryologist has yet taken the trouble to construct a single monolithic volume in which all known embryological data are subjugated to generalization in terms of fields. The closest approach to such a treatment is that of Huxley and De Beer (1934), who have accounted for a number of morphogenetic data on the basis of what they call gradient-fields; these however are probably more closely identical to Child's axial gradients than now, more than twenty years later, seems appropriate or desirable.

While the field theory has not yet been adequately developed, Weiss (1926) deserves considerable credit for having generalized it on a theoretical basis to cover morphogenetic phenomena. Analogy with a strictly physical concept is explicit in it—at a much more sophisticated level than in Driesch's metaphor referred to above. While at the moment its value is descriptive rather than analytical, it may yet become useful in fostering comprehension of the newer embryological data, within the limitations, of course, that circumscribe the applicability of 19th century physical theory to 20th century embryological interpretation.

The field concept as such has, however, so far led less directly in the direction of the more modern work than its components, the organizer and gradient concepts, and it is a distinction of both of these that they have each directly stimulated the study of morphogenetic phenomena on other than a cellular level. The work on abnormal inductors carried out in Spemann's laboratory and by Holtfreter in Dahlem was one of the principal factors responsible for turning embryology directly toward its present chemical phase. Child's theories had a similar effect by virtue of their emphasis, new in their time, on the metabolic basis of differentiation; and in fact, it has proved highly significant that this was expressed by Child in terms of the utilization of oxygen. From this point of view, even though vertebrate embryologists have found the concepts of Spemann more compatible to elucidation of what is known of vertebrate development, the work of Child has been of inestimable general influence.

It was Child who first systematically applied the methods of general physiology to the study of morphogenesis. The program of J. Loeb (1905), who was also treating the egg and embryo as a physico-chemical system, was like that of so many of his embryological contemporaries at the turn of the century far more varied and variable. Although repetition of Child's experiments by techniques more critical than poisoning an organism by cyanide failed to confirm his results, and while Warburg's studies in 1908 and 1910 on respiration in the sea urchin egg were other contributing factors, it seems safe to say that the wide dissemination, in doctrinaire tone, of Child's generalizations among biological investigators at least accelerated, if in fact it did not do more, the progress of the more accurate and more fruitful studies on respiratory systems within the egg which were to be performed by Brachet (1934), Boell *et al.* (1939) and the many others who have carried these investigations farther (Boell, 1955). Needham (1942, p. 605), himself an interested party of the top rank in this connection, believes too that

. . . it is sure that embryology owes a considerable debt to Child, who by introducing his gradient concept was one of the first to recognize those invisible dispositions of order with which the organism imposes its organization on the matter of which it is made. Today the gradient theory has merged in the general theory of morphogenetic fields, already discussed. . . . It is not likely we shall be able to do without this in the future progress of embryology.

Furthermore, it cannot be denied that for some particular organisms the existence of gradients has not only been confirmed but demonstrably related to the activities of specific metabolic systems, respiratory and otherwise (Hörstadius, 1928, 1935, 1939, 1949; Runnström, 1928, 1954; Lindahl, 1936, 1942; Gustafson and Lenique, 1952, 1955). In fact, if this essay were being written by an echinoderm rather than a vertebrate, the establishment and elaboration of gradients would almost certainly be considered to be the most highly significant of the organizing mechanisms in development that relate a governed part to a governing whole.

Yet even the echinoderms might be driven to the admission that the concepts of gradients and fields describe principally differences in action and reaction between parts of an organism at a specified moment in time; and dynamic though they may be in other respects, they have perhaps their greatest value in the delineation of spatial rather than temporal situations. Something further is requisite to account for changes in gradients and fields in time. The concepts implicit in organizer action, based as they are on mechanisms of induction, deal to a far greater degree with processes responsible for the progression of events through time; and in fact it is when these are superimposed on gradient concepts, as for instance when von Ubisch (1925) and Hörstadius (1928, 1935) alter the later development of echinoderm embryonic cells at one end of a gradient by the addition or subtraction of cells originating from elsewhere along the gradient, that they achieve their most spectacular success. Since differentiation is a process in time rather than a fixed state (a fact which many contemporary biologists tend to neglect), the ultimate task of embryology and developmental physiology becomes the analysis of sequences of events in time, and theories which account for spatial distinctions between parts of embryos, no matter how profound these may be, must always remain subservient to hypotheses which emphasize the progressive element in differentiation. The experiments on which the organizer concept was based have made manifest the degree to which phenomena and events of any one particular moment in development are dynamically related to events that have occurred at previous moments. Further, they have provided incontrovertible proof that a mutual influence between embryonic parts lies at the basis of the complex interrelationships of embryonic processes. Thus they have imputed the ultimate validity and significance to the fundamental principle of progressive differentiation which has dominated all of the concepts of embryology since the time of Aristotle.

Considerable space has been devoted in the immediately foregoing pages to the origins and consequences, to the likenesses and similarities, of the notions of organizers and gradients and fields, not only because of the intrinsic interest of these ideas but also because they have been extended during the first third of the century to the proportions of rather grandiose conceptual schemes. Such concentration of attention on a few major formulations may seem to savor of inconsistency in the light of the emphasis placed in the introductory remarks on diversification of activity as a particular attribute of the embryology of the beginning part of the century.

At least certain of the laws of probability are as applicable to the study of the development of developmental ideas as to any other natural phenomena. The more words written, the more words read, and the greater the probability of their striking fire to stimulate further work; and it is hardly to be denied that a goodly number of words have been indited in relation to organizers and gradients and fields. The laws of probability are however notoriously refractory of application to a single case, and there are a number of individual circumstances where investigation cloaked by fewer generalizing words may be equally interesting in its conception and pregnant in its influence. Especially is this true of the studies by Harrison, which, although they contributed heavily to the development of the concepts both of organizers and fields, originated quite independently of these and have been no less significant in their weight of influence, though never unified into a single didactic theory. If it was Roux who insisted that understanding of the *Causalnexus* of events in morphogenesis must rest on a knowledge of the behavior of cells in terms of their relationships, positive or negative, with their neighbors, it was Harrison who made this goal possible and actual of attainment by hastening the introduction into the embryological laboratories of the techniques whereby cells could be isolated and recombined.

Granted that he may not have been the first to isolate and grow cells separated after the blastomere stage from the whole organism (see L. Loeb, 1912), he first had the intuition to devise and utilize the technique of tissue culture to perform a crucial experiment for the solution of an embryological problem (Harrison, 1907). One might be tempted to assert that his originality of insight, as evidenced by his application of this new technique towards the solution of an old morphogenetic problem, was almost unique, were it not for the fact that he himself had previously (Harrison, 1898, 1904) matched this accomplishment by recognizing in the fusion of embryonic parts by the method of Born (1897) the way to recombine cells which subsequently became the means by which their interrelationships were put to the crucial test. The first published descriptions of Harrison's grafting experiments antedated those of Spemann (1901, 1906a, b) and were independent of them. The written record fails to make clear whether Spemann knew of Harrison's paper of 1898 when he performed his own first transplantations. While he did not mention it in 1901, when he first wrote of the desirability of transplanting the optic cup or of replacing the lens epidermis with a piece of belly skin, or in his Nobel Prize Lecture (appended to his autobiography, 1943), he did refer to the work of Harrison in his own first publications dealing methodologically with transplantation (Spemann, 1906a, b). The second of these, in fact, discusses the work of Harrison at great length. In any case, Harrison's work was strongly instrumental in demonstrating to all embryologists the potentialities of the transplantation technique for performing crucial experiments. In the first transplantation experiments he ever reported (Harrison, 1898), by using organisms of different species and different specific coloring, he even introduced the very refinement which was later to allow the framing of the most

critical question ever to be addressed to the organizer (Spemann and H. Mangold, 1924). His influence in this connection
has been gratefully acknowledged by Spemann, who described
the work on the lateral line as "that classical investigation . . .
from which I have learned more than from almost any other
investigation, not only for technique, but also for the methodically advancing analysis" (Spemann, 1938, p. 131).

The ultimate value of Harrison's contribution to the embryology of the 20th century transcends, however, its technical
importance. What distinguished his attainments even on the
methodological side were the originality[8] and the imagina-
tiveness which enabled him to transform mere method into
an intellectual tool adaptable to probing the embryo at depths
at which it had never before been investigated. He himself
turned the various manipulative operations which he innovated towards a solution of some of the profoundest problems
of embryonic organization. Intrigued, like so many others,
by the phenomena of polarity, he was able to reduce some
of these in his mind to coordinates of bilateral symmetry
which he could recognize as manipulable in the embryo in a
series of experiments (Harrison, 1918, 1921) which represented a study of one of the most fundamental aspects of embryonic wholeness, a performance characterized by a freshness
of approach almost unparalleled in modern embryology. The
specific results of these experiments, fascinating in their own
right, were important also in that they provided a firm and
concrete foundation for the concept of fields. His own interpretations were of no less significance in that they were expressed in terms of spatial transformations in time, and they

8 No ideas in science are of course completely original. It is extremely interesting,
in view of much that is said in this essay and elsewhere, that in private conversations
Harrison has frequently stated that the work and writing which most strongly influenced his own ideas when he was young was that of Sachs. This fact happens to
have been reported to me only after the virtual completion of the text of this paper,
and is therefore not in any way responsible for the frequent references to the strong
influences of Sachs on other investigators.

were timely in their attempts to refer both gross and subtle morphogenetic effects to molecular phenomena: a mere analogy to the tetrahedral carbon atom in 1921 was followed in 1936 by a "conclusion that the transformation from the first to the second phase [in the step-wise differentiation of asymmetry] and probably, in some measure at least, that from the second to the third phase involve changes in the orientation of ultramicroscopic elements" (Harrison, 1936, p. 246). The ultramicroscopic elements were revealed in the Harvard Tercentenary address (delivered as a lecture in 1936; published 1945) as none other than protein molecules, whose arrangement could be postulated as accounting for a number of polar and other phenomena.

This hypothesis was however at most a modest and tentative one which was never aggrandized to a comprehensive theory. In fact, in his avoidance of general theorizing in favor of investigation of a wide variety of developmental phenomena Harrison's mind has exemplified the vigorously progressive tendencies distinctive of the beginning of the century. In his own work he dealt specifically with material as widely divergent as the outgrowing axone, the medullary plate, the lens, the lateral line, the ear, the fin, the limb, and the manifold derivatives of the neural crest. While he confined his own efforts, after the very first, to the amphibian, experimental investigations on fish and mammal were pursued in his laboratory at the instigation of Nicholas (1927, 1934), and scarcely an organ or organ system has escaped investigation in his laboratory or by its members (see, for instance, for the range of material covered, and the varied nature of the particular problems attacked, the tables of contents of the *Festschrift* volumes 113 (1950) and 129 (1955) of the *Journal of Experimental Zoology*). These investigations have provided fundamental data which, while they have answered some of the familiar questions of the past, have in the main raised new ones to be solved by the future. If they have been constructed principally in terms of organs or organ-systems, this serves only to emphasize the fact that these too, like the whole embryo, function on a high plane of integration.

III. THE EMBRYO AS CONSTRUCTED OF GERM LAYERS

If too much significance may seem to have been attributed in the preceding section to the concept of the axial gradient, nevertheless such emphasis can be defended by the insistence that this concept has been one of the funnels through which the 19th century has poured its ideas into the 20th. Another concept which to some extent has filled a like function is the germ layer doctrine, which during the 19th century not only interpreted the layers as primary entities in the developing organism, but went so far as to raise their specificity of origin and action to the level of a formal generalizing principle for embryology (witness, for instance, the statement in Ziegler's textbook in 1902, cited from Mangold, 1923, p. 272):

. . . Wenn bei den Wirbeltieren die Gastrulation beendet ist und die Keimblätter gebildet sind, so haben diese Keimblätter ganz getrennte Aufgaben in bezug auf ihre Beteiligung an den Organen und die Bildung der Gewebe. Dieser Satz spricht die Lehre von der Spezifizität der Keimblätter aus, welche eines der wichtigsten allgemeinen Resultate der embryologischen Forschung ist.[9]

To formulate a romantic analogy, the 19th century might have intimated that the germ layers are the phrases in which the embryo composes its melodies.

The development of the germ layer concept through to the beginning of the 20th century has been presented in another place (Oppenheimer, 1940). Suffice it to state here that by

[9] When gastrulation is completed in the vertebrates and the germ layers are formed, these layers have quite separate tasks with regard to their participation in organs and the construction of tissues. This proposition expresses the doctrine of the specificity of the germ layers, which is one of the most important general results of embryological research.

the end of the 19th century an unquestioning belief in the specificity of the layers was so widely, although not universally maintained (see Mangold, 1923, and Oppenheimer, 1940, for discussion of some 19th century doubts concerning the dogmatic value of the principle), that on a conceptual plane one of the more progressive contributions of the early part of the 20th century was the demonstration by operative techniques of the modifiability of the layers in a number of organisms; in the amphibians, for instance, first as an extension of the investigations on the organizer (Mangold, 1923); and later in the echinoderms (von Ubisch, 1925; Hörstadius, 1928) as related to polar gradients. (It had in fact already in the previous century been demonstrated for the echinoderms by Herbst, 1892, 1893 by chemical means.) The indication that even within each germ layer prospective potency, to borrow for a moment some old-fashioned but useful terminology, may be greater than prospective significance, and that the increment varies for different organisms and for different layers in the same organism, has resulted on the negative side in the weakening of the firm ideas of germ layer fixity and specificity as a generalizing principle; and on the positive, it has pointed up the need for formulating new interpretations of regulation and regulability, and thus of epigenesis and preformation. It was in part the breaking of the absolute rule of the old germ layer dogma that released the energies of embryologists to treat morphogenesis in the wide variety of manners which has been described as characteristic of the early 20th century.

But if the degree of specificity formerly attributed to the layers now seems devaluated, and if the present assessments of the layers are now so changed that, for instance, von Baer and Haeckel might have difficulty in recognizing their legacy in the chemical coinage of Toivonen and Yamada, nevertheless an intimate continuity has obtained between the rigorous concept developed during the 19th century and some of the more modern investigations carried out during the 20th. Vogt's magnificent studies on morphogenetic movements considered the rearrangements of cells in groups, and except for the chorda his groups were principally the old germ layers. Thus in a way he substituted dynamic and material reality for what had been previously formal. Spemann analyzed the operations of the organizer in terms of the action of an underlying layer of cells on an overlying one. The fact that chorda could be demonstrated by modern methods as having position and function in its own right, as distinct from both mesoderm and endoderm, would have given small comfort to the adherents of the older and stricter theory. Yet the embryo itself has proved that prospective notochord adapts its migrations to those of prospective mesoderm and that it cooperates with this layer, at least in the urodele, in affecting the actions of the overlying ectoderm.

But Spemann and his immediate collaborators were not the last to utilize distinctions between the actions and reactions of the conventional layers as keys by which to investigate induction. When Dalcq (Dalcq and Pasteels, 1937) explains qualitative diversity along the amphibian embryonic axis by postulating quantitative distribution of a hypothetical substance (organisine) along a hypothetical morphological gradient in the mesoderm, he evinces his debt for the only certainty in his explanation to the germ layer concept which has defined for him the existence of mesoderm as a distinct entity. The same holds true for Nieuwkoop (1952), whose complicated theory to account for regional differentiation calls on two different actions, one succeeding the other in time, of chordamesodermal substrate on overlying cells.

Furthermore, individual differences between the layers have provided the starting point for some of the recent chemical approaches towards the solution of enigmas concerning induction which the old transplantation methods have thus far been inadequate to unriddle. Specifically, the work currently attempting to identify the chemical substances involved in the production of regional differentiation in the amphibian (Toivonen and Kuusi, 1948; Toivonen, 1949, 1950, 1951; Yamada, 1950; Kuusi, 1951; Hayashi, 1956; Yamada and Ta-kata, 1956) is a direct outgrowth of the demonstration by Chuang (1939) that the abnormal inductors evoking the differentiation of mesoderm may differ from those responsible for the production of neural tissue. Thus the lively activity now being pursued in this field, even though now carried out by means of chemical analyses, is witness to the tremendous weight of influence not only of the organizer and gradient concepts, but also to that of the authority of the older germ layer concept, from which at most a small minority of contemporary investigators has been able completely to emancipate itself.

The possibility has already been lightly touched upon that the concepts of the 19th century did not necessarily suffer in comparison with those of the 20th so far as their dynamic qualities were concerned; and the degree to which chemical analyses are in fact more dynamic than other morphological descriptions is a moot question. In any case, it is eminently certain that at the supracellular as well as the cellular level, even the 19th century viewed the germ layers as highly dynamic entities and investigated their transformations as events succeeding one another in time. The concepts of motion which dominated physical science by the end of the 19th century were clearly reflected not only in general biological but also in specifically embryological interpretation, see Roux (1885a, p. 412):

Dies wäre die descriptive Definition der vor uns liegenden weiteren Aufgabe der Embryologie; kurz gefasst also: die vollkommene Beschreibung aller, auch der kleinsten Entwicklungsvorgänge als Substanzbewegungen der Theile des Eies und der von ihm aufgenommenen Theile bis zur vollen Entwicklung des Individuums, gestützt auf die vollkommene Kenntnis der Anordnung und aüsseren Beschaffenheit jedes kleinsten Theilchens des befruchteten Eies: eine "Kinematik der Entwicklung," wenn wir, wie wohl zu empfehlen ist, uns an AMPÈRE'S Eintheilung der Bewegungslehre anschliessen.[10]

If current attempts to account for the mechanics of movements of cell aggregates seem a modern feature of the contemporary scene, these have their counterparts in studies dating far back into the previous century. His in 1876, was, like Lewis (1943), Devillers (1950), and Trinkaus (1951), profoundly concerned with the relationships of epiboly to the establishment of the embryonic axis in the teleost, and it is very nearly superfluous to mention that he considered unequal growth of layers[11] and their consequent foldings as primary mechanisms in morphogenesis in his pioneering attempts to interpret development in terms of mechanical principles (His, 1874).

Furthermore, Vogt was by no means the first modern to concern himself with the ordered migrations of cells in groups. Roux before him, already as a student in 1874, had made an attempt at vital staining of the whole endoderm in the chick embryo (Roux, 1885b, p. 435; not referred to, by the way, by Vogt, 1925, 1929):

Ich verfolgte bei ihm den utopischen Zweck, durch Injection von Farbstoffen in die Keimhöhle, das untere Keimblatt und damit auch alle seine Derivate zu kennzeichnen. Der Eingriffe wurde mit einer fein ausgezogenen Glascanüle ausgeführt und war an sich nicht absolut

[10] This would be the descriptive definition of the further task of embryology which still remains before us, to sum it up briefly: The complete description of all, even the most minute developmental processes, as material movements of the parts of the egg and of their constituent parts, until the full development of the individual is attained, based on complete knowledge of the arrangement and the external conditions of every smallest particle of the fertilized egg: a "cinematics of development," if we adhere, as highly to be recommended, to Ampère's subdivision of the theory of motion.

[11] See also Roux (1885b, p. 429): "Schon Chr. Pander und H. Lotze vermutheten in ungleichem Wachsthum der verschiedenen Theile der Keimblätter den ursachlichen Vorgang für die Entstehung der Formen des Embryo."

Already Chr. Pander and H. Lotze suspected unequal growth of different parts of the germ layers as the causative process in the origin of embryonic form.

tödtlich. Durch Niederschlag aus sehr verdünnten Carminlösungen erzeugte feine Carminkörnchen, sowie auch Anilinblau wurden festgehalten; der Zweck wurde natürlich nicht erreicht. Von Interesse war aber das Verhalten des Keimes gegen Körnchen von sog. unlöslichem Berlinerblau. Dieser Farbstoff war nämlich nach weiterer Bebrütung des Eies nicht mehr aufzufinden; dagegen zeigte die Umgebung der Einstichstelle, welche bei der Injection der erst erwähnten Farbstoffe immer am intensivsten gefärbt war, sowie einige andere Stellen des Keimes eine intensiv gelbe Färbung, so dass wohl anzunehmen ist, dass das eisenhaltige Material hier zu einem gelben Farbstoff umgearbeitet worden ist.[12]

Roux (1895), as previously noted (Oppenheimer, 1955a), considered movements of the blastomeres as tropistic, and Driesch (1894) too, also before Vogt, and also under the influence of the theories on tropisms, which were themselves deeply concerned with motion, built a whole and comprehensive theory of induction on observations of selective movements of specific groups of mesenchyme cells towards a region of predilection in the embryonic ectoderm.

The modern field of investigation of morphogenetic movements opened up by the brilliant studies of Vogt, though it has been subject to sporadic exploration, has however been slow of complete invasion subsequent to his time. Now that experimental studies still in progress are imputing a high degree of developmental significance to selective migration (in tissue culture, Grobstein, 1954, 1955; in other types of explants, Townes and Holtfreter, 1955; and even, and espe-

12 I pursued [in the chick] the utopian goal of earmarking the lower germ layer and thus also all of its derivatives by the injection of dyes into the blastocoele. The operation was carried out with a finely drawn-out glass cannula and was in itself not completely fatal. Fine granules of carmine obtained by the precipitation of very dilute carmine solutions, and also those of aniline blue, were retained; naturally the goal was not attained. The behavior of the embryo with respect to granules of so-called insoluble Berlin blue was however of interest. This dye, especially after continued incubation of the egg, was no longer to be found; on the other hand, the region surrounding the point of injection, which was always the most intensively stained when this latter dye was used, and also a few other places in the embryo, showed an intense yellow color, so that it stands to reason that the iron-containing substance was here converted to a yellow dye.

28

cially, in the whole embryo, Oppenheimer, 1955b), it is to be hoped that this area of investigation will finally become more adequately exploited. Other pioneer studies such as those of Nicholas (1945; see also a related paper by Ballard, 1955) on earlier stages of amphibian development than those investigated by Vogt open up other widening vistas which can provide entirely new perspectives for the embryologists of the future.

Certainly one reason for a half century of skirting rather than penetrating the field has been the highly elusive nature of the factors — except those operating at the level of the cell itself — which account for the migrations of cells in groups. One highly conspicuous exception to what has just been re-marked concerning the evasion of grappling with the funda-mental factors controlling morphogenetic movements is the work of Holtfreter, whose article (1943a) demonstrating the integrative importance of the amphibian surface coat in cel-lular movements has proved to be a descriptive contribution of the first order of significance. It places a new emphasis on a supercellular entity governing the movements of the cells, which now supplants the germ layer as the next higher order of integration above the individual cell. While the 20th cen-tury has as yet formulated no new specific generalizing con-cept in cellular terms to supplant the germ layer theory, it has through this simple and original contribution of Holt-freter turned the investigation of morphogenesis to an entirely different direction than has been followed for many years.

IV. THE EMBRYO AS CONSTRUCTED OF CELLS
1. The Whole Cell

The developmental significance of Holtfreter's surface coat is of course primarily that this is an agent which organizes the movements of cells. To further embellish our earlier meta-phor, if the germ layers, designated as such by the 19th century, represent the phrases of the embryo's tunes, the cells represent the notes. "The reference of developmental processes to the cell," wrote Harrison in 1937 (p. 372), "was the most important step ever taken in embryology," and it seems unlikely that he is soon to be contradicted.

In the same way as the embryology of the 20th century has retained yet altered the 19th century concept of germ layers, so does it still bear the clear marks of influence, however modified these may have become, of the 19th century cell doctrine; to confirm this point, one has only to regard the titles of many of the periodicals in which embryological articles are now being published: The Journal of *Cellular* and Comparative Physiology; Experimental *Cell* Research; The Proceedings of the Congresses of *Cell* Biology; and so forth. In fact, while our views of the cell theory itself have, as other historians have pointed out (J. W. Wilson, 1944, 1947a, b; Baker, 1948, 1949, 1952, 1953, 1955), undergone a process of gradual change, it may well be mainly by virtue of the heritage of 19th century dogma that the word cell is such a frequent biological term; yet much of what is being discussed by so-called cell biologists impinges less on cells *qua* cells than on their mere constituents, whether membranes and inclusions on the morphological side, or enzyme systems on the functional. Indeed, some of the work on homogenates is so far from cellular that it might more befittingly be called uncellular biology or uncellular physiology.

But if the division of biology which today encompasses much of embryology is called cell biology, this results only partly from the proverbial weight of the dead hand of the past. It is still true, as Harrison is not the only one to have pointed out, that the cell remains a natural unit for the embryo. To continue with one of the examples utilized in the previous section, Vogt, to repeat what has been said of him above, interpreted morphogenetic movements in terms of groups of cells. Holtfreter has enabled separate cells to reveal their independence and individuality of movement; in fact, it is only in the light of the considerable autonomy of the individual cells that the role of the surface coat in organizing their activities becomes so dramatic. The significance of the cell for 20th century embryology is that, while it maintains all the dignity as the structural unit which the 19th century bestowed upon it (and indeed, paradoxically enough, in the mid-20th century this is being enhanced rather than otherwise as a result of the application of phase and especially electron microscopy to embryological material; see for instance Porter, 1954), it has also acquired fresh merit as a functional unit, functioning *as* a unit rather than as the sum of its various inclusions.

Investigation of its activities at this functional level is one of the popular fashions of the midcentury, of which the work of Holtfreter represents only a single aspect. That of Niu (1956), which purports to analyze induction as a cell-to-cell rather than a layer-to-layer relationship, is another; and all of the studies which exploit disaggregation as an embryological tool (Moscona and Moscona, 1952; Weiss and Andres, 1952; Grobstein, 1954, 1955) offer tacit admission of the supremacy of the cell over the simple cell aggregate as a primary unit of developmental function, insofar as aggregation is accomplished by the selective migration of individual cells.

However, even these studies are not an exclusive product of the middle of the 20th century. The very flask cells whose activity Holtfreter (1943b) has demonstrated as so vital in the transformations of the amphibian gastrula were the subject of a great monograph published over 25 years ago (Ruffini, 1925), and indeed were most vividly described in action for the gastrulating frog's egg in 1900 by H. V. Wilson (who was also, by the way, the first to study systematically the selective recongregation of disaggregated cells in the modern sense, see p. 33). Notions of cellular autonomy date back at least as far as to Virchow (see J. W. Wilson, 1947b), whose influence on later recognition of the cell as a dynamic independent entity is usually most unjustly underestimated by biologists of whatever stamp. The studies on cell lineage so popular around the turn of the century implied an interest in cellular autonomy, though in the minds of the wise, such as E. B. Wilson (1892, 1899) and Conklin (1897, 1905), the whole was never forgotten for the part. And as for the supracellular coat, it is in a way far less significant that in 1956 Spratt, after Holtfreter, sees intercellular bridges in the chick blastoderm than that Rhumbler (1899, 1902) believed the amphibian egg to be invested with a special coat whose mechanical functions had to be taken into account in connection with the displacements of cells during invagination, or than that in 1897 Andrews not only observed and described intercellular bridges in the echinoderm egg (Andrews, 1897a) but recognized them for quite what they are worth today (Andrews, 1897b, p. 87):

The true nature and mode of formation of cell walls seem to be that they are but pellicular modifications of the continuous substance of masses into plates, which are as readily formed internally as externally, that they do not differ either in origin or constitution from other internal and external pellicles or ectosarcal formations; that they are, in short, not substance dividers nor substance isolators, but *substance structures, substance differentiators, and differentiations, substance organs; and finally, that they belong primarily to the mass and but secondarily to cells.*

We can no longer regard these formations as having for the living substance the value of a prison wall. We must look upon them as *substance strengtheners;* as devices for securing a qualified independence for areas which yet maintain absolute physical and physiological continuity. . . . *Cell division is mass differentiation; that is its true meaning — making it one with all the host of substance organizations of the elements of the living substance for physiological function.* (Italics those of the original author.)

Finally, if the 20th century views the cell as a unit of embryonic function both in its own right and as subservient to the total mass of cells constituting the whole embryo, a primary importance of the contemporary work on a conceptual plane is that it seems at last once more to be reconsidering the interrelationships of cells as such to each other in other ways than from the sole point of view of induction. The reversion of attention towards supracellular protoplasmic coats and intercellular bridges is only one example of this tendency. Another is the present ruling emphasis on affinity as a fundamental principle in development, and it is making no new and profound revelation to say that modern study of cell-to-cell relationships in development now hangs heavily on concepts of affinity, thanks once more to the insight of Holtfreter (1939).

The history of the concepts of affinity in biology is another fascinating chapter not yet written. These ideas must certainly have been intimately related to the whole sequence of allied concepts in chemistry from the time of the alchemists to that of Berzelius and of those responsible for contemporary resonance theories. They have however also a rich background in the biological concepts of the late 19th and early 20th century. Haeckel's motive in dividing siphonophore larvae (1869) was to verify his hypothesis that amoebae, ontogenetically as well as phylogenetically, aggregate to form these organisms. The tropism theories, already pointed out as so significant in the development of concepts of induction by Herbst and Roux and Driesch and Harrison and Spemann, were essentially mechanistic explanations of selective affinity, whether of the sunflower for the sun or of the moth for the flame. Born (1897) already in the first communication describing the union of embryonic parts in the amphibian placed heavy emphasis on the junction of like to like. H. V. Wilson, in the first decade of the new century (1907, 1911), dissociated the cells first of sponges, then of hydroids, by squeezing them through bolting cloth, and described with consummate accuracy their selective reaggregation to form new organisms.

The significance of the current studies of affinity however runs far deeper than that they represent a transition between the past and present. They also form a new bridge between studies at the supracellular level at one side, and at the subcellular on the other, and thus also between the present and the future. On the supracellular level they have led, again through the insight of Holtfreter (Townes and Holtfreter, 1955), to new concepts of the mechanisms responsible for folding and cavitation, thus relating cells to layers in a new sense of the 20th rather than the old of the 19th; and on the subcellular, attempts to explain affinities in terms of subcellular constituents are already beginning to lead towards the explanation of gross morphogenetic phenomena in terms of demonstrable protein activity [see for instance Spiegel, 1955, who relates cell-to-cell adhesion to the presence of demonstrated surface antigens; immunological studies on fertilization (Tyler, 1955); and various genetic studies of development].

2. *Cellular Components: Microscopic and Submicroscopic*

Cellular affinity, no matter how analyzed or described, implies either cellular or subcellular specificity, and it remains to discuss the development of latter-day concepts of specificity in development. Specificity is of course no purely developmental phenomenon, it can fairly be designated as the key characteristic not only of all embryological but of all biological systems, as is self-evident from the application of the name *species* to the organism as the fundamental biological unit. In one way, problems which relate to specificity are the central target of all biological investigations. In embryology in the 19th century the fixity of the germ layers was defined by the very word *specificity*. Roux used the word *Specification* as we do the word differentiation [see his article Ueber die Spezifikation der Furchungszellen und über die bei der Postgeneration und Regeneration anzunehmenden Vorgänge,[13] 1893; or his definition of *Specification* in his "Terminologie" (Roux *et al.*,

[13] On the Specification of the Cleavage Cells and on the Processes Presumed to Occur in Postgeneration and Regeneration.

1912, p. 385), as "die Entstehung, Bildung der Specietät, der Eigenart. Sie kann betreffen die Potenz . . . oder die entwickelte Beschaffenheit, die Differenzierung"[14]. Thus in his meaning of the word all research directed toward the study of differentiation is concerned also with specificity.

More particularly, however, 20th century biology analyzes specificity, developmental or otherwise, with reference to the concepts of two special areas of thought, one of them genetics, and the other, the so-called molecular biology. Ideally these two methods approach each other very closely; even at a realistic level they share in common the fact that they consider cells in terms of agents functioning at the subcellular level. They deal with cellular inclusions, visible or otherwise, as primary factors, and it is a feature of the 20th century, as opposed to the 19th, that investigations of cellular inclusions of microscopically visible dimensions can no longer be considered apart from those treating of systems of molecular size or nature. The mid-20th century's interest in Gustafson's correlation of gradients with mitochondrial distribution is measured by its reference of mitochondria to their metabolic action.

To take up first genetics: The practice of considering hereditary factors in relation to morphogenetic factors is very ancient. In the period to which this essay limits itself, attempts to verify or refute an embryological theory based by Roux on Weismann's concept of the qualitative distribution of the chromosomes are commonly recognized as having been highly influential by providing a vigorous impetus for the new experimental investigations of development at the turn of the century. Boveri's study (1907) on the development of dispermic echinoderm eggs demonstrating the existence of qualitative differences between the chromosomes, and more important, the importance to normal development of their equable

---

[14] The origin, the production of speciety, of specialty. It can concern potentiality . . . or developed characteristics, differentiation.

distribution to all cells was worked out with the utmost in-
genuity on strictly embryological material, without recourse
to the type of knowledge of hereditary factors that was con-
temporaneously beginning to be investigated in what were to
grow into the schools of genetics proper. When Briggs, in the
1950's (Briggs and King, 1952, 1955; King and Briggs, 1955),
continues his artful experiments which attempt to delimit the
time at which the nucleus of an embryonic cell is no longer
totipotent to govern development, he carries to a logical extreme a line of thought and experiment begun by Spemann
(1914, 1928), by the latter carried only through the 32-cell
stage, but completely unequivocal in disproving for that stage
the Roux-Weismann theory. (Roux, by the way, opinionated
though he was in many other respects, gracefully relinquished
this theory once it had been experimentally invalidated.)

The early studies designed to test the Roux-Weismann
hypothesis were, as already pointed out, performed independently of studies of genetics as such. The bringing to light
of their results, and the subsequent establishment of the gene
theory by Morgan and his group might have been expected,
especially since Morgan himself had begun his career as an
embryologist, to have led immediately to the realization that
the fundamental problem of biological specificity can be
viewed as an embryological one: by what chain of mechanisms
does the action of the genes specify a cell or group of cells to
become different from others? Morgan's own book "Embryology and Genetics" as late as 1934 considered just precisely
what its title implies, the two disciplines as completely separate, and the word *"and"* in his title is as diagnostic of the
book's contents as are the two nouns. This is in sharp opposition to the great work of E. B. Wilson, "The Cell in Development and Inheritance" which already in its first edition (1896)
on the cytological side ventured to include not only in its title
but also in its text as full and general a view as was possible
at the time of the relationships of cytological data to the study

of embryology and heredity. In this and in subsequent editions (1900, 1925) Wilson set a fashion for the cytological investigations of developmental and genetic phenomena which has not only culminated in the modern studies of cytogenetics and cytochemistry, but which has linked the study of the structure and function of the cell to its development and inheritance inseparably for all time.

The evasion for many years of embryological considerations by the formal American schools of genetics, which has a moment ago been contrasted with their recognition by the most influential of American cytologists, was fortunately not a universal phenomenon, and some of those who have investigated heredity on a broader physiological basis than Morgan and his colleagues and successors have always remained far closer to the study of development. Goldschmidt has always not only accepted but attributed supreme significance to the developmental action of the hereditary factors (see his "Theoretical Genetics," 1955, for an exhaustive historical review); and he explained their developmental functions specifically on the basis of enzyme activity (Goldschmidt, 1916) a number of decades before the propagation of the one-gene–one-action theories (Beadle, 1945, 1949; Haurowitz, 1950) still so popular in certain quarters, and long before Spiegelman (1948) was to evoke the concept of competition for enzymes as explanatory of differentiation.

The fact remains, however, that the conceptual chasm between the gene and the finally differentiated cell continues wide and deep, and in spite of early beginnings by Wright (1916, 1945) it is only relatively lately that successful progress is being made toward bridging it, with the work for instance of Poulson (1940, 1945), Landauer (1948), Gluecksohn-Schoenheimer (1949), Gluecksohn-Waelsch (1951, 1953, 1954), and Hadorn (1951, 1955), to mention only a few selected arbitrarily. When biochemical steps intervening between the gene and its effect can be followed (Ephrussi, 1942) or postulated

37

(Landauer, 1954), the study of development becomes itself molecular biology, although unfortunately it must be remembered that the ultimate and really only significant step leading directly back to the gene itself remains as yet to be followed for metazoan material.

Goldschmidt, of all the students concentrating on heredity one of the most acute in his intuitive and analytical understanding of embryological problems, was one of those who recognized fairly early the possibility that extranuclear as well as nuclear factors might be instrumental in various ways in the regulation of differentiation (Goldschmidt, 1924, 1938; see also Part II of "Theoretical Genetics," 1955, which is devoted to The Cytoplasm as Seat of Genetic Properties). For all his vision, however, and for all the emphasis placed on cytoplasmic inclusions by such influential embryologists as E. B. Wilson, Boveri, and Conklin, any postulate that differentiation might be controlled by extranuclear factors in the genetic sense would have been viewed as wholly untenable, at least on this side of the Atlantic Ocean, throughout by far the greatest part of the first half of this century, as all of us will remember who are more than 40 years of age. Had Spemann concluded his Silliman Lectures in 1933, for instance, by interpreting his results in terms of plasmagenes, as Holtfreter and Hamburger (1955) have just now attempted, his audience no doubt would have suspected him of showing signs of senility or something worse.

Goldschmidt (1955) has suggested that what has restored respectability in America to an interest in cytoplasmic inheritance has been the work of Sonneborn (1943a, b, 1947, 1951) on the genetics of the killer effect in *Paramecium*. While the work on plastid inheritance may have been equally influential in this particular connection, it would be extremely interesting to try to take measure of the strong influence on embryology that has emanated from the various disciplines that are now encompassed in microbiology. It is of course not only in relation to current notions of plasmagenes adopted from or by microbiologists (Ephrussi, 1953) that microbiological concepts have affected embryological ideas. But while embryology, like all modern biology, benefits from the metabolic and genetic studies currently being performed by microbiologists, these have a very special relevance for morphogenetic investigation. The experimental material of the microbiologists shares with that of the embryologists one completely unique feature: namely, that it consists of cells which are not *only* single cells, but which are also whole organisms in their own right. It is inevitable, therefore, that much that is of value for the one group of investigators becomes highly meaningful to the other.

But it may also be remembered that if microbiology has underlined for embryology the importance of a concept of plasmagenes which may prove useful in the further analysis of developmental specificity, embryology may have earlier facilitated the progress of the microbiologists towards this new direction. Visible particles within the cytoplasm were of special interest to embryologists from the time they were first made investigable during the 19th century by the perfection of achromatic lenses; and when the behavior of these visible inclusions was insufficient to account for observed morphogenetic phenomena, the ground substance of the cytoplasm was invoked as an organizing agency by many of the great pioneers of the beginning of the 20th century. Lillie (1909) explained the inequality of the spindle poles in *Nereis* on the basis of the molecular structure of the ground substance, and Boveri, Conklin, and Harrison were continually attributing vast significance to the ground substance. Thus during the years when most other biological attention was concentrated solely on the nucleus, the embryologists continued to drum on the note that situations exist which demonstrate the importance of the cytoplasm itself — though not necessarily in the genetic sense — in controlling the differentiation of the cell.

Interpretations involving cytoplasmic inheritance are, however, not the only ideas borrowed from microbiology which are now in the course of becoming incorporated into embryological concepts of specificity. Another not wholly unrelated pattern of ideas is in course of transfer with respect to immunology, over and above Sonneborn's concern with an immunological phenomenon. As a matter of fact, the significance of immunological interpretations of developmental specificity was recognized very early for the case of fertilization by Lillie (1919), in work which was of the greatest importance because, along with those of Child and J. Loeb cited above, his was one of the strongest voices earlier in this century to argue for the investigation of developmental phenomena according to physiological as well as cytological principles. There were others, too, whose interest in immunology as a developmental phenomenon long antedated the current flare of enthusiasm. Studies of tissue specificity in transplantations, begun during the First World War by L. Loeb (summarized in full, 1945), were interpreted on the basis of compatibility between like and like, and incompatibility between unlike and unlike, in an immunological framework, and these ideas probably fed into the newly developing embryological concepts to a degree that is rarely acknowledged. The supposedly new embryology of the mid-20th century is thus highly obligated to Leo as well as to his brother Jacques Loeb.

Yet while investigation of the field in which embryology and immunology overlap has not, as was earlier the case for conventional nuclear genetics, suffered a long delaying action at the level of study of visible inclusions, nonetheless, after an early start (see the work of Boucek, 1927, 1928, suggested by Nicholas), it is only now showing a rapid spurt of progress (Cooper, 1946, 1948, 1950; Ebert, 1950, 1952, 1954; Irwin, 1949, 1955; Schechtman, 1947, 1952, 1955; Gluecksohn-Waelsch, 1954; Brambell *et al.*, 1951; Brambell, 1954). Since it relates problems of developmental specificity to those of

cellular affinity and disaffinity at one level, to those of hereditary factors at another, and finally to protein and other molecular systems at still another, it shows, just past the middle of
the century, promise of serving for a time at least a useful
synthesizing function.

It is clearly apparent, however, from much that has been
said before, that the immunological approach has not been
the only avenue followed by 20th century embryology down
(or up?) towards the molecule. It is one of the curiosities of
almost all of the embryological studies of the century that
they have followed convergent paths leading in this direction.
In fact, the embryology of the whole century has been so cen-
trally reliant on molecular explanations that it seems almost
justifiable to inquire whether, because perhaps of the recondite nature of the phenomena to be explained, embryologists
may not have been for longer than other biological specialists
cognizant of the possibilities of interpretation at the molecular
level. Much of the work cited above in this essay has been
mentioned as instrumental in leading towards molecular embryology: Child's studies on the axial gradients; the Scandi-
navian studies on polar gradients in echinoderm eggs; Warburg's respiratory studies on sea urchin eggs; Harrison's
investigations on symmetry; the discovery of abnormal inductors. Considerable additional work which has not been specifically cited here has similarly been of inestimable influence
in this direction: not least, the publication of Needham's large
treatise (1931). If, however, all of these investigations and
others unnamed helped to move embryology towards its present position, they were able to do so not only as a result of
prior progress in chemistry and biochemistry, but also — and
let it not be forgotten — because the position had been prepared by others who had been strictly embryological in their
inclinations.

Roux, while he despaired in some of his moods, mechanist
though he was, of explaining embryological phenomena in

molecular terms, at least recognized this possibility. Herbst first demonstrated the transformability of the germ layers in 1892 by the use of the lithium ion. One of the subsections of Driesch's (1894) book on development was entitled Contact Induction (Berührungsinduktion); the section following it was entitled, Chemical Inductors, with two subsections called, respectively, Chemical Induction as Growth Regulator and Chemical Induction of Oriented Movements. Driesch, furthermore, was almost obsessed by the importance of enzymes, with an interest which once more he may have acquired from Sachs (Driesch, 1894, p. 44). The first attempt at a complete chemical and biochemical description of the egg (in this case that of *Ascaris*) was made as early as 1913, by Fauré-Fremiet, himself a microbiologist as well as an embryologist.

In other words, though chemical embryology has certainly of late fallen under the influence of the discoveries of fundamental mechanisms worked out on nonembryonic material, it has had an illustrious past all of its own. It might even prove an interesting gambit to explore to what degree investigation of some of these fundamental biochemical mechanisms may have been encouraged by the asking of opportune questions by some of the more progressive embryologists.

What is of course characteristic of the chemical and biochemical studies is that at the present time, as in fact during all previous periods when they were utilized at all, molecular explanations have been applied to embryological considerations at every level. Molecular orientation is called upon as explanatory of such fundamental properties of the whole organism as polarity and symmetry; specificity of organs, of tissues, of layers, and of cells has been analyzed on a molecular basis, as have the functions of cell inclusions of all varieties and magnitudes. As a result, a new concept has arisen during this century as a synthesizing concept for coordination of all embryological explanation: the *Unity of Biochemistry* of the 20th century supplants the *Unity of Descent* of the 19th century and the *Unity of Type* of the 18th as a synthesizing scheme. It purports to explain in different terms than these that unity in diversity which is the primary distinguishing feature of the developing embryo, a unity no longer now being accounted for by an *Urbild* in the mind of nature, or merely by common ancestry, but rather by the ubiquity of action of ATP or DNA. The century which began its efforts by diversification has reached its turning point by attempting again to construct a centralizing doctrine, this time on a chemical basis.

This is a synthesizing scheme insofar as it is single and emphasizes singleness, in a manner which would have appealed to an 18th century *Naturphilosoph* or a 19th century Haeckelian. Whether if it is not false, it is truly synthetic, or simply analytic after all; whether it explains, or merely describes, only what is made of it during the final half of the 20th century will reveal. If actually it remains but analytical, which is a patent possibility, at least it describes more quantitatively and in richer precision than before some of the mechanisms whereby progressive differentiation manifests itself, bringing this principle closer to the point where truly synthetic investigations can begin.

V. SOME CONCLUDING FANCIES

There are no conclusions in the accepted sense to be drawn from the foregoing. Only a few arbitrarily chosen aspects of embryological investigation have been selected for comment, those which have happened to appeal subjectively to a most subjective critic either for their apparent relationships to the past, or their seeming potentialities for the future. Such is the waywardness of the course of that will-of-the-wisp, scientific progress, that its future path is unpredictable,

> "Und wenn ein Irrlicht Euch die Wege weisen soll,
> So müsst Ihr's so genau nicht nehmen."

But if there is to be no formal epilogue, a few random and fragmentary concluding notes may be appended.

An article preliminary to this one (Oppenheimer, 1955a) rather labored the possibility that the development of embryological concepts up into the 19th century could be characterized by a gradual transition from metaphysical towards physical interpretations. The question then arises, has the threshold of the metaphysical in embryology continued to recede during the present century? This is not so easy to answer as it might seem. When Lillie, for instance, at the beginning of the century, invoked the qualities of the ground substance of the cytoplasm to account for what he could not explain on the basis of visible inclusions, he was retreating not away from but towards the metaphysical. When contemporary embryology turns to the ground substance in its now known ultramicroscopic structure to elucidate, say, the development of the nervous system (Weiss, 1955), it believes it passes from the metaphysical towards the physical. Making the invisible visible and the minute mathematically comprehensible is not necessarily synonymous, however, with leading away from the metaphysical towards the physical. The difficulty is to calculate the measure in which descriptions and explanations couched in terms of the ultramicroscopic, when this is molecular, are themselves physical or mathematical. This becomes a function of what physical science itself makes of the molecule and the atom; and some possibility surely exists in the middle of the 20th century that these entities may be now less physically and more metaphysically conceived than they were at the end of the 19th.

If so — and indeed in any case — the highly pertinent question arises as to the extent to which 20th century embryology stands in peril of remaining under domination by 19th century rather than 20th century physical concepts. To return again for a moment to Roux, one importance of his contribution lay in his recognition of time as a prime factor whose effects were open to experimental investigation. As a creature of the 19th century he related his primary question concerning it to a 19th century conception of causality which 20th century physical science considers outdated. Yet all of our embryological principles, such as they are, developed as they have been in the wake of Roux's passage, suffer the same defect. We have said earlier that the methods of 20th century embryology began by being essentially those of the 19th. So also began, and still continue to be, its philosophical foundations.

Occasionally, in the text of this essay, a musical metaphor has been followed. This was something more than a frivolous literary conceit; it has been designed to draw attention to the fact that there may be more ways than one of looking at a sequence of events in time. It happens that very occasionally either a romantic biologist (see von Uexküll in his enchanting piece "Der unsterbliche Geist in der Natur," 1946) or a romantic aesthetician (Carriere, 1859) has drawn an analogy between a developing organism and a musical composition, but this has been on the whole an exceptional rather than a usual occurrence.[15] Now this is in very curious contrast to another group of investigators who are as perpetually plagued as are the embryologists by the relationships of sequences of events in time to properties of integration; namely, the neurologists concerned with higher brain function, who much more often than the embryologists fall back on the musical analogy. Investigators of the caliber of Wilder Penfield, Russell Brain, and Stanley Cobb, for instance, have all recently done so.

The kind of metaphor by which one illustrates one's mental processes is hardly fraught with significance for the progress of science. What is essential is that in every manner possible

---

15 One is tempted to wonder what might have been the outcome for embryology — and indeed for teleology more generally — had the music of Aristotle's day been such that he could have compared the development of an embryo to composing a musical opus rather than painting a picture.

present energies be concentrated on the efforts of trying in a new way to break into the problem of coping with differentiation as change in time (a problem which has never been more lucidly posed for embryology than by Harrison in 1937). We have been speaking of differences between the 19th and 20th centuries. Toying with the romantic musical analogy is a 19th century, not a 20th century, conception. What may be its 20th century equivalent? The embryologists, beyond Harrison, have not framed it. Have the neurologists succeeded where the embryologists have not?

It is just possible that they may have bared the clue, in that they have at least publicly recognized (see the completely brilliant article by Fessard, 1954, on the relations of nervous integration to conscious experience) that microphysicists, confronted by similar difficulties of explaining an internal multiplicity of objects and the fundamental unity of their behavior, have found useful the invention of the concept of stationary states, during which the passage of time is said to have no meaning, and have at least raised the question as to the significance of this concept for the study of consciousness. Has such a concept nothing to say to embryology? The embryology of the 20th century has been rapid to borrow technological method from 20th century physical science. It might well, during the remaining half of the century, dip more consistently into some of its deeper resources.

These remarks have not been framed with the intent to express dismay at the extent of what has so far been accomplished in embryology — in fact, quite the opposite. Many embryologists seem all too prone at the moment to apologize for the present state of what they consider the decadence of embryology. The record suggests that they are quite unfair in doing so.

The principle of progressive differentiation, of which we keep speaking, is as old as Aristotle, it is true. But it is almost wholly within the present century that its significance has been made clear by analytical rather than descriptive studies, in the light first of what is now called classical experimental embryology (which, though it is fashionable to consider it old fashioned, *was* contemporary in its origins with Einstein and Freud), and next of the descriptive analytic studies which are now attempting to relate the visible effects of morphogenesis to the biochemical processes and mechanisms which are their concomitants. It would seem quite justifiable to maintain that the elucidation of this principle on an experimental and analytical basis is alone — quite aside from any of the contributions which embryology may have made towards the development of concepts in other now vigorous fields of biology — very much worth the labors of a mere half century.

The first paragraph of this essay spoke somewhat guardedly of the generalization that the ideas of the present are to be understood only in the light of their precursors. This is a dictum which is accepted as absolute by a number of writers in the field of the history of science, but it remains, unfortunately, to justify its validity to many scientists. One real difficulty is, of course, that if it is to be exalted to the rank of an axiom, greater historical reliability is required than is now attainable. It is a far cry from the ferments of Sachs and Driesch, for instance, to the particular protein groups studied by Ebert, and our evidence is inadequate as to the full pattern of thoughts and influences that may or may not have intervened in 60 years. Spemann has expressed well, in the quotation cited above (p. 14), the impossibility of knowing even the source of one's own specific ideas.

But there are further hazards to surmount beyond the inevitable uncertainties of historical certitude. Geoffrey Scott wrote a book a number of years ago (1914; second edition reprinted in 1954) which was essentially a history of taste, in which he evaluated the aesthetic judgments placed on Renaissance architecture by later centuries. In a perceptive chapter, The Biological Fallacy, which for a number of reasons deserves to be read thoughtfully by every historian of biology, he suggests some very profound and perplexing problems about the study of sequences of ideas which raise grave doubts as to the value of the philosophy of evolution as applied to the study of a succession of styles in art. So far as art is concerned, he worries as to how this may have diminished, for instance, the engrossment of men's thoughts with style itself, in contrast to its history; and thus, by implication, man's very creativity. But he even goes so much further than this as to question the actual relations of the ideas to each other. In considering, for instance, the sequence between Brunelleschi, the herald as he names him, and Bramante, the achiever, and Bernini, the fall, he concludes that "to Brunelleschi there was no Bramante; his architecture was not Bramante's unachieved, but his own fulfilled. His purpose led to the purpose of Bramante: they were not on that account the same" (1954, p. 134).

The question is worthy of brief examination, not only because it is an interesting one as raised in its own right by Scott, but because, ironically, so many of the new young generation of scientists belittle the historical approach, just at the very time when history has learned to traffic as profitably in ideas as in events. Scott claims, in his own words, that "the values of art do not lie in the sequence but in the individual terms" (Scott, 1954). It cannot be denied that for the growth of science as of art the study of a succession of past changes can never substitute for the creative impulse that itself creates change. But neither can it be denied, for science or for art, that the new creativity is always somehow related to the old. Insofar as the whole essence of science is that it builds upon what has been built before, the new and the old become inseparable.

What Scott has failed to remember, in his treatment of the biological fallacy, is that biology has exploded a fallacy of its own, namely, the one which used to be embodied in the now no longer tenable biogenetic law. What Scott has perhaps been thinking about is the phylogeny of ideas, not their ontogeny. In embryology, we now consider ontogeny to be responsible for phylogeny, rather than the reverse. If we can continue to see value in studying the ontogeny, not the phylogeny, of ideas, by concentrating on this we not only avoid the pitfall of Scott's biological fallacy, but we furthermore place ourselves in a position in which we can judge our own creative contributions from at least an improved, if not yet an ideal, point of perspective. It has just been said above, that the study of a succession of past changes can never substitute for the creative impulse; it can, however, in the best event, guide it. As the foremost experimentalist of us all has predicted, "Die Universalmethode des causalen Anatomen wird ebensowenig die Anwendung des Messers wie des Farbstoffes oder des Maasses, sondern die Geistesanatomie, das analytische, causale Denken sein" (Roux, 1885a, pp. 22–23).

REFERENCES

ANDREWS, G. F. 1897a. Some spinning activities of protoplasm in starfish and *Echinus* eggs. *J. Morphol.* **12:** 367-389.

ANDREWS, G. F. 1897b. The living substance as such: and as organism. *J. Morphol.* **12,** Suppl. No. **2:** 1-176.

BAKER, J. R. 1948. The cell-theory: a restatement, history, and critique. Part I. *Quart. J. Microscop. Sci.* **89:** 103-125.

BAKER, J. R. 1949. The cell-theory: a restatement, history, and critique. Part II. *Quart. J. Microscop. Sci.* **90:** 87-108.

BAKER, J. R. 1952. The cell-theory: a restatement, history, and critique. Part III. The cell as a morphological unit. *Quart. J. Microscop. Sci.* **93:** 157-190.

BAKER, J. R. 1953. The cell-theory: a restatement, history, and critique. Part IV. The multiplication of cells. *Quart. J. Microscop. Sci.* **94:** 407-440.

BAKER, J. R. 1955. The cell-theory: a restatement, history, and critique. Part V. The multiplication of nuclei. *Quart. J. Microscop. Sci.* **96:** 449-481.

BALLARD, W. W. 1955. Cortical ingression during cleavage of amphibian eggs, studied by means of vital dyes. *J. Exptl. Zool.* **129**: 77-98.

BAUTZMANN, H. 1955. Die Problemlage des Spemannschen Organisators. *Naturwissenschaften* **42**: 286-294.

BEADLE, G. W. 1945. Biochemical genetics. *Chem. Revs.* **37**: 15-96.

BEADLE, G. W. 1949. Genes and biological enigmas. *Science Progr.* **6**: 184-249; 313-317.

BILIKIEWICZ, T. 1932. Die Embryologie im Zeitalter des Barock und des Rokoko. *Arb. Inst. Geschichte Med. Univ. Leipzig* **2**: 1-184.

BOELL, E. J., NEEDHAM, J., AND ROGERS, V. 1939. Morphogenesis and metabolism. I. Anaerobic glycolysis of the regions of the amphibian gastrula. *Proc. Roy. Soc.* **B127**: 322-356.

BOELL, E. J. 1955. Energy exchange and enzyme development during embryogenesis. *In* "Analysis of Development" (B. H. Willier, P. A. Weiss, and V. Hamburger, eds.), Section VIII, pp. 520-555. Saunders, Philadelphia.

BORN, G. 1897. Ueber Verwachsungsversuche mit Amphibienlarven. *Wilhelm Roux' Arch. Entwickelungsmech. Organ.* **4**: 349-465; 517-623.

BOUCEK, C. M. 1927. The permeability of the placenta of the white rat to a specific hemolysin. *Proc. Soc. Exptl. Biol. Med.,* **24**: 607-608.

BOUCEK, C. M. 1928. A study of the placental permeability of the white rat, as determined by its reaction to hemolysins. *Am. J. Anat.* **41**: 1-24.

BOVERI, T. 1901. Die Polarität von Ovocyte, Ei und Larve des *Strongylocentrotus lividus. Zool. Jahrb. Abt. Anat. u. Ont.* **14**: 630-653.

BOVERI, T. 1907. Zellenstudien. VI. Die Entwicklung dispermer Seeigeleier. Ein Beitrag zur Befruchtungslehre und zur Theorie des Kernes. *Jena. Z. Naturw.* **43**: 1-292.

BOVERI, T. 1910. Die Potenzen der *Ascaris*-Blastomeren bei abgeänderter Furchung. Zugleich ein Beitrag zur Frage qualitativungleicher Chromosomen-Teilung. "Festschrift z. 60. Geburtstag R. Hertwigs," Vol. 3, pp. 133-214. Gustav Fischer, Jena.

BRACHET, J. 1934. Étude du métabolisme de l'oeuf de grenouille (*Rana fusca*) au cours du développement. 1. La respiration et la glycolyse de la segmentation à l'éclosion. *Arch. biol. (Liège)* **45**: 611-727.

BRAMBELL, F. W. R., HEMMINGS, W. A., AND HENDERSON, M. 1951. "Antibodies and Embryos." Athlone Press, London.

BRAMBELL, F. W. R. 1954. Transport of proteins across the fetal membranes. *Cold Spring Harbor Symposia Quant. Biol.* 19: 71-81.

BRIGGS, R., AND KING, T. J. 1952. Transplantation of living nuclei from blastula cells into enucleated frogs' eggs. *Proc. Natl. Acad. Sci. U.S.* 38: 455-463.

BRIGGS, R., AND KING, T. J. 1955. Specificity of nuclear function in embryonic development. *In* "Biological Specificity and Growth" (E. G. Butler, ed.), Chapter XI, pp. 207-228. Princeton U.P., Princeton.

CARRIERE, M. 1859. "Aesthetik. Die Idee des Schönen und ihre Verwirklichung durch Natur, Geist und Kunst." 2 vols. F. A. Brockhaus, Leipzig.

CHILD, C. M. 1911. Studies on the dynamics of morphogenesis and inheritance in experimental reproduction. I. The axial gradient in *Planaria dorotocephala* as a limiting factor in regulation. *J. Exptl. Zool.* 10: 265-320.

CHILD, C. M. 1912. The process of reproduction in organisms. *Biol. Bull.* 23: 1-39.

CHILD, C. M. 1928. The physiological gradients. *Protoplasma* 5: 447-476.

CHILD, C. M. 1941. "Patterns and Problems of Development." Univ. Chicago Press, Chicago.

CHILD, C. M. 1946. Organizers in development and the organizer concept. *Physiol. Zool.* 19: 89-148.

CHUANG, H. H. 1939. Induktionsleistungen von frischen und gekochten Organteilen (Niere, Leber) nach ihrer Verpflanzung in Explantate und verschiedene Wirtsregionen von Tritonkeimen. *Wilhelm Roux' Arch. Entwicklungsmech. Organ.* 139: 556-638.

CONKLIN, E. G. 1897. The embryology of *Crepidula. J. Morphol.* 13: 1-226.

CONKLIN, E. G. 1905. The organization and cell-lineage of the ascidian egg. *J. Acad. Natural Sci. Philadelphia* [2] 13: 5-119.

COOPER, R. S. 1946. Adult antigens (or specific combining groups) in the egg, embryo and larva of the frog. *J. Exptl. Zool.* 101: 143-171.

COOPER, R. S. 1948. A study of frog egg antigens with serum-like reactive groups. *J. Exptl. Zool.* 107: 397-437.

COOPER, R. S. 1950. Antigens of frog embryos and of adult frog serum studied by diffusion of antigens into agar columns containing antisera. *J. Exptl. Zool.* **114**: 403-420.

DALCQ, A., AND PASTEELS, J. 1937. Une conception nouvelle des bases physiologiques de la morphogénèse. *Arch. biol. (Liège)* **48**: 669-710.

DEVILLERS, C. 1950. Mécanisme de l'épibolie gastruléenne. *Compt. rend. soc. biol.* **230**: 2232-2234.

DRIESCH, H. 1894. "Analytische Theorie der organischen Entwicklung." Wilhelm Engelmann, Leipzig.

EBERT, J. D. 1950. An analysis of the effects of anti-organ sera on the development, in vitro, of the early chick blastoderm. *J. Exptl. Zool.* **115**: 351-377.

EBERT, J. D. 1952. Appearance of tissue-specific proteins during development. *Ann. N.Y. Acad. Sci.* **55**: 67-84.

EBERT, J. D. 1954. Some aspects of protein synthesis in development. *In* "Aspects of Synthesis and Order in Growth" (D. Rudnick, ed.), Chapter IV, pp. 69-112. Princeton U.P., Princeton.

EPHRUSSI, B. 1942. Chemistry of "eye color hormones" of *Drosophila*. *Quart. Rev. Biol.* **17**: 327-338.

EPHRUSSI, B. 1953. "Nucleo-Cytoplasmic Relations in Micro-Organisms, Their Bearing on Cell Heredity and Differentiation." Oxford U.P., New York.

FAURÉ-FREMIET, M. E. 1913. Le cycle germinatif chez l'*Ascaris megalocephala*. *Arch. Anat. microscop.* **15**: 435-757.

FESSARD, A. E. 1954. Mechanisms of nervous integration and conscious experience. *In* "Brain Mechanisms and Consciousness" (J. F. Delafresnaye, ed.), pp. 200-236. Blackwell Scientific Publications, Oxford.

GLUECKSOHN-SCHOENHEIMER, S. 1949. Causal analysis of mouse development by the study of mutational effects. *Growth* **13** (Suppl.): 163-176.

GLUECKSOHN-WAELSCH, S. 1951. Physiological genetics of the mouse. *Advances in Genet.* **4**: 1-51.

GLUECKSOHN-WAELSCH, S. 1953. Lethal factors in development. *Quart. Rev. Biol.* **28**: 115-135.

GLUECKSOHN-WAELSCH, S. 1954. Some genetic aspects of development. *Cold Spring Harbor Symposia Quant. Biol.* **19**: 41-49.

GOLDSCHMIDT, R. B. 1916. Genetic factors and enzyme reaction. *Science* **43**: 98-100.

GOLDSCHMIDT, R. B. 1924. Untersuchungen zur Genetik der geographischen Variation. I. *Arch. mikroskop. Anat. u. Entwicklungs-mech.* **101:** 92-337.

GOLDSCHMIDT, R. B. 1938. A *Lymantria*-like case of intersexuality in plants. *J. Genet.* **36:** 531-535.

GOLDSCHMIDT, R. B. 1955. "Theoretical Genetics." Univ. California Press, Berkeley.

GROBSTEIN, C. 1954. Tissue interaction in the morphogenesis of mouse embryonic rudiments in vitro. *In* "Aspects of Synthesis and Order in Growth" (D. Rudnick, ed.), Chapter X, pp. 233-256. Princeton U.P., Princeton.

GROBSTEIN, C. 1955. Tissue disaggregation in relation to determination and stability of cell type. *Ann. N.Y. Acad. Sci.* **60:** 1095-1107.

GUSTAFSON, T., AND LENIQUE, P. 1952. Studies on mitochondria in the developing sea urchin egg. *Exptl. Cell Research* **3:** 251-274.

GUSTAFSON, T., AND LENIQUE, P. 1955. Studies on mitochondria in early cleavage stages of the sea urchin egg. *Exptl. Cell Research* **8:** 114-117.

HADORN, E. 1951. Developmental action of lethal factors in *Drosophila*. *Advances in Genet.* **4:** 53-85.

HADORN, E. 1955. "Letalfaktoren in ihrer Bedeutung für Erbpathologie und Genphysiologie der Entwicklung." Georg Thieme, Stuttgart.

HAECKEL, E. 1869. "Zur Entwickelungsgeschichte der Siphonophoren." C. Van der Post, Jr., Utrecht.

HARRISON, R. G. 1898. The growth and regeneration of the tail of the frog larva. Studied with the aid of Born's method of grafting. *Wilhelm Roux' Arch. Entwicklungsmech. Organ.* **7:** 430-485.

HARRISON, R. G. 1904. Experimentelle Untersuchungen über die Entwicklung der Sinnesorgane der Seitenlinie bei den Amphibien. *Arch. mikroskop. Anat. u. Entwickelungsmech.* **63:** 35-149.

HARRISON, R. G. 1907. Observations on the living developing nerve fiber. *Anat. Record* **1:** 116-118.

HARRISON, R. G. 1918. Experiments on the development of the forelimb of *Amblystoma*, a self-differentiating equipotential system. *J. Exptl. Zool.* **25:** 413-461.

HARRISON, R. G. 1921. On relations of symmetry in transplanted limbs. *J. Exptl. Zool.* **32:** 1-136.

HARRISON, R. G. 1936. Relations of symmetry in the developing ear of *Amblystoma punctatum*. *Proc. Natl. Acad. Sci. U.S.* **22:** 238-247.

HARRISON, R. G. 1937. Embryology and its relations. *Science* **85**: 369-374.

HARRISON, R. G. 1945. Relations of symmetry in the developing embryo. *Trans. Conn. Acad. Arts Sci.* **36**: 277-330.

HAUROWITZ, F. 1950. "Chemistry and Biology of Proteins." Academic Press, New York.

HAYASHI, Y. 1956. Morphogenetic effects of pentose nucleoprotein from the liver upon the isolated ectoderm. *Embryologia* **3**: 57-67.

HERBST, C. 1892. Experimentelle Untersuchungen über den Einfluss der veränderten chemischen Zusammensetzung des umgebenden Mediums auf die Entwicklung der Thiere. I. Versuche an Seeigeleiern. *Z. wiss. Zool.* **55**: 446-518.

HERBST, C. 1893. Experimentelle Untersuchungen über den Einfluss der veränderten chemischen Zusammensetzung des umgebenden Mediums auf die Entwicklung der Thiere. II. Weiteres über die morphologische Wirkung der Lithiumsalze und ihre theoretische Bedeutung. *Mitt. Zool. Stat. Neapel* **11**: 136-220.

HIS, W. 1874. "Unsere Körperform und das physiologische Problem ihrer Entstehung. Briefe an einen befreundeten Naturforscher." F. C. W. Vogel, Leipzig.

HIS, W. 1876. Untersuchungen über die Entwickelung von Knochenfischen besonders über diejenige des Salmens. *Z. Anat. Entwickelungsgesch.* **1**: 1-40.

HOLTFRETER, J. 1939. Gewebeaffinität, ein Mittel der embryonalen Formbildung. *Arch. exptl. Zellforsch. Gewebezücht.* **23**: 169-209.

HOLTFRETER, J. 1943a. Properties and functions of the surface coat in amphibian embryos. *J. Exptl. Zool.* **93**: 251-323.

HOLTFRETER, J. 1943b. A study of the mechanics of gastrulation. Part I. *J. Exptl. Zool.* **94**: 261-318.

HOLTFRETER, J., AND HAMBURGER, V. 1955. Embryogenesis: progressive differentiation. Amphibians. *In* "Analysis of Development" (B. H. Willier, P. A. Weiss and V. Hamburger, eds.), Section VI, Chapter 1, pp. 230-296. Saunders, Philadelphia.

HÖRSTADIUS, S. 1928. Ueber die Determination des Keimes bei Echinodermen. *Acta Zool. Stockholm* **1**: 1-191.

HÖRSTADIUS, S. 1935. Ueber die Determination im Verlaufe der Eiachse bei Seeigeln. *Pubbl. staz. zool. Napoli* **14**: 251-479.

HÖRSTADIUS, S. 1939. The mechanics of sea urchin development, studied by operative methods. *Biol. Revs.* **14**: 132-179.

HÖRSTADIUS, S. 1949. Experimental researches on the developmental physiology of the sea urchin. *Pubbl. staz. zool. Napoli* **21** (Suppl.): 131-172.

HUXLEY, J. S., AND DE BEER, G. R. 1934. "The Elements of Experimental Embryology." Cambridge U.P., London.

IRWIN, M. R. 1949. Immunological studies in embryology and genetics. *Quart. Rev. Biol.* **24:** 109-123.

IRWIN, M. R. 1955. Immunogenetics. *In* "Biological Specificity and Growth" (E. G. Butler, ed.), Chapter III, pp. 55-71. Princeton U.P., Princeton.

KERR, J. G. 1919. Vertebrata with the exception of Mammalia. "Textbook of Embryology." Vol. II. Macmillan, London.

KING, T. J., AND BRIGGS, R. 1955. Changes in the nuclei of differentiating gastrula cells, as demonstrated by nuclear transplantation. *Proc. Natl. Acad. Sci. U.S.* **41:** 321-325.

KÖLLIKER, A. 1861. "Entwicklungsgeschichte des Menschen und der höheren Thiere." Wilhelm Engelmann, Leipzig.

KUUSI, T. 1951. Ueber die chemische Natur der Induktionsstoffe, mit besonderer Berücksichtigung der Rolle der Proteine und der Nukleinsäure. *Ann. Zool. Soc. Zool. Botan. Fennicae Vanamo* **14:** 1-98.

LANDAUER, W. 1948. Hereditary abnormalities and their chemically induced phenocopies. *Growth* **12** (Suppl.): 171-200.

LANDAUER, W. 1954. On the chemical production of developmental abnormalities and of phenocopies in chicken embryos. *J. Cellular Comp. Physiol.* **43,** Suppl. **1:** 261-305.

LEWIS, W. H. 1943. The role of the superficial gel layer in gastrulation of the zebra fish egg. (Abstract.) *Anat. Record* **85:** 326.

LILLIE, F. R. 1909. Polarity and bilaterality of the annelid egg. Experiments with centrifugal force. *Biol. Bull.* **16:** 54-79.

LILLIE, F. R. 1919. "Problems of Fertilization." Univ. Chicago Press, Chicago.

LINDAHL, P. 1936. Zur Kenntnis der physiologischen Grundlagen der Determination im Seeigelkeim. *Acta Zool. Stockholm* **17:** 179-365.

LINDAHL, P. 1942. Contributions to the physiology of form generation in the development of the sea urchin. *Quart. Rev. Biol.* **17:** 213-227.

LOEB, J. 1905. "Studies in General Physiology" (Decennial Publications of the University of Chicago, 2nd Series, Volume XV, Parts I and II). Univ. Chicago Press, Chicago.

LOEB, L. 1912. Growth of tissue in culture media and its significance for the analysis of growth phenomena. *Anat. Record* **6:** 109-120.

LOEB, L. 1945. "The Biological Basis of Individuality." C. C Thomas. Springfield, Illinois.

MANGOLD, O. 1923. Transplantationsversuche zur Frage der Spezifität und der Bildung der Keimblätter. *Arch. mikroskop. Anat. u. Entwicklungsmech.* **100:** 198-301.

MEYER, A. W. 1939. "The Rise of Embryology." Stanford U.P., California.

MORGAN, T. H. 1934. "Embryology and Genetics." Columbia U.P., New York.

MOSCONA, A., AND MOSCONA, H. 1952. The dissociation and aggregation of cells from organ rudiments of the early chick embryo. *J. Anat.* **86:** 287-301.

NAGEL, E. 1954. Malicious philosophies of science. *In* "Sovereign Reason," Chapter 1, pp. 17-35. Free Press, Glencoe, Illinois.

NEEDHAM, J. 1931. "Chemical Embryology," 3 vols. Cambridge U.P., London.

NEEDHAM, J. 1934. "A History of Embryology." Cambridge U.P., London.

NEEDHAM, J. 1942. "Biochemistry and Morphogenesis." Cambridge U.P., London.

NICHOLAS, J. S. 1927. Application of experimental methods to the study of developing *Fundulus* embryos. *Proc. Natl. Acad. Sci. U.S.* **13:** 695-698.

NICHOLAS, J. S. 1934. Experiments on developing rats. I. Limits of foetal regeneration; behavior of embryonic material in abnormal environments. *Anat. Record* **58:** 387-413.

NICHOLAS, J. S. 1945. Blastulation, its role in pregastrular organization in *Amblystoma punctatum. J. Exptl. Zool.* **100:** 265-299.

NIEUWKOOP, P. D. 1952. Activation and organization of the central nervous system in amphibians. *J. Exptl. Zool.* **120:** 1-108.

NIU, M. C. 1956. New approaches to the problem of embryonic induction. *In* "Cellular Mechanisms in Differentiation and Growth" (D. Rudnick, ed.), Chapter 7, pp. 155-171. Princeton U.P., Princeton, New Jersey.

OPPENHEIMER, J. M. 1940. The non-specificity of the germ-layers. *Quart. Rev. Biol.* **15:** 1-27. Reprinted in this volume, pp. 256-294.

OPPENHEIMER, J. M. 1955a. Problems, Concepts and their History.

In "Analysis of Development" (B. H. Willier, P. A. Weiss and V. Hamburger, eds.), Section I, pp. 1-24. Saunders, Philadelphia. Reprinted in this volume, pp. 117-172.

OPPENHEIMER, J. M. 1955b. The differentiation of derivatives of the lower germ layers in *Fundulus* following the implantation of shield grafts. *J. Exptl. Zool.* **128**: 525-559.

PANTIN, C. F. A. 1955. The journal and its editors. *J. Exptl. Biol.* **32**: 1-3.

PORTER, K. R. 1954. Cell and tissue differentiation in relation to growth (animals). *In* "Dynamics of Growth Processes" (E. J. Boell, ed.), Chapter V, pp. 95-110. Princeton U.P., Princeton.

POULSON, D. F. 1940. The effects of certain X-chromosome deficiencies on the embryonic development of *Drosophila melanogaster*. *J. Exptl. Zool.* **83**: 271-325.

POULSON, D. F. 1945. Chromosomal control of embryogenesis in *Drosophila*. *Am. Naturalist* **79**: 340-363.

RHUMBLER, L. 1899. Physikalische Analyse von Lebenserscheinungen der Zelle. III. Mechanik der Pigmentzusammenhäufungen in den Embryonalzellen der Amphibieneier. *Wilhelm Roux' Arch. Entwickelungsmech. Organ.* **9**: 63-102.

RHUMBLER, L. 1902. Zur Mechanik des Gastrulationsvorganges insbesondere der Invagination. Eine entwickelungsmechanische Studie. *Wilhelm Roux' Arch. Entwicklungsmech. Organ.* **14**: 401-476.

ROUX, W. 1885a. "Einleitung" zu den "Beiträgen zur Entwickelungsmechanik des Embryo." *Z. Biol.* **21**: 411-428.

ROUX, W. 1885b. Beiträge zur Entwickelungsmechanik des Embryo. Nr. I. Zur Orientirung über einige Probleme der embryonalen Entwickelung. *Z. Biol.* **21**: 429-524.

ROUX, W. 1893. Ueber die Spezifikation der Furchungszellen und über die bei der Postgeneration und Regeneration anzunehmenden Vorgänge. *Biol. Zentr.* **13**: 612-625; 656-672.

ROUX, W. 1895. Ueber den "Cytotropismus" der Furchungszellen des Grasfrosches (Rana fusca). *Wilhelm Roux' Arch. Entwickelungsmech. Organ.* **1**: 43-68; 161-202.

ROUX, W. *et al.*, eds., 1912. "Terminologie der Entwicklungsmechanik der Tiere und Pflanzen." Wilhelm Engelmann, Leipzig.

RUFFINI, A. 1925. "Fisiogenia." F. Vallardi, Milan.

RUNNSTRÖM, J. 1928. Zur experimentellen Analyse der Wirkung des Lithiums auf den Seeigelkeim. *Acta Zool. Stockholm* **9**: 365-424.

RUNNSTRÖM, J. 1954. Die Analyse der primären Differenzierungs-vorgänge im Seeigelkeim. *Verhandl. deut. zool. Ges. Tübingen,* pp. 32-68.

SCHECHTMAN, A. M. 1947. Antigens of early developmental stages of the chick. *J. Exptl. Zool.* 105: 329-348.

SCHECHTMAN, A. M. 1952. Physical and chemical changes in the circulating blood. *Ann. N.Y. Acad. Sci.* 55: 85-98.

SCHECHTMAN, A. M. 1955. Ontogeny of the blood and related anti-gens and their significance for the theory of differentiation. *In* "Biological Specificity and Growth" (E. G. Butler, ed.), Chapter I, pp. 3-31. Princeton U. P., Princeton.

SCHLEIP, W. 1929. "Die Determination der Primitiventwicklung. Eine zusammenfassende Darstellung der Ergebnisse über das Deter-minationsgeschehen in den ersten Entwicklungsstadien der Tiere." Akademische Verlagsgesellschaft, Leipzig.

SCOTT, G. 1954. "The Architecture of Humanism. A Study of the History of Taste." Doubleday, New York.

SEIDEL, F. 1955. Geschichtliche Linien und Problematik der Ent-wicklungsphysiologie. *Naturwissenschaften* 42: 275-286.

SONNEBORN, T. M. 1943a. Gene and cytoplasm. I. The determina-tion and inheritance of the killer character in variety 4 of *Para-mecium aurelia. Proc. Natl. Acad. Sci. U.S.* 29: 329-338.

SONNEBORN, T. M. 1943b. Gene and cytoplasm. II. The bearing of the determination and inheritance of characters in *Paramecium aurelia* on the problems of cytoplasmic inheritance, pneumococcus transformations, mutations and development. *Proc. Natl. Acad. Sci. U.S.* 29: 338-343.

SONNEBORN, T. M. 1947. Developmental mechanisms in *Parame-cium. Growth* 11 (Suppl.): 291-307.

SONNEBORN, T. M. 1951. The role of the genes in cytoplasmic in-heritance. *In* "Genetics in the Twentieth Century" (L. C. Dunn, ed.), Chapter 14, pp. 291-314. Macmillan, New York.

SPEMANN, H. 1901. Ueber Correlationen in der Entwickelung des Auges. *Verhandl. anat. Ges.* 15: 61-79.

SPEMANN, H. 1906a. Ueber eine neue Methode der embryonalen Transplantation. *Verhandl. deut. zool. Ges. Marburg,* pp. 196-202.

SPEMANN, H. 1906b. Ueber embryonale Transplantation. *Naturw. Rundschau* 21: 543-546; 557-560.

SPEMANN, H. 1914. Ueber verzögerte Kernversorgung von Keimtei-len. *Verhandl. deut. zool. Ges. Freiburg,* pp. 216-221.

SPEMANN, H. 1921. Die Erzeugung tierischer Chimären durch heteroplastische embryonale Transplantation zwischen *Triton cristatus* und *taeniatus*. *Wilhelm Roux' Arch. Entwicklungsmech. Organ.* 48: 533-570.

SPEMANN, H. 1928. Die Entwicklung seitlicher und dorso-ventraler Keimhälften bei verzögerter Kernversorgung. *Z. wiss. Zool.* 132: 105-134.

SPEMANN, H. 1936. "Experimentelle Beiträge zu einer Theorie der Entwicklung." Springer, Berlin.

SPEMANN, H. 1938. "Embryonic Development and Induction." Yale U. P., New Haven, Conn.

SPEMANN, H. 1943. "Forschung und Leben" (F. W. Spemann, ed.). J. Engelhorns Nachf. Adolf Spemann, Stuttgart.

SPEMANN, H., AND MANGOLD, H. 1924. Ueber Induktion von Embryonalanlagen durch Implantation artfremder Organisatoren. *Arch. mikroskop. Anat. u. Entwicklungsmech.* 100: 599-638.

SPIEGEL, M. 1955. The reaggregation of dissociated sponge cells. *Ann. N.Y. Acad. Sci.* 60: 1056-1078.

SPIEGELMAN, S. 1948. Differentiation as the controlled production of unique enzymatic patterns. *Symposia Soc. Exptl. Biol.* 2: 286-325.

SPRATT, N. 1956. Form changes in early chick blastoderms and the probable role of intercellular fibers. (Abstract.) *Anat. Record* 124: 364-365.

TOIVONEN, S. 1949. Zur Frage der Leistungsspezifität abnormer Induktoren. *Experientia* 5: 323-326.

TOIVONEN, S. 1950. Stoffliche Induktoren. *Rev. suisse zool.* 57: 41-56.

TOIVONEN, S. 1951. Verschiedenheit der Induktionsleistungen des Lebergewebes von hungernden und gut ernährten Meerschweinchen in Implantatversuch bei *Triturus*. *Arch. Soc. Zool. Botan. Fennicae Vanamo* 6: 63-71.

TOIVONEN, S., AND KUUSI, T. 1948. Implantationsversuche mit in verschiedener Weise vorbehandelten abnormen Induktoren bei Triton. *Ann. Zool. Soc. Zool. Botan. Fennicae Vanamo* 13: 1-19.

TOWNES, P. L., AND HOLTFRETER, J. 1955. Directed movements and selective adhesion of embryonic amphibian cells. *J. Exptl. Zool.* 128: 53-120.

TRINKAUS, J. P. 1951. A study of the mechanism of epiboly in the egg of *Fundulus heteroclitus*. *J. Exptl. Zool.* 118: 269-319.

TYLER, A. 1955. Gametogenesis, fertilization and parthenogenesis.

In "Analysis of Development" (B. H. Willier, P. A. Weiss, and V. Hamburger, eds.), Section V, Chapter 1, pp. 170-212. Saunders, Philadelphia.

VON UBISCH, L. 1925. Entwicklungsphysiologische Studien an Seeigelkeimen. II. Die Entstehung von Einheitslarven aus verschmolzenen Keimen. *Z. wiss. Zool.* **124:** 457-468.

VON UEXKÜLL, J. 1946. "Der unsterbliche Geist in der Natur. Gespräche." Christian Wegner, Hamburg.

VOGT, W. 1925. Gestaltungsanalyse am Amphibienkeim mit örtlicher Vitalfärbung. Vorwort über Wege und Ziele. I. Teil. Methodik und Wirkungsweise der örtlichen Vitalfärbung mit Agar als Farbträger. *Wilhelm Roux' Arch. Entwicklungsmech. Organ,* **106:** 542-610.

VOGT, W. 1929. Gestaltungsanalyse am Amphibienkeim mit örtlicher Vitalfärbung. II. Teil. Gastrulation und Mesodermbildung bei Urodelen und Anuren. *Wilhelm Roux' Arch. Entwicklungsmech. Organ.* **120:** 384- 706.

WARBURG, O. 1908. Beobachtungen über die Oxidations-Prozesse vom Seeigelei. *Z. physiol. Chem.* **57:** 1-16.

WARBURG, O. 1910. Ueber die Oxidationen in lebenden Zellen nach Versuchen am Seeigelei. *Z. physiol. Chem.* **66:** 305-340.

WEISS, P. 1926. Morphodynamik. *Abhandl. theoret. Biol.* **23:** 1-43.

WEISS, P. 1955. Nervous System (Neurogenesis). *In* "Analysis of Development" (B. H. Willier, P. A. Weiss, and V. Hamburger, eds.), Section VII, Chapter 1, pp. 346-401. Saunders, Philadelphia.

WEISS, P., AND ANDRES, G. 1952. Experiments on the fate of embryonic cells (chick) disseminated by the vascular route. *J. Exptl. Zool.* **121:** 449-487.

WILSON, E. B. 1892. The cell-lineage of *Nereis. J. Morphol.* **6:** 361-480.

WILSON, E. B. 1896. "The Cell in Development and Inheritance." Columbia U.P., New York.

WILSON, E. B. 1899. Cell-lineage and ancestral reminiscence. *Biol. Lectures Marine Biol. Lab. Woods Holl* **1898:** 21-42.

WILSON, E. B. 1900. "The Cell in Development and Inheritance," 2nd ed. Columbia U. P., New York.

WILSON, E. B. 1925. "The Cell in Development and Heredity," 3d ed. Columbia U. P., New York.

WILSON, H. V. 1900. Formation of the blastopore in the frog egg. *Anat. Anz.* **18:** 209-239.

WILSON, H. V. 1907. On some phenomena of coalescence and regeneration in sponges. *J. Exptl. Zool.* **5**: 245-258.

WILSON, H. V. 1911. On the behavior of the dissociated cells in hydroids, *Alcyonaria,* and *Asterias. J. Exptl. Zool.* **11**: 281-338.

WILSON, J. W. 1944. Cellular tissue and the dawn of the cell theory. *Isis* **35**: 168-173.

WILSON, J. W. 1947a. Dutrochet and the cell theory. *Isis* **37**: 14-21.

WILSON, J. W. 1947b. Virchow's contribution to the cell theory. *J. Hist. Med. & Allied Sci.* **2**: 163-178.

WRIGHT, S. 1916. An intensive study of the inheritance of color and of other coat characters in guinea pigs with especial reference to graded variation. *Carnegie Inst. Washington Publ.* **241**: 59-160.

WRIGHT, S. 1945. Genes as physiological agents: general considerations. *Am. Naturalist* **79**: 289-303.

YAMADA, T. 1950. Regional differentiation of the isolated ectoderm of the *Triturus* gastrula induced through a protein extract. *Embryologia* **1**: 1-20.

YAMADA, T., AND TAKATA, K. 1956. Spino-caudal induction by pentose nucleoprotein isolated from the kidney. *Embryologia* **3**: 69-79.

Questions Posed
by Classical Descriptive
and Experimental Embryology*

E MBRYOLOGY is surely one of the oldest scientific interests of man. The nature of generation and of development was the subject of a special treatise at least as early as the time of Hippocrates, and has never during the intervening centuries lost its interest either for professional investigators or for ordinary or extraordinary laymen, and even the *nouvelle vague* with DNA at its crest has increased rather than decreased this interest. The problems of development are central to all biology, since organisms are as they are by virtue of the manner by which they have become what they are as individuals.

My assignment differed somewhat from that of the other speakers in the Plenary Symposia. They were asked to discuss the present status of work in their fields; my task was defined as describing the accomplishments of the scientists whose work

* A lecture delivered at the Plenary Session on Development, XVI. International Congress of Zoology, Washington, D. C., 1964, sponsored by the National Academy of Sciences of the United States of America. Reprinted from *Ideas in Modern Biology*, edited by John A. Moore (*Proc. XVI. Intl. Congr. Zool.*, Vol. VI), Chap. VI, pp. 205–227, Natural History Press (Doubleday & Company, Inc.), Garden City, N.Y., 1965. Written at the Department of Biology, Brown University. Part of the material overlaps that in an essay-review on F. Baltzer's *Theodor Boveri* ("Theodor Boveri: the Cell Biologists' Embryologist," *Quart. Rev. Biol.*, Vol. XXXVIII, 1963, pp. 245–249.

preceded that of present-day developmental biologists, and to evaluate the work that made it possible to begin the embryological investigations that are being carried on with such vigor today. Thus my design has been to discuss the contributions made by classical embryology toward a solution of the problem of how an egg and embryo develop an adult organism. Since I believe that the principal contribution science can make is to ask questions, I have tried to address myself to the problem of ascertaining the questions asked by classical embryologists.

One primary difficulty about this assignment is to know what "classical" means. Classical is an adjective that is now too often used to signify the old-fashioned in contrast to the modern and up-to-date. In its more respectful connotation, it is used to refer to the great pioneering works upon which later investigations have followed. It is in this sense that I shall discuss some of the important contributions of some of our predecessors. What is most fascinating about them is that the questions they asked are the questions we are still asking today.

Thus, in considering the contributions of the past I do not wish merely to list discoveries. Surely by now it has been said often enough, if not too often, that Aristotle observed chick embryos, as did Albertus Magnus after him; that Fabricius described the anatomy of embryos, that Harvey used the phrase *ex ovo omnia* and discovered the role of the blastoderm; that embryologists of the 17th and early 18th centuries thought they saw the adult preformed in the egg or in what we should now call the spermatozoon, and that embryologists after them were sure that they did not; that building upon the work of Caspar Friedrich Wolff, and especially of Pander, Karl Ernst von Baer observed the importance of the germ layers in all vertebrates, discovered the mammalian egg, and brought embryology into its full dignity as a science.

I am not sure, by the way, whether von Baer's work completes, or simply commences, classical embryology. If the latter, we might continue the list of familiar events: that Haeckel, who depended too little on precise observations, related ontogenetic phenomena causally to phylogenetic ones, that His and Goette related them to mechanical ones; that Roux began to experiment on embryos and thought a half egg formed a half embryo, that Driesch followed him and thought it did not. And so on, and so on, until we come to the modern period and the discoveries and outlooks of Harrison and Spemann, whose standards of insight and workmanship would be called classical by any definition. All these predecessors of Harrison and Spemann made contributions whose importance has not been, and ought not to be minimized, but I have no more to say about most of them here than has already been said elsewhere.

One of the things I do wish to emphasize, however, is the nature of the *first* questions asked by each of those I discuss, its relationship to his own later thought, and to the thought of later embryologists. How did each investigator's own questions change as he worked? Which of these questions, the earlier or later ones, were to prove of most influence?

Wilhelm Roux, who was the founder of what he called *Entwickelungsmechanik*, of what we have been calling experimental embryology but now are beginning to call by the better name analytical embryology, tells the story of a visit by the Emperor Franz Josef to the Anatomical Institute in Innsbruck when Roux was working there. Roux showed him that isolated cleavage cells of a frog's egg attracted each other when explanted, as he thought, by what he called cytotropism. The Emperor asked Roux, "How does one discover something like this?" and Roux replied, "Your Majesty, you must first have a question in mind, and then look for an appropriate means of extorting an unequivocal answer to it" (Roux, 1922, p. 166). What we shall discuss here are the questions that our heroes began by having in mind, rather than the techniques and

64

means of extorting the answers — though we recognize, of course, the great importance of the methodology.

Roux was not the first to recognize, privately or publicly, the importance of the manner of framing the question for an understanding of development. The asking of specific answerable questions went at least as far back as Aristotle, who asked perhaps the most important one: When one organ follows another in development, is there a causal relationship? (Aristotle, *Generation of Animals,* 1953 ed., p. 149.) Wolff recognized that a defect of preformationism was the closing of the possibility of asking questions concerning the nature of development in our sense. Von Baer, too, usually accredited as the greatest of embryologists largely for his descriptive studies and his interpretations of them, asked important questions as to mechanisms of development. The eye rudiments, he said, develop as if they were actively pushed out [*hervorgetrieben*] from the foremost brain vesicle. But what, asked von Baer, pushes them out [*Was ist nun aber das Hervortreibende*] (von Baer, 1828, I, 24)? This is still a question to which we have no complete answer; we know the mesoderm has something to do with it, but the means to answer the question are not yet in embryologists' minds; and von Baer had many other such insights for which he is not usually given credit (Oppenheimer, 1963).

Discussion of all the questions raised by all our forerunners would occupy a whole book; I shall therefore take up here the contributions and questions of a few individuals only — Roux, Driesch, and Boveri — and the choice is dictated, as you will see, by the fact that they were the most adventurous of the pioneers. I believe you will be startled, as I have been, to learn the degree to which they were concerned with the same problems that confront us today. Let us begin with Wilhelm Roux. Even Driesch, who disagreed with him on many issues, said that for Roux's work "the often mis-used word 'classic' is suitable" (Driesch, 1951, p. 98).

WILHELM ROUX 1850–1924

It is usually Roux who is given the credit for pioneering work in first raising the questions we still try to answer now; and it was surely he who placed embryology on its present analytical footing by trying to answer them experimentally. Roux raised a great number of trenchant questions. He was technically not very adept in his attempts to solve them experimentally, but he did not hesitate to write about them, and to write about them again and again, so that there are abundant sources of information concerning the development of his thought.

One of the first questions he raised with respect to development concerned the nature of the forces responsible for what he was later to call functional adaptation, and he discussed this problem at great length in 1881 in a work entitled *Der Kampf der Theile im Organismus. Ein Beitrag zur Vervollständigung der mechanischen Zweckmässigkeitslehre* [*The struggle of parts in the organism. A contribution towards the completion of a mechanical theory of teleology*] (Roux, 1881). His analogy between the struggle for existence of organisms in nature, on the one hand, and the competition of parts in a developing organism, on the other, led him to question the relative significance of dependent versus independent differentiation, a question that was to dominate embryology after his time. Ten years later he thought he answered it in favor of independent differentiation by killing one blastomere of the frog's egg at the two-cell stage and finding that the surviving blastomere formed a half embryo (Roux, 1888). Roux was never one to hide his light under a bushel, and even went so far as to predict, at one point, that in several centuries young students would read his work with the same interest with which he had studied Descartes' (Roux, 1923, p. 170). He never went so far as to claim identity, in print at least, with Jupiter, but he did say that the ideas expressed in the *Kampf der Theile* came full-blown into his mind [*Diese Theorie bildete sich in meinem Gehirn ganz von selbst aus, jedenfalls aus den in der Studienzeit aufgenommenen Gedankenkeimen*] (Roux, 1923, p. 149).

One of the things that is less often remembered today is that Roux, at least in his early days, in opting for self-differentiation, did not exclude that dependent differentiation is an integral part of it. He was interested from early on in the influence of the environment in development. In his thesis, his first publication, when he was searching for factors determining the manner of branching of the blood vessels, he already posed the possibility of three causes of development (Roux, 1878, p. 243): "(1) Originally inherited modes of development, conditioned by the laws of growth and the specific functions of organs. (2) External transforming influences impinging on individual organs and on the whole organism." His third set of causes, hydraulic forces, was highly particular to blood-vessel formation and need not be further discussed here.

His early interest in the influence of the environment on development was not merely theoretical; he performed experiments testing the effects on development of stimuli from the external surroundings. The first question he asked directly of the egg was: What are the factors determining its three planes of symmetry? Are they within the egg, or external to it? In 1884 he tested the effects of gravity on amphibian development by placing frogs' eggs in a rotating wheel; he also evaluated the effects on them of light, heat, and terrestrial magnetism (Roux, 1884; Pflüger, 1883, independently attempted to assess by a different method the effects of gravity on the determination of the median plane of symmetry of the frog's egg). Roux later (1885c, 1891) was to test also the effects of "free" electricity and of alternating and direct current on early and later development of amphibian and other eggs. When, in Roux's 1884 experiments on altered gravity, the embryos developed normally, and self-differentiation might have seemed assured, Roux did not stop, but went on to demonstrate (Roux, 1887) that the point of entrance of the spermatozoon and the so-called copulation path of the sperm nucleus does in fact determine the median plane.

Roux wrote in his autobiography (Roux, 1923, p. 163) that after forty years his doctrine of self-differentiation was still misunderstood, in that self-differentiation was construed as a mode of operation [*Wirkungsweise*], whereas he had in reality meant by it merely a topographical causal principle, which determines the differentiation of a delimited part of the egg or embryo, but that the realizing factors can and must be added from outside. Self-differentiation occurs, he adds in the autobiography, like every other change in the world, as a result of the operation [*Wirken*] of parts upon each other, by the effects of parts of the self-differentiating region upon each other, thus by dependent differentiation of sometimes very small subsidiary parts one upon the other.

By 1923, interactions between developing parts had been demonstrated experimentally by transplantation methods, and the statement just cited might seem possibly to have been thought up after the fact. But two years before the publication of the article on the determination of the plane of bilateral symmetry, Roux wrote a theoretical introduction (Roux, 1885a) to his *Beiträge zur Entwickelungsmechanik des Embryo* in which he explicitly emphasized the distinction between self-differentiation, dependent differentiation, and the *combined* differentiation of structures or parts of embryos through self- and dependent differentiation. The first *Beitrag* contains the specific statement, with respect to correlative development, that "it must always be remembered that many of these processes may be released [*ausgelöst*] by nearer or farther parts of the organism, or influenced by them in their differentiation" (Roux, 1885b, p. 523).

If this has a surprisingly Spemannish ring, so has some of the terminology that Roux developed during the course of his considerations. When Roux summarized these concepts in his autobiography (Roux, 1923, p. 161) he stated that it was on the basis of separation of determining [*determinierende*] factors and realizing [*realisierende*] factors that the distinction between self-differentiation and dependent differentiation, and their combination, rests. Although the concepts, as intimated above, had their origin in 1881 in the *Kampf der Theile*, I do not find the *words* "determining" and "realizing" used in the 1881 or 1885 writings; but they are specifically used, and discussed at some length, in 1905 in the first number of his *Vorträge und Aufsätze* (Roux, 1905, pp. 31, 39, 41, 43, 139, 172, 183, 206–210). And he even went so far in this work as to consider successive determination, writing that he had built upon Wolff's concepts of epigenesis to come to the concept of "successive determination of new form," thus to the concept of "gradual repeated, degree by degree, new determination of manifoldness through subsequent effects by what is already determined" (Roux, 1905, p. 244).

He ultimately performed his own experiments, or tried to, on the relations of developing parts to each other; here is where the cytotropism experiments (Roux, 1894) come in that were demonstrated to Franz Josef. Holtfreter, in his pioneering paper on tissue affinity (Holtfreter, 1939), which has led to the modern work on aggregation and disaggregation of cells, states that the original point of departure for such studies was Roux's postulate of a mutual attraction of living cells.

But to return to our chronology. Even before the experiment of separating the blastomeres Roux came to the formulation of other important questions and conceptions that still dominate us today and that some of us forget that Roux expressed. His definition of development in the introduction to the *Beiträge* has never been improved upon. He defined development as the production of perceptible manifoldness [*das Entstehen von wahrnehmbarer Mannigfaltigkeit*] (Roux, 1885a, p. 414). But the important thing is that he immediately recognized that this process is divisible into two principal processes, which are usually combined. The first is a true increase in manifoldness. The second is a transformation of imperceptible manifoldness. These processes he was later to call neo-epigenesis and neopreformation (Roux, 1905, pp. 101–103). Embryologists ever since have addressed themselves to the problem of to what degree, at a particular moment in differentiation, these two phases of development are in their ascendency. We still today, and even more so than ever, are examining it when we inquire, for instance, to what degree enzymes are induced in embryos. Are they formed anew, or are their precursors present? To what degree are their precursors similar to the finished product? The work of Markert on isozymes is intimately related to this question.

The posing of this particular question in this particular way was perhaps the most important contribution of Roux. It is quite possible, however, that it might have had little influence had he not performed his dramatic experiments separating the blastomeres of the frog (Roux, 1888), which led ultimately to the experiments and analyses we perform today.

But again, before he performed these experiments of dividing the frog's egg, and even before he wrote some of the other works we have been discussing, he wrote another theoretical paper of the greatest influence and import, raising questions concerning the significance for development of the division of the chromatin (Roux, 1883a). Even if he made the wrong option, postulating that its division is qualitative, his consideration of the role of the chromatin in development led to a great deal of experimentation to test his hypothesis. To him, and to others to follow, the importance of apparent mosaic development or self-differentiation was that it seemed to support the opinion that the chromatin is divided qualitatively. The revelation by some of his followers that eggs could be regulative in development negated this hypothesis in their minds, as in ours, and thus made way for new ones.

When Roux told the Emperor that there were two things an embryologist had to do to make a discovery, he omitted a third. He did not state that the question asked of an embryo had to be intelligible not only to the embryo, but also to embryologists—that is, it had also to be couched in terms of interest and relevance to the embryology of the day if it was to bear influence. Roux asked other questions of embryos, or knew that they had to be asked, that only now are recognized as being important. For instance, when he wrote about the role of competition between cells, he related it to concepts of immunology, and in the same connection he discussed the significance of cell death. When L. von Liebermann in 1918 wrote a paper entitled "A selection hypothesis. Attempt at a unified explanation of immunity, tissue immunity and manifestations of immunity" [*Selektionshypothese. Versuch einer einheitlichen Erklärung der Immunität, Gewebsimmunität und Immunitätserscheinungen*], Roux replied to it in an article (Roux, 1918), published in a bacteriological journal, entitled "Immunization by the selection of parts, a reaction to poisoning and diminished nutrition. An old hypothesis" [*"Immunisierung durch Teilauslese" gegen Vergiftung und verminderte Ernährung. Eine alte Hypothese*]. He called it an old hypothesis, already in 1918, because he had previously expressed it tentatively in the *Kampf der Theile*, implying that cells subjected to poisoning, for instance, are eliminated, and that cells immune to the effects of the poison are those that give rise to progeny that survive. In the preface to the second printing in 1881 of the *Kampf der Theile* (not in the preface to the first printing published the same year), he postulates that the organism becomes more resistant to poison by overcoming poisoning, "and so resistance to poisons can come about just as does immunity to infectious germs" (cited from reprint of second printing in Roux, 1895, I, 147), and he repeated the analogy in 1883 (Roux, 1883b, p. 425). In 1918 he discussed toxins, fevers, and generalized diseases as agents leading to cell necrosis, cell degeneration, and cell atrophy, thus as agents leading to selection within the organism of cell strains resistant to them, or of strains that develop resistance after exposure to them (see also entry *Immunität* in Roux, 1912, p. 201). Roux's 1918 paper is well worth reading by investigators now working in the field of immuno-embryology and by immunologists concerned with selection theories. In Roux's own day, the value of these concepts and the questions he asked concerning them were not yet apparent.

Before leaving Roux, we may point to one more of his theoretical questions; this concerns the relationship of quantity to quality. The analysis of development, he wrote, must first be qualitative, a breaking down of complicated events into different modes of action and the factors related to them. Only when one of these factors is ascertained can the magnitude of its effect be investigated. Thus, Kant's dictum that science is only true science insofar as it is mathematical is not pertinent to developmental mechanics. A correct qualitative analysis of developmental events is also true science, and in fact in this science it is primary, according to Roux (1923, p. 175).

HANS DRIESCH 1867–1941

Hans Driesch, in the history books, is usually introduced by the description of his strictly qualitative experiments (Driesch, 1891b) separating blastomeres of echinoderm eggs. His results, indicating that early blastomeres form whole, not half embryos, were opposed to those of Roux on the frog; Driesch thus demonstrated the epigenetic and non-mosaic non-self-differentiating nature of development, and Driesch interpreted the embryo (and even its parts) as a harmonious equipotential system. This answered one old question and proved that the division of the chromatin could not be qualitative as Roux had postulated. But it raised many new ones.

A corollary of Driesch's epigenetic concepts was his comparison of the presumptive significance of an embryonic part (that is, what it usually forms) with its prospective potency (that is, what it might form in a variety of situations). The results of separating the blastomeres showed that the prospective potency is far wider than the prospective significance. What the history books report less often is that he performed a number of other experiments confirming this; for instance, in the winter of 1892–1893, he displaced cells of sea urchin embryos into atypical relationships with each other by shaking them into abnormal positions [*Verlagerung*]; the developing plutei were normal. In these experiments Driesch demonstrated the interchangeability [*Vertretbarkeit*] of ectoderm and endoderm (Driesch, 1893a, 1893c).

But even earlier, in experiments reported in 1892, he compressed the four-cell stage of sea urchin eggs between a microscope slide and a cover slip, with the result that the third cleavage plane was vertical, rather than horizontal; again, the plutei developing from such eggs were normal, and the specific positions of the cleavage planes were thus seen not to be critical determining factors so far as later development is concerned. To Driesch, this too negated Roux's concepts of mosaic development, and he was thus led to the conclusion that "the relative position of a blastomere in the whole will determine in general what will develop from it; . . . its prospective significance is a function of its position" [*Die relative Lage einer Blastomere im Ganzen wird wohl ganz allgemein bestimmen was aus ihr hervorgeht; . . . ihre prospektive Beziehung ist eine Funktion des Ortes*] (Driesch, 1892, p. 39).

This conclusion so well fits what we think of cellular differentiation that we tend to overlook Driesch's original meaning. To him, the dictum that the fate of a cell is a function of its position in the whole lacked causal implication. Function to him, he emphasized later, meant function in a mathematical sense: a particular cell has a particular position with respect

73

to over-all symmetry in terms of up-and-down, fore-and-hind, left-and-right, "as in a system of coordinates in analytical geometry," as he put it (Driesch, 1951, p. 87; for earlier comment see Driesch, 1893b, p. 305; Driesch, 1894, p. 12).

In fact, an interest in mathematics and physics was of inestimable influence on Driesch's early work. He wrote his thesis (1889) under the tutelage of Haeckel, on hydroids. At this time, according to his autobiography, he became skeptical of the notion that phylogeny and ontogeny could be causally related in Haeckel's sense. Two vague questions became outlined in his mind: (1) If there could be a "dynamic" geology that studies the forces by which the earth has been brought to its present state, could there not also be a "dynamic" biology, a science of the forces bringing about the configuration of organisms? (2) Could not cleavage patterns be mathematically defined, so that a finite system of comparisons could be drawn up — so that, just as in crystallography, it could be said that only these particular forms of cleavage can exist, and none other (Driesch, 1951, pp. 67–68)?

Here is an important question raised by Driesch, the nature of the mathematical and physical characteristics of the cleaving egg. He was not able to answer it, and it is still today a subject of active research. It was only after he first thought in these terms that he first read Roux's 1889 lecture on developmental mechanics as a science of the future (Roux, 1890). In 1891 he published a small book entitled *Die mathematisch-mechanische Betrachtung morphologischer Probleme der Biologie. Eine kritische Studie* (Driesch, 1891a). This was a rather philosophical discussion of what mechanics (in the sense that the word was then used in biology) and mathematics could contribute to the understanding of causality in development. "A problem is mechanically elucidated if, mathematically formulated, it can be reduced to mechanical principles, and can be considered their result" (1891a, p. 9). He considered, among other biological phenomena, the relationships of the position

74

of cleavage planes to mathematical formulations and to various physical considerations, and he concluded with some speculation on purposiveness in relationship to mechanical explanation. He knew his book would not be looked upon with favor by Haeckel, but he sent him a copy, together with a letter asking whether development of the individual might not be considered from this new point of view. Neither the letter nor the book was acknowledged, but in due time Haeckel sent him an unwritten message, through a mutual friend, suggesting that Driesch take some time off in a mental hospital.

Only after the preparation of this little book — in fact, in 1891, the year it was published — did Driesch perform his experiment of separating blastomeres. But after this time, he began to read more philosophy than he had read before, and as early as 1892 when he wrote the first discussion of the theoretical significance of his experimental results (Driesch, 1892, Section VI) he raised the possibility that vitalistic interpretations are not incompatible with scientific methodology. One is reminded of the advice given to Roux by Schwalbe immediately after the publication of the *Kampf der Theile*: "Never write so philosophical a book again, or you will never be appointed to a professorship in anatomy" (Roux, 1923, p. 152).

Well, Driesch read philosophy, to which he was inclined, and became lost in admiration of the regulatory powers of the embryo, and eventually, after performing a number of other important experiments, he became a professor of philosophy and a vitalist. But a number of years before he abandoned embryology, he wrote another remarkable book, *Analytische Theorie der organischen Entwicklung* (Driesch, 1894), and many of the concepts and questions expressed in it deserve mention here; in fact, the content of this little book deserves an essay, or a series of essays, in itself.

Chemismus — that is, chemism as distinguished from chemistry — is emphasized as the basis of ontogenetic processes, and the rhythmicity of chemical action is pointed out. "The production of a substance at a specific time is . . . a chemical process; since this occurs in cells, chemical processes must occur in cells. . . . The results of ontogenesis come about by chemical phases. . . . There is nothing to hinder us from conceiving of the majority of these chemical effects as completely comprehensible; that is, we can learn to recognize the newly-formed substances that lead to the new morphological process, even though we may never be able to say why they are formed, and why at a particular moment" (Driesch, 1894, pp. 43–44).

He devotes a whole chapter (*op. cit.*, pp. 48–64) to *Auslösung,* the release, the triggering, the induction of ontogenetic processes, all implied by the word *Auslösung.* He discusses it in terms of energy relationships; he discusses position and induction [*Position und Induktion*] (p. 50), and in this connection states that perhaps it is not an organ itself that is induced but a sphere of activity [*Umfangskreis*] in which it exists, clearly foreshadowing the field theory (p. 51). He speaks of induction by push-and-pull [*Zug- und Druckinduktion*], of contact induction [*Berührungsinduktion*], of chemical induction [*chemische Induktion*], of chemical induction as a growth regulator (p. 57). Chains of effects are postulated. Roux's manifoldnesses, he writes, by affecting each other create new manifoldnesses, and these, affecting the original manifoldnesses, create new differences (p. 86). Here are acting and reacting systems working together by what we would now call feedback.

Although in a sentence already cited he might seem to have despaired of analyzing time-sequences of such actions, he devotes a full chapter (pp. 64–110) to time-sequences in ontogenetic processes. Induced effects show a definite fixed order in time; development exhibits phases, he repeats, and then he asks the questions (p. 65), "On what do the phases of development depend in the final instance? What are they, in the final instance?" Are not these the questions we are asking today when we analyze, or attempt to analyze, the time of action of genes?

In fact, Driesch himself discusses causes and effects in terms of nucleus and cytoplasm. "Insofar as it contains a nucleus, every cell, during ontogenesis, carries the totality of all primordia; insofar as it contains a specific cytoplasmic cell body, it is specifically enabled by this to respond to specific effects only" (p. 81). And in accounting for interaction between cytoplasm and nucleus he attributes a primary role to enzymes (the "ferments" in his terminology and in that of his contemporaries): "The determining organogenic materials are not produced directly by the nucleus, but arise in the cytoplasm only under the direction of the nucleus. We interpret this direction by the nucleus as fermentative action. Thus we think of the nucleus as a mixture [*Gemenge*] of ferment-like materials, of which each represents a kind of elementary process of the development in question. . . . By a releasing process [*Auslösungsvorgang*] a specific one of these ferments is set into action, and this may be a definite specific ferment, because the cytoplasm that functions as stimulus receiver and as intermediary between stimulus and response possesses a specific chemical constitution. When nuclear material is activated, then, under its guidance, the cytoplasm of its cell that had first influenced the nucleus is in turn itself changed, and thus the basis is established for a new elementary process, which itself is not only a result but also a cause" (*op. cit.*, p. 88). Here is feedback, again, if you will, between nucleus and cytoplasm.

Driesch even postulated nuclear exchange as a method of testing differences between nuclei (*op. cit.*, p. 72); modern embryologists who believe nuclear exchange a brand-new technique may be reminded that Rauber had already in 1886 interchanged cleavage nuclei between frogs and toads (Rauber, 1886); Roux referred to these experiments in passing (Roux, 1892, p. 90). Did Driesch know of these experiments? He does not refer to them, nor have many others since Roux; the em-

bryos died, and the results were negative, but Rauber expressed doubts, when he reported the experiments, that a
toad's egg developing with a frog's nucleus would become a
frog.

Why do we place now so little emphasis on Roux's strong
emphasis on the interrelationship of parts, and on Driesch's
remarkable materialistic analysis? Perhaps in part because we
no longer read what they wrote, but in part also because these
were early, not late concepts in the minds of Roux and Driesch
themselves. Roux had a defect of character that led him to
overdogmatism, and after he performed the separation of the
blastomeres his dogma was self-differentiation; he could brook
no dispute, and those who read only his later works have only
a bare glimmering of the richness of his earlier thought. But
his early words may well have found their way into conscious
or subconscious memories. Driesch's case was different. In
becoming a philosopher, and a vitalist at that, he emphasized
the nonchemical and the nonmechanical in all but the earliest
of his writings; but his early words too may have had their
influence on the great minds that must have been exposed to
them in the happy days when there seems to us to have been
more time for reading and contemplation.

THEODOR BOVERI 1862–1915

It would take all too little browsing in general textbooks of
the history of biology to ascertain that Roux and Driesch
usually share the honors of being considered the patron saints
of early experimental embryology. Their contributions, in the
framing of embryological concepts and questions, were, as we
have seen, considerable. Yet in some ways their work, in terms
of classical quality, is almost overshadowed by that of another
pioneer in embryology, Theodor Boveri, whose name is rarely
mentioned in the general — or even the special — texts. Yet it
was he who, in E. B. Wilson's words, "by the slow and pains-

taking processes of observation, experiment and analysis, accomplished the actual amalgamation between cytology, embryology and genetics — a biological achievement which . . . is not second to any of our time" (Wilson, 1918, p. 69). He made an indelible mark upon his science, said Wilson; but somehow the mark has become obscured. Baltzer has recently published a superb analysis of Boveri's work (Baltzer, 1962) and it is to be hoped that this may help to bring Boveri once more into his own.

For Boveri, there was no aberration of thought, no before nor after; he was steadfast as a star. He never abandoned attempts to solve what was, in his mind, the fundamental problem of development, which was a very general one; he investigated, in his own words, the processes "by which a new individual with particular characteristics arises from the reproductive products of its parents" (Boveri, 1910, p. 133). "What is the egg, and what does it contain? How are hereditary traits represented in the egg and determined during its development? What is the background from which they emerge into view, one after another, as development goes forward? By what mechanism (if mechanism it be) do the unseen potentialities hidden within the germ become the actualities that appear before our eyes in the embryo and adult?" Thus Wilson (1918, p. 68) paraphrased it. These are general problems, but Boveri approached them specifically.

He studied the role of the nucleus in development, the role of the centrosome, as he called it, and the role of the cytoplasm. While the experimental analysis of visible processes was his method of attack, his true goal was to ascertain the physiological relationships between cell structure and cell processes, and from this, as we shall see, he never deviated.

We have said that he studied centrosome, nucleus, and cytoplasm. Let us first mention Boveri's contribution with respect to the centrosome. Van Beneden and Neyt (1887) and Boveri himself (1887) had observed this organelle in cleaving *Ascaris* eggs. Boveri's question was, "What is its origin?" and he demonstrated that the centrosome that functions in the zygote is the centrosome of the spermatozoon introduced at fertilization (1887, 1888).

In his studies on fertilization, he was already interested (as who could not be, in his day as in ours?) in the structure and functions of the chromatic substance, our chromatin. In part as a result of his happy choice of material — in this case the eggs of *Ascaris*, with a small number of large chromosomes — but in much greater part as the result of the sharpness and depth of his own insight, he proved what by his time had not yet been assured, that chromosomes have their own individuality, and that they are the same before and after the resting stage (Boveri, 1888).

He viewed the chromosomes, in fact, in what was the terminology of his day, as "independent elementary organisms" [*selbständige elementare Lebewesen*] and suggested that the manner in which the chromosomes make a unity with the cytoplasm might be likened to a very close symbiosis. "Yes," he wrote, "I hold it to be a question open to discussion whether this may not even be more than a metaphor" (Boveri, 1904b, p. 90). Virologists, and speculators as to the role of nucleic acids in the origin of life, take note.

While Boveri, of course, did not define the chromosomes as constructed of nucleic acid, he recognized the importance of the discovery of the nucleic acids. "F. Miescher [the discoverer of nucleic acids]," Boveri wrote, "the distinguished founder of cell chemistry, prophesied in one of his last letters in 1895 that in the twentieth century there would be great struggles between the morphologists and the biochemists in the field of nuclear constitution and the related problems of heredity, and Miescher's whole life work expresses clearly enough the conviction that the victory would fall to his science. The morphologist," continued Boveri, "will show sufficient self-abnegation in the search for knowledge to wish the final victory to go to his competitor. But even he, the morphologist, would wish nothing better than to have morphological analysis carried to a point where his ultimate elements would be specific chemical entities" (Boveri, 1904b, pp. 122-123). Boveri himself expressed some doubt as to whether this goal would ever be attained. The contents of these Proceedings of a Zoological Congress provide sufficient commentary.

But to return to his earlier questions and views concerning the functions of the visible, rather than the chemical, chromosomes as structural entities. At the time when Boveri began his studies, the fusion of the nuclei of the egg and the spermatozoon was considered to be the important event at fertilization. Van Beneden, however, had shown in 1883 that nuclear fusion fails to occur in *Ascaris*. Boveri (1890) confirmed this observation for a number of other eggs, and demonstrated also that the nuclei of egg and spermatozoon furnish to the zygote equivalent complements of chromosomes. As Baltzer (1962) puts it, these results shifted the emphasis from the nucleus as a whole to the chromosomes. The significance of this shift for the interpretation of the chromosomes as the carriers of the hereditary factors is apparent.

In the previous year, however, Boveri had already described experiments demonstrating the role of the nucleus in heredity (Boveri, 1889). He fertilized nonnucleated fragments of uncleaved sea urchin eggs and found that in some cases, at least, normal larvae developed, as they did also on occasion from unfertilized egg fragments containing only the egg nucleus. This was a clear demonstration of the equivalence, for development, of the maternal and paternal nuclei.

But Boveri's most important contribution to genetic theory was his proof, on strictly cytological and embryological grounds, by a most ingenious experimental analysis of the development of sea urchin eggs fertilized by two spermatozoa, that "not a definite number, but a *definite combination of chromosomes* is essential for normal development, and this means nothing else than that the *individual chromosomes must possess different qualities*" (Boveri, 1902, p. 75; see Boveri, 1907, for a full description of these experiments). By the establishing of the differential value of the chromosomes, Roux's concept of qualitative division of the chromosomes was dealt a death blow, and the direct influence of chromosomes in development, as modern genetics envisions it, was recognized. And a cytological explanation of Mendel's results could now be expected.

In fact, in a footnote to his 1902 paper on dispermic sea urchin eggs, Boveri mentioned the relevance of the proof of the differential value of the chromosomes to "the results of botanists in studies of hybrids and their descendants" (Boveri, 1902, p. 81, fn. 1). This was the very year in which Sutton (1902) called "attention to the probability that the association of paternal and maternal chromosomes in pairs and their subsequent separation during the reducing division . . . may constitute the physical basis of the Mendelian law of heredity" (Sutton, 1902, p. 39). Sutton's work had been started independently, but he began his 1902 paper by saying that he was prompted to communicate his results at that time by "the appearance of Boveri's recent remarkable paper on the analysis of the nucleus by means of observations on double-fertilized eggs" (Sutton, 1902, p. 24).

Boveri, in fact, went still further in his thinking concerning the operations of the chromosomes in heredity. In the small monograph of 1904 on the constitution of the chromatic substance, from which we have already quoted, he prophesied linkage: "When in continued breeding experiments two characters either always appear together, or disappear together, the conclusion may be drawn with the greatest probability that the factors for the two characters are located on the same chromosome," and he continued by saying that when in the course of continued breeding the number of combinations in which traits actually appear is larger than the number of possible combinations, this might be a result "of an exchange of parts between homologous chromosomes" (Boveri, 1904b, p. 118).

But returning again to the more specific role of the chromosomes in development, he also recognized the importance of the time phases of development as related to its chromosomal control. If Driesch asked a question as to what is responsible for the timing of developmental rhythms, Boveri began to answer it. He fertilized enucleated eggs of one species with the spermatozoa of another species (1895, 1903, 1904a, 1914a), and the resulting androgenetic merogons developed normally to the blastula or gastrula stage, and then in many cases ceased to develop or began to develop abnormally, as had also been the case for dispermic eggs. This could be interpreted on the basis that before gastrulation the chromosomes exert only general effects; after gastrulation, the factors for species-specific characters come into play, in interaction between nucleus and cytoplasm. This, as Baltzer points out (1962, p. 109), was the first expression of the concept of phase-specific and time-bound action of genes during development, and, as Baltzer also emphasizes, it attributed to the cytoplasm a more specialized significance than had heretofore been acknowledged.

One of the greatest of Boveri's virtues as an investigator was that no matter how strongly his work pointed to the importance of the nucleus in development and heredity, he never minimized the developmental role of the cytoplasm, and according to Wilson (1918, p. 80) it was he "who first gave an experimental demonstration of the determinative activity of the protoplasm in ontogeny." He even inquired into its influence in heredity, and it was in fact to answer the latter question that he performed the androgenetic merogony experiments that we have already mentioned. He fertilized the enucleated eggs of one species of sea urchin, *Sphaerechinus*, with spermatozoa of another, *Psammechinus* or *Paracentrotus;* the eggs were enucleated by fragmentation. When some plutei proved maternal in character he thought these had developed from nucleated fragments; plutei of the paternal type he thought to have developed from enucleated fragments. Thus he thought once more to have demonstrated the primary role of the nucleus in the determination of hereditary traits (Boveri, 1889). He never succeeded in performing the experiments successfully in other than mass cultures, and he recognized later, in despair, that he had ignored several sources of experimental error and that he might have interpreted his results incorrectly (Boveri, 1918). Yet the same experiments, performed on the same species by von Ubisch 65 years later in experiments that were technically more critical showed that Boveri's conclusions may well have been correct, at least for the early stages Boveri studied, although in von Ubisch's material, plutei originally of the paternal type showed some maternal traits at stages far older than those Boveri was able to study (von Ubisch, 1954, 1957a, 1957b).

If, however, Boveri failed in these experiments to demonstrate any direct influence on heredity by the cytoplasm, he performed the most dramatic demonstration that has ever been made of the direct influence of the cytoplasm on the nucleus. He was interested in polarity and was a pioneer in its study in the egg; he recognized that it was associated with particular qualities of the cytoplasm in sea urchin eggs (Boveri, 1901a, 1901b). In *Ascaris*, in which the chromosomes at one pole of the egg exhibit a peculiar visible behavior not exhibited by those at the other pole, he could bring about the unusual behavior in two cells rather than one, either by dispermy or by centrifuging the eggs and shifting the plane of the spindle through 90 degrees, thus bringing two nuclei, instead of only one, into the proximity of a particular part of the cytoplasm with a particular quality (Boveri, 1910). To repeat, no more clear-cut evidence of the influence of cytoplasm on nucleus has ever been brought forward.

But long before these experiments were ever performed, he

knew of the importance of interaction between nucleus and cytoplasm. In the 1902 article on multipolar mitosis in dispermic eggs, he summarized his current views then as follows: "It appears to me that the quite peculiar interaction of the cytoplasm with its simple structure and differential division and the nucleus with its complex structure and manifold total multiplication may still achieve what Weismann and Roux attempted to explain with the help of differential nuclear division. When the primitive differences of the cytoplasm, as expressed in the existence of layers, are transferred to the cleaved egg without any change in the relationships of the layers, they affect the originally equal nuclei unequally by unfolding (activating) or suppressing certain nuclear qualities, as may be visualized directly in the cleavage of *Ascaris*. The inequalities of the nuclei, in some cases perhaps of temporary nature only, lend different potencies to the cytoplasm, that to begin with was differentiated only by degrees. Thus new cytoplasmic conditions are created which again release in certain nuclei the activation or suppression of certain qualities thus imprinting on these cells in turn a specific character and so on, and so on. In short: a continually increasing specification of the originally totipotent complex nuclear structure, and consequently, indirectly, of the cytoplasm of the individual cells, appears conceivable on the basis of physico-chemical events once the machine has been set in motion by the simple cytoplasmic differentiation of the egg" (Boveri, 1902, p. 85). This is what we all say today, I believe.

Let us come back once more to stratification and polarity. When Boveri compared the development of isolated upper and lower portions of sea urchin eggs, he observed that the isolated upper portion could not gastrulate, while the lower could do so and could also differentiate primary mesenchyme (Boveri, 1901a). The lower part of the egg or of each fragment he conceived of as a privileged region [*Vorzugsbereich*]: "here differentiation began, and from here all other regions are influenced in their differentiation" (Boveri, 1901a, p. 167). Spemann himself acknowledged later how akin this interpretation was to his own ideas (Spemann and Mangold, 1924), and admitted that "it may have been working subconsciously after I had encountered it in the publication, . . . or even in oral communication, or it may have been part of our common stock of ideas in those invaluable years of daily intercourse with that great investigator" (Spemann, 1938, p. 142).

One more point may be added, at the end. We remarked how Roux had anticipated the future in relating developmental to immunological problems. Boveri, too, looked into pathology, and his concern was the origin of malignant tumors (Boveri, 1914b). He emphasized that this was a cellular problem and interpreted a tumor cell as one in which the number of chromosomes is atypical; the metabolic derangements of the tumor cell are, in his view, secondary to this. This is an idea only now becoming accepted. Boveri even related the metastatic character of tumor cells to the modified chromosome numbers; modern investigators interested in the aggregation and disaggregation of cells might well contemplate Boveri's question as to whether the normal nucleus provides a substance necessary for cellular adhesion.

Time has sufficed to present only a brief outline of Boveri's work, but hopefully what has been said may be sufficient to indicate the degree to which today we occupy ourselves with attempts to answer his questions, as well as those raised by Roux and Driesch. Had I the space to continue, it would of course be devoted to the work of Harrison and Spemann that began the modern period. They defined the problems growing out of Roux's and Driesch's and Boveri's work in such a way that they became open to analysis by what we call modern methods. But that must await another occasion.

REFERENCES

ARISTOTLE. *Generation of Animals,* with an English translation by A. L. Peck. 1953. Harvard University Press, Cambridge, Mass.

VON BAER, K. E. 1828, 1837. *Ueber Entwickelungsgeschichte der Thiere. Beobachtung und Reflexion.* Gebrüder Bornträger, Königsberg. 2 vols.

BALTZER, F. 1962. *Theodor Boveri. Leben und Werk eines grossen Biologen 1862–1915.* Wissenschaftliche Verlagsgesellschaft M. B. H., Stuttgart.

VAN BENEDEN, E. 1883. Recherches sur la maturation de l'oeuf, la fécondation et la division cellulaire. Arch. de Biol., *4:*265–641.

VAN BENEDEN, E., AND A. NEYT. 1887. Nouvelles recherches sur la fécondation et la division mitotique, chez l'Ascaride mégalocéphale. Bull. Acad. Roy. Belgique, Sér. *3, 14:*215–295.

BOVERI, T. 1887. Ueber den Anteil des Spermatozoon an der Teilung des Eies. Sitz.-Ber. d. Ges. f. Morph. u. Phys. München, *3:*71–80.

BOVERI, T. 1888. Zellenstudien II. Die Befruchtung und Teilung des Eies von Ascaris megalocephala. Jenaische Zeitschr. f. Naturwiss., *22:*685–882.

BOVERI, T. 1889. Ein geschlechtlich erzeugter Organismus ohne mütterliche Eigenschaften. Sitz.-Ber. d. Ges. f. Morph. u. Phys. München, *5:*73–80.

BOVERI, T. 1890. Zellenstudien III. Ueber das Verhalten der chromatischen Kernsubstanz bei der Bildung der Richtungskörper und bei der Befruchtung. Jenaische Zeitschr. f. Naturwiss., *24:*314–401.

BOVERI, T. 1895. Ueber die Befruchtungs- und Entwicklungsfähigkeit kernloser Seeigeleier und über die Möglichkeit ihrer Bastardierung. Roux' Arch. f. Entw.-mech., *2:*394–443.

BOVERI, T. 1901a. Ueber die Polarität des Seeigeleies. Verh. d. phys.-med. Ges. Würzburg, NF. *34:*145–176.

BOVERI, T. 1901b. Die Polarität von Oocyte, Ei und Larve des Strongylocentrotus lividus. Zool. Jahrb., Abt. f. Anat. u. Ont., *14:*630–653.

BOVERI, T. 1902. Ueber mehrpolige Mitosen als Mittel zur Analyse des Zellkerns. Verh. d. phys.-med. Ges. Würzburg, NF. *35:*67–90. English translation, from which excerpts in text are cited, by S. Glueck-sohn-Waelsch in *Foundations of Experimental Embryology,* B. H. Willier and J. M. Oppenheimer (Eds.). 1964. Prentice-Hall, Inc., Englewood Cliffs, N.J.

BOVERI, T. 1903. Ueber den Einfluss der Samenzelle auf die Larven-charaktere der Echiniden. Roux' Arch. f. Entw.-mech. d. Org., *16:* 340–363.

BOVERI, T. 1904a. Noch ein Wort über Seeigelbastarde. Roux' Arch. f. Entw.-mech. d. Org., *17:*521–525.

BOVERI, T. 1904b. *Ergebnisse über die Konstitution der chromatischen Substanz des Zellkerns.* Gustav Fischer, Jena.

BOVERI, T. 1907. Zellenstudien VI. Die Entwicklung dispermer Seeigel-eier. Ein Beitrag zur Befruchtungslehre und zur Theorie des Kerns. Jenaische Zeitschr. f. Naturwiss., *43:*1–292.

BOVERI, T. 1910. Die Potenzen der Ascaris-Blastomeren bei abgeänder-ten Furchung. Zugleich ein Beitrag zur Frage qualitativ ungleicher Chromosomenteilung. In *Festschrift für Richard Hertwig,* Gustav Fischer, Jena, *III:*133–214.

BOVERI, T. 1914a. Ueber die Charaktere von Echiniden-Bastardlarven bei verschiedenem Mengenverhältnis mütterlicher und väterlicher Substanzen. Verh. d. phys.-med. Ges. Würzburg, NF. *43:*117–135.

BOVERI, T. 1914b. *Zur Frage der Entstehung maligner Tumoren.* Gus-tav Fischer, Jena. Also available in English translation by Marcella Boveri: *The Origin of Malignant Tumors.* 1929. The Williams and Wilkins Company, Baltimore.

BOVERI, T. 1918 (posthumous). Zwei Fehlerquellen bei Merogonieversu-chen und die Entwicklungsfähigkeit merogonischer und partiell-merogonischer Seeigelbastarde. Roux' Arch. f. Entw.-mech. d. Org., *44:*417–471.

DRIESCH, H. 1889. Tektonische Studien an Hydroidpolypen. Jenaische Zeitschr. f. Naturwiss., *24:*189–226.

DRIESCH, H. 1891a. *Die mathematisch-mechanische Betrachtung mor-phologischer Probleme der Biologie. Eine kritische Studie.* Gustav Fischer, Jena.

DRIESCH, H. 1891b. Entwicklungsmechanische Studien. I. Der Werth der beiden ersten Furchungszellen in der Echinodermenentwick-lung. Experimentelle Erzeugung von Theil- und Doppelbildun-gen. II. Ueber die Beziehungen des Lichtes zur ersten Etappe der thierischen Formbildung. Zeitschr. f. wiss. Zool., *53:*160–183.

DRIESCH, H. 1892. Entwicklungsmechanische Studien. III. Die Vermin-derung des Furchungsmaterials und ihre Folgen (Weiteres über Theilbildungen). IV. Experimentelle Veränderungen des Typus der Furchung und ihre Folgen (Wirkungen von Wärmezufuhr und von Druck). V. Von der Furchung doppeltbefruchteter Eier. VI. Ueber einige allgemeine Fragen der theoretischen Morphologie. Zeitschr. f. wiss. Zool., *55:*1–62.

Driesch, H. 1893a. Zur Verlagerung der Blastomeren des Echinideies. Anat. Anz., *8*:348–357.

Driesch, H. 1893b. Zur Theorie der tierischen Formbildung. Biol. Centralbl., *13*:296–312.

Driesch, H. 1893c. Entwicklungsmechanische Studien. VII. Exogastrula und Anenteria (über die Wirkung von Wärmezufuhr auf die Larvenentwicklung der Echiniden). VIII. Ueber Variation der Mikromerenbildung (Wirkung von Verdünnung des Meereswassers). IX. Ueber die Vertretbarkeit der "Anlagen" von Ektoderm und Entoderm. X. Ueber einige allgemeine entwicklungsmechanische Ergebnisse. Mitt. zool. Stat. Neapel, *11*:221–254.

Driesch, H. 1894. *Analytische Theorie der organischen Entwicklung.* Wilhelm Engelmann, Leipzig.

Driesch, H. 1951 (posthumous). *Lebenserinnerungen. Aufzeichnungen eines Forschers und Denkers in entscheidender Zeit.* Ernst Reinhardt, Basel.

Holtfreter, J. 1939. Gewebeaffinität, ein Mittel der embryonalen Formbildung. Arch. f. exp. Zellforsch., *23*:169–209.

von Liebermann, L. 1918. Selektionshypothese. Versuch einer einheitlichen Erklärung der Immunität, Gewebsimmunität und Immunitätserscheinungen. Deutsche med. Wochenschr., *44*:313–314.

Oppenheimer, J. M. 1963. K. E. von Baer's beginning insights into causal-analytical relationships during development. *Dev. Biol.,* *7*:11–21. Reprinted in this volume, pp. 295–307.

Pflüger, E. 1883. Ueber den Einfluss der Schwerkraft auf die Theilung der Zellen. Pflügers Arch. ges. Physiol., *31*:311–318.

Rauber, A. 1886. Personaltheil und Germinaltheil des Individuum. Zool. Anz., *9*:166–171.

Roux, W. 1878. Ueber die Verzweigungen der Blutgefässe des Menschen. Eine morphologische Studie. Jenaische Zeitschr. f. Naturwiss., *12*:205–266. Also in W. Roux, 1895. Ges. Abh., I:1–76.

Roux, W. 1881. *Der Kampf der Theile im Organismus. Ein Beitrag zur Vervollständigung der mechanischen Zweckmässigkeitslehre.* Wilhelm Engelmann, Leipzig. Also in W. Roux, 1895. *Ges. Abh.,* I:135–422, under title "Der züchtende Kampf der Theile oder die 'Theilauslese' im Organismus, zugleich eine Theorie der functionellen Anpassung."

Roux, W. 1883a. *Ueber die Bedeutung der Kerntheilungsfiguren.* Wilhelm Engelmann, Leipzig. Also in W. Roux, 1895. *Ges. Abh.,* II:125–143.

Roux, W. 1883b. Beiträge zur Morphologie der functionellen Anpassung. II. Ueber die Selbstregulation der "morphologischen" Länge der Sceletmuskeln des Menschen. Jenaische Zeitschr. f. Naturwiss., *16*:358–427. Also in W. Roux, 1895. *Ges. Abh., I*:575–661.

Roux, W. 1884. Beiträge zur Entwickelungsmechanik des Embryo. II. Ueber die Entwickelung der Froscheier bei Aufhebung der richtenden Wirkung der Schwere. Breslauer ärztl. Zeitschr., 22. März, pp. 1–16. Also in W. Roux, 1895. *Ges. Abh., II*:257–276.

Roux, W. 1885a. Einleitung zu den Beiträgen zur Entwickelungsmechanik des Embryo. Zeitschr. f. Biol., *21*:411–428. Also in W. Roux, 1895. *Ges. Abh., II*:1–21.

Roux, W. 1885b. Beiträge zur Entwickelungsmechanik des Embryo. I. Zur Orientirung über einige Probleme der embryonalen Entwickelung. Zeitschr. f. Biol., *21*:429–524. Also in W. Roux, 1895. *Ges. Abh., II*:144–255.

Roux, W. 1885c. Beiträge zur Entwickelungsmechanik des Embryo. III. Ueber die Bestimmung der Hauptrichtungen des Froschenembryo im Ei und über die erste Theilung des Froscheies. Breslauer ärztl. Zeitschr., Nos. 6–9. Also in W. Roux, 1895. *Ges. Abh., II*:277–343.

Roux, W. 1887. Beiträge zur Entwickelungsmechanik des Embryo. IV. Die Bestimmung der Medianebene des Froschembryo durch die Copulationsrichtung des Eikernes und des Spermakernes. Arch. mikr. Anat., *29*:157–211. Also in W. Roux, 1895. *Ges. Abh., II*: 344–418.

Roux, W. 1888. Beiträge zur Entwickelungsmechanik des Embryo. V. Ueber die künstliche Hervorbringung "halber" Embryonen durch Zerstörung einer der beiden ersten Furchungszellen, sowie über die Nachentwickelung (Postgeneration) der fehlenden Körperhälfte. Virchows Arch. path. Anat. u. Physiol. u. klin. Med., *114*: 113–153; 246–291. Also in W. Roux, 1895. *Ges. Abh., II*:419–521.

Roux, W. 1890. *Die Entwicklungsmechanik der Organismen, eine anatomische Wissenschaft der Zukunft.* Urban und Schwarzenberg, Vienna. Also in W. Roux, 1895. *Ges. Abh., II*:24–54.

Roux, W. 1891. Beiträge zur Entwickelungsmechanik des Embryo. VI. Ueber die "morphologische Polarisation" von Eiern und Embryonen durch den electrischen Strom sowie: über die Wirkung des electrischen Stromes auf die Richtung der ersten Theilung des Eies. Sitz.-ber. d. k. Akad. d. Wissensch. Wien, Math.-naturw. Klasse, *101*(Abt. III): 27–228. Also in W. Roux, 1895. *Ges. Abh., II*:541–765.

Roux, W. 1892. Ziele und Wege der Entwickelungsmechanik. Merkel-Bonnet's Erg. d. Anat. u. Entw.-gesch., 2:417–445. Also in W. Roux, 1895. *Ges. Abh.*, II:55–94.

Roux, W. 1894. Ueber den "Cytotropismus" der Furchungszellen des Grasfrosches (Rana fusca). Roux' Arch. f. Entw.-mech. d. Org., 1:43–68; 161–202.

Roux, W. 1895. *Gesammelte Abhandlungen über Entwickelungs-mechanik der Organismen.* Wilhelm Engelmann, Leipzig. 2 vols.

Roux, W. 1905. Die Entwickelungsmechanik, ein neuer Zweig der biologischen Wissenschaft. In W. Roux, ed. *Vorträge und Aufsätze über Entwickelungsmechanik der Organismen.* Wilhelm Engelmann, Leipzig, I:i–xiv, 1–283.

Roux, W., et al., eds. 1912. *Terminologie der Entwicklungsmechanik der Tiere und Pflanzen.* Wilhelm Engelmann, Leipzig.

Roux, W. 1918. "Immunisierung durch Teilauslese" gegen Vergiftung und verminderte Ernährung. Eine alte Hypothese. Zeitschr. f. Hyg. u. Infektionskrankh., 87:283–302.

Roux, W. 1923. Wilhelm Roux in Halle a. S. In R. L. Grote, ed. 1923. *Die Medizin der Gegenwart in Selbstdarstellungen.* Felix Meiner, Leipzig, I:141–206.

Spemann, H. and H. Mangold. 1924. Ueber Induktion von Embryo-nalanlagen durch Implantation artfremder Organisatoren. Arch. f. mikr. Anat. u. Entw.-mech., 100:599–638.

Spemann, H. 1938. *Embryonic development and induction.* Yale University Press, New Haven.

Sutton, W. S. 1902. On the morphology of the chromosome group in *Brachystola magna.* Biol. Bull., 4:24–39.

von Ubisch, L. 1954. Ueber Seeigelmerogone. Pubbl. Staz. Zool. Napoli, 25:246–340.

von Ubisch, L. 1957a. Merogone und Bastarde von Seeigeln. Nova Acta Leopoldina, NF. 19:1–22 (Nummer 129).

von Ubisch, L. 1957b. Ueber Seeigelmerogone II. Pubbl. Staz. Zool. Napoli, 30:279–308.

Wilson, E. B. 1918. Theodor Boveri. In W. C. Roentgen, ed. *Erinnerungen an Theodor Boveri.* J. C. B. Mohr. Tübingen, pp. 67–89.

Ross Harrison's Contributions to Experimental Embryology[*]

IN THE MEMOIR concerning Ross Harrison prepared for the
Royal Society of London, Abercrombie has stated: ". . .
one suspects that Harrison, for all his objectivity in obtaining
and assessing evidence, worked on strongly held hunches at
least until the evidence was available."[1] Harrison did not live
his intellectual life by hunches; in contrast, he lived by reason
and logic, and the inner coherence of his thought was extraordinary. What I wish to examine here, therefore, is primarily
the patterns of integration within his own thought; but it
proves highly illuminating to see also how the ideas threading
through them were interwoven with those of some of his contemporaries and predecessors.

Harrison is commonly praised for the innovation — a word
used advisedly here — of the technique of tissue culture and
for his adaptation of Born's method of embryonic grafting for
the purposes of answering particular embryological questions.
Harrison's real contribution, however, was in formulating the
questions, which could be answered by the use of simple techniques, and it was the questions, not the techniques, that were
of principal interest to him and of primary influence on biol-

* This essay is based on a paper presented to the American Association for the
History of Medicine at its meetings in Philadelphia, April 30, 1965. Reprinted from
Bulletin of the History of Medicine, Vol. XL, 1966, pp. 525–543. The Johns Hopkins
Press, Baltimore, Md.

1 Michael Abercrombie, "Ross Granville Harrison 1870–1959," *Biogr. Mems. Fel-
lows Roy. Soc. London*, 1961, 7: 111–126; see p. 113.

ogy. Harrison's gift was an ability both to frame the questions and to devise ways and means of enticing the embryo to answer them unequivocally. The questions that he set for the embryo were more specific than those posed by Wilhelm Roux, who formulated the program for the new experimental embryology, and this was one factor responsible for Harrison's success. But the problems with which he dealt were wide in their implications, and their solutions provided a number of replies to Roux' philosophically more generalized inquiries.

Harrison received his Ph.D. at the Johns Hopkins University in 1894 under the egis of William Keith Brooks; his doctoral dissertation was a morphological study of the development of the median and paired fins of teleost fishes. Harrison's definitive publication on this subject appeared in 1895;[2] he had published several shorter papers on this and on related morphological subjects in 1894,[3] and his first paper, published in 1893,[4] had been a description of the development of the fin rays of bony fishes.

The two of his papers on fins that were the most extensive[2,4] were both published in the German language, in one of the leading German periodicals on developmental morphology. In the 1890's, Germany was intellectual Mecca for embryologists, and Harrison spent considerable time in Bonn, both before and after receiving his Ph.D. degree, between 1892 and 1899. In fact, his work on the fins was begun in Bonn, at the suggestion of Moritz Nussbaum; Brooks was happy to have Harrison continue it at Hopkins. Harrison was awarded the degree of Doctor of Medicine at Bonn in 1899, but perhaps

[2] R. G. Harrison, "Die Entwicklung der unpaaren und paarigen Flossen der Teleostier," *Arch. f. mikr. Anat. u. Entwcklngsgesch.*, 1895, *46:* 500–578.

[3] R. G. Harrison, "The development of the fins of teleosts," *John Hopkins Univ. Circ.*, 1894, No. 111; "The metamerism of the dorsal and the ventral longitudinal muscles of the teleosts," *ibid.;* "Ectodermal or mesodermal origin of the bones of teleosts?", *Anat. Anz.*, 1894, *10:* 138–143.

[4] R. G. Harrison, "Ueber die Entwicklung der nicht knorpelig vorgebildeten Skelettheile in den Flossen der Teleostier," *Arch. f. mikr. Anat.*, 1893, *42:* 248–278.

more important than the diploma to Harrison's future progress was his temporary absorption into the new world of German experimental embryology.

Among other events that occurred on the German scene, in 1896, not long after Harrison's dissertation was published, was the publication by Gustav Born of a description of a method of embryonic grafting in amphibians. Born's definitive paper[5] was long and sober, but a preliminary one,[6] based on a report he gave orally to the medical section of the Schlesische Gesellschaft für vaterländische Kultur, was full of verve. Born's discovery, like so many in science, had been in a way accidental. He cut young amphibian larvae in half, crosswise, in order to test their relative powers of regeneration anteriorly and posteriorly. Between some of the halves a small slip of epidermis near the dorsal fin was permitted to remain unsevered, so that the head and body could be identified as having originally belonged to the same donor. Born was surprised, the morning after performing the experiment, to find that the separated portions had fused together at their cut surfaces. He was even more astonished to find that two trunk portions left in close proximity in a dish had also fused together overnight, and this led him to perform a great variety of combinations. Born died too soon to be able to exploit his own discovery, but his long 1896 paper proves that he recognized its theoretical value.

Born's paper was published as of the date December 31, 1896; Harrison began grafting experiments of his own in 1897. These are described in a paper published in 1898[7] that dealt with the growth and regeneration of the tail of frog

5 G. Born, "Ueber Verwachsungsversuche mit Amphibienlarven," *Roux' Arch. f. Entwcklngsmechn. d. Organ.*, 1896, *4*: 349–465.

6 G. Born, "Ueber die künstliche Vereinigung lebender Theilstücke von Amphibienlarven," *72. Jahresb. d. Schles. Gesellsch. f. vaterländ. Kultur, I. Abth., Medicin. Sektion,* Sitzung vom 8. Juni 1894, pp. 79–91.

7 R. G. Harrison, "The growth and regeneration of the tail of the frog larva. Studied with the aid of Born's method of grafting," *Roux' Arch. f. Entwcklngsmechn. d. Organ.*, 1898, *7*: 430–485.

ROSS HARRISON

larvae studied by the aid of Born's method of grafting. Subjects taken up in the paper included the growth of the tail and its bearing upon the mode of distribution of the cutaneous nerves, the regeneration of the tail as related to heteromorphosis,[8] the regeneration of tails grafted in reverse position, and reactions between tissues derived from different species.

Some details of these experiments will be mentioned later, as will Harrison's interpretation of them; here a comment about technique may be relevant. The dissecting microscope seems to have been first used for embryological experiments in 1903 by Warren Lewis, then a colleague of Harrison's at Hopkins.[9] Harrison's own first grafting experiments were carried out with the aid of only a simple Lupe. That the head of one embryo heals well enough to the body of another for the resultant chimera to survive is in itself remarkable. Born had carried through to metamorphosis larvae combining heads and bodies of the same species; Harrison's dexterity is attested to by his having brought to metamorphosis one chimera consisting of a *Rana virescens* head and a *Rana palustris* body. It died, probably of overfeeding according to Harrison, at the age of four months and twenty days. Harrison remembered these experiments with particular pleasure in the 1930's when Thomas Mann published his short novel *Die vertauschten Köpfe.*

The heads in Mann's romance were exchanged between men, in Harrison's laboratory intergenerically between frogs. Born himself had performed interordinal grafts and had fused

[8] Harrison did not define heteromorphosis, but placed in a footnote the definition of it by Jacques Loeb, who had proposed the term: "the phenomenon that there grows in the place of one organ in an animal, another organ typically different from it in form and function [Lebenserscheinungen]"; Harrison, 1898, *op. cit.,* ftn. 7 above, p. 466. Harrison quoted Loeb's definition in German; the English translation is mine.

[9] Described by W. H. Lewis, "Experimental studies on the development of the eye in Amphibia. I. On the origin of the lens. *Rana palustris,*" *Am. J. Anat.,* 1904, *3:* 505–536.

95

the heads and trunks of frog larvae to tails of newts, although none of these chimerae survived much over three weeks. During the course of Harrison's first grafting experiments, he made some incidental observations on the position of the lateral line in embryos in which tails of *R. palustris* embryos were grafted to *R. virescens* bodies, noting that the "sense organs of the lateral line in the grafted larvae just described form a complete series extending to the extreme tip of the tail and continuing without break or bend from the integument of one component to that of the other";[10] he soon followed up this observation with work forming the basis of an extensive paper on the development of the lateral line.[11] This article described a number of chimerae, among others, in which heads of dark *Rana sylvatica* larvae were united with paler bodies of *R. palustris* larvae. Harrison observed that the lateral line organs exhibited the pigmentation characteristic of the *sylvatica* larvae; a beautiful colored lithographic plate illustrates the development of the lateral line as it proceeds posteriorly from the brown head onto and along the yellow trunk. These experiments provided valuable and hitherto unknown information as to the mode of development of the lateral line sense organs, but equally important was their demonstration of the value of heteroplastic grafting for the performance of crucial investigations. This was both recognized and acknowledged by Spemann, whose own most important paper, if a particular one can be singled out, was based on the use of this method.[12] But Spemann, in pointing

10 Harrison, 1898, *op. cit.* ftn. 7 above, p. 444.

11 R. G. Harrison, "Experimentelle Untersuchungen über die Entwicklung der Sinnesorgane der Seitenlinie bei den Amphibien," *Arch. f. mikr. Anat. u. Entwcklngsgesch.*, 1903, *63:* 35–149.

12 The historical relationships of Harrison's grafting experiments to those of Spemann have been reviewed briefly elsewhere by Jane M. Oppenheimer, "Embryological concepts in the twentieth century," *Survey Biol. Progr.*, 1957, *3:* 1–46; see pp. 15–16; reprinted in this volume, pp. 1–61. Also, *Idem,* "Ross Granville Harrison," in *Geschichte der Mikroskopie. Leben und Werk grosser Forscher,* eds. H. Freund and A. Berg, Frankfurt am Main: Umschau Verlag, 1965, Vol. 2, pp. 117–126; see p. 120.

out the importance of the technique, also praised the paper equally for its "methodically advancing analysis."[13]

Abercrombie, in writing of the lateral line paper, praised it as excellent, but found it "rather isolated from the main stream of Harrison's work."[14] This is a judgment with which I cannot concur. Harrison included in the paper on the lateral line a discussion of the relationship of the lateral line sense organ to its nerve and in fact, as Abercrombie admits, made some observations on the outgrowth of the *ramus lateralis vagi* into the sense organ. Furthermore, Harrison's interest in the *ramus lateralis vagi* and its peripheral destination reached at least as far back as the time he was performing the work for his dissertation on the origin of the paired and unpaired fins in fishes. His dissertation is usually described as a morpho-logical study, which it principally was, but in it Harrison described having performed experiments involving the me-chanical stimulation of *r. lateralis vagi* in decapitated *Carassius* of two species, in which the spinal cord had been destroyed, in order to prove that the lateral line nerve did not innervate the fin musculature.

Thus his interest in the outgrowth, course, and destination of the lateral line branch of the vagus nerve was not isolated from the rest of his thought. It was not only related, as we have seen, to the work he performed for his dissertation, but it also fell in the main line of his thinking which led to his work on the outgrowth of the nerve fiber.

One of the principal subjects taken up by his first paper on embryonic grafting was, as we have said, the bearing of the manner of growth of the tail on the mode of distribution of the cutaneous nerves. Harrison observed during the growth of the grafted tails a remarkable shifting of the epidermis over the underlying organs. In his own words:

13 H. Spemann, *Embryonic Development and Induction,* New Haven: Yale Univ. Press, 1938, p. 131.
14 Abercrombie, *op. cit.,* ftn. 1 above, p. 113.

As is well known, the integument of the trunk is divisible into a series of zones, each of which corresponds to the area of distribution of a given spinal nerve . . . . The portion of the skin innervated by a given spinal nerve does not necessarily exactly overlie the muscular zone which is supplied by the ventral root of the same nerve . . . . The shifting of the epidermis during development over the subjacent muscle plates, as ascertained above experimentally, corresponds in direction and in relative amount in the different regions with the displacement of the sensory area as compared with the motor belt of the same segmental nerve . . . .

Wandering of the skin, then, like wandering of muscles, occurs during development, but the nerves remain to indicate the course of this ontogenetic wandering of the one as well as of the other.

These considerations suggest that a connection between each ganglion cell and its end organs in the integument is established early in development, and that each nerve rudiment in its first stage passes from its origin in the ganglion cell by the shortest path to the integument.[15]

A footnote on the following page comments that the observations just described do not provide evidence as to how and when the connection between nerve cell and end organ arises, but adds that they are "not to be construed as necessarily contradicting the view, at present almost generally accepted, that each axis cylinder grows out centrifugally from the ganglion cell to the end organ."[16] And here again, the lateral line branch of the vagus came in for its share of attention. When the lateral line follows from the integument of one component into that of the other, when tails are grafted, wrote Harrison, all of its organs "receive fibers from the *ramus lateralis vagi,* which are derived entirely from the ganglion cells of the anterior component. This must mean that in this case a connexion is established secondarily between these ganglion cells and the sensory cells in the epidermis of the transplanted piece. This probably takes place in the same manner as a severed nerve grows out again to its end organ."[17]

15 Harrison, 1898, *op. cit.,* ftn. 7 above, pp. 442–443.
16 Harrison, 1898, *op. cit.,* ftn. 7 above, p. 444 ftn.
17 Harrison, 1898, *op. cit.,* ftn. 7 above, p. 444.

In 1901, he published an extensive treatise on the histogenesis of the peripheral nerves in the salmon;[18] his observations on the outgrowth of the spinal nerves in *Salmo salar* embryos, already familiar to him from the earlier fin studies, had led him to throw his weight to the side of those holding the opinion that the nerve fiber grows out from the neuroblast, and the observations, in the 1903 paper on the lateral line, on the outgrowth of the lateral line nerve, supported him in this stand. But the then moot problem of the origin of the nerve fiber — whether from the neuroblast, from Schwann cells, or from protoplasmic bridges in the embryo — could not be solved by observation alone. Experiment was required.

Harrison performed the experiment.[19] He explanted parts of the nerve tube, removed from frog larvae at stages before the neuroblasts had formed their outgrowths, into clotted frog lymph on cover slips inverted over depression slides, and he watched the living neuroblasts spinning their fibers into the clots. This was a true *experimentum crucis* and answered unequivocally the neuroembryologist's question as to the mode of origin of the nerve fiber. It also provided embryology with a new technique as powerful as it was simple. Wilhelm Roux had said, when he dictated the program for experimental embryology, that in order to understand how an embryonic part develops, one of the things that the investigator must know is how it develops in isolation. Harrison showed embryologists how to study parts of an embryo in isolation. This was the effective beginning of tissue culture.

I said in my introductory remarks not that Harrison invented the method of tissue culture, but that he innovated it. This was intended as a reminder of the word renovate. He was not the first investigator to attempt to grow cells or tissues

18 R. G. Harrison, "Ueber die Histogenese des peripheren Nervensystems bei Salmo salar," *Arch. f. mikr. Anat. u. Entwcklngsgesch.*, 1901, 57: 354–444.

19 R. G. Harrison, "Observations on the living developing nerve fiber," *Anat. Rec.*, 1907, 1: 116–118; also *Proc. Soc. Exp. Biol. & Med.*, 1907, 4: 140–143.

separated from the organism; he was the first to do so successfully by a method that was later to permit body constituents to
develop outside the body under rigorously controlled experimental conditions.

Roux himself in 1885, according to White, "isolated the
chick medullary plate and kept it alive for some days in saline
solution in an effort to determine the factors involved in the
closure of the medullary tube."[20] Paul, also, states that
"Wilhelm Roux's experiment of maintaining the medullary
plate of a chick embryo in warm saline for a few days was
performed in the year 1885 and is the first recorded instance
of a successful explantation."[21] Both White and Paul docu-
ment their statements by referring to a paper published by
Roux in volume 21 of the *Zeitschrift für Biologie*.[22] It is true
that this paper describes the placing of large fragments of
chick embryos of early incubation age into warm physiological
saline solution to test His' hypothesis, which Roux did not
confirm, that the folding of the neural folds results from
mechanical pressures due to unequal growth, but according to
my reading of the paper, both in the original journal and in
Roux' *Gesammelte Abhandlungen,* the longest period of isolation that he specifies is two hours, and it would seem unlikely
in the extreme that his crude methods would have permitted
the survival of the explants over a period of days.

Neither White nor Paul, furthermore, refer to the fact that
about a decade later Roux[23] studied the behavior in salt solu-

20 Philip R. White, *The Cultivation of Animal and Plant Cells,* New York: The
Ronald Press, 1954, p. 15.

21 John Paul, *Cell and Tissue Culture,* 2d ed., Baltimore: Williams & Wilkins
Company, 1960, p. 1.

22 Wilhelm Roux, "Beiträge zur Entwickelungsmechanik des Embryo. I. Zur
Orientirung über einige Probleme der embryonalen Entwickelung," *Ztschr. f. Biol.,*
1885, Neue Folge *3,* der ganzen Reihe *21:* 429–524; also in Wilhelm Roux, *Gesammelte Abhandlungen über Entwickelungsmechanik der Organismen,* Leipzig: Engelmann, 1895, II: 144–255.

23 Wilhelm Roux, "Ueber den 'Cytotropismus' der Furchungszellen des Grasfrosches (Rana fusca)," *"Roux' Arch. f. Entwcklngsmechn. d. Organ.,* 1894, *1:* 43–68,

tion of isolated cells from amphibian morulae, blastulae, and gastrulae. Neither do the historical reviews by White, Paul, or by Fischer[24] refer to what Harrison surely knew, namely, that Born in 1896, at the very end of his paper on transplantation, reported unsuccessful attempts made in 1894 to cultivate "larger and smaller" fragments of amphibian blastulae and gastrulae, as well as of older larvae, in the dorsal lymph sac of the frog, expressing the opinion that if such fragments survived for days in salt solution, it might be possible that they would continue to live and to *develop* in the more favorable milieu provided by lymph.[25]

But other less embryologically oriented investigators were also beginning to study cells or tissues in isolation experiments of one sort or another, and a number of these, unlike Born, are referred to by White, Paul, or Fischer. Arnold, in 1887,[26] placed thin slices (0.05 to 0.25 mm thick) of pith into the dorsal lymph sacs or into the peritoneal cavity of frogs; he removed them, after they had been invaded by leucocytes, into warm aqueous humor. He watched the leucocytes migrate from the pith into the fluid, where they survived for four to five days. Ljunggren, in 1898, maintained human skin *in vitro* in ascitic fluid and then reimplanted it.[27] Jolly, in 1903, cultured salamander leucocytes in serum,[28] and Beebe and Ewing

161–202; "Ueber die Selbstordnung (Cytotaxis) sich 'berührender' Furchungszellen des Froscheies durch Zellenzusammenfügung, Zellentrennung und Zellengleiten," *Roux' Arch. f. Entwcklngsmechn. d. Organ.*, 1896, *3:* 381–468.

24 Albert Fischer, *Tissue Culture. Studies in Experimental Morphology and General Physiology of Tissue Cells in Vitro,* London: Heinemann (Medical Books), 1925.

25 Born, 1896, *op. cit.,* ftn. 5 above, p. 617; my italics.

26 Julius Arnold, "Ueber Theilungsvorgänge an den Wanderzellen, ihre progressiven und retrogressiven Metamorphosen," *Arch. f. mikr. Anat.*, 1887, *30:* 205–310.

27 C. A. Ljunggren, "Von der Fähigkeit des Hautepithels, ausserhalb des Organismus sein Leben zu behalten, mit Berücksichtigung der Transplantation," *Deutsche Ztschr. f. Chir.*, 1898, *47:* 608–615.

28 J. Jolly, "Sur la durée de la vie et de la multiplication des cellules animales en dehors l'organisme," *Compt. Rend. Soc. de Biol.*, 1903, *55:* 1266–1268.

reported in 1906 the cultivation in blood of a canine lympho-sarcoma.[29]

But Born, Arnold, and Ljunggren were not alone in attempting to combine *in vivo* with *in vitro* experiments as a way to study tissues in isolation. That great investigator Leo Loeb, in 1898,[30] reported a different kind of transplantation than Harrison's and Born's, although like them he was using it in an attempt to study regeneration. He found that after transplantation, epithelium of the guinea pig could grow and migrate in blood clots and coagulated lymph, although separated from the neighboring host tissues. This, he said later, suggested to him at the time "that it should be possible to cultivate tissues on solid culture media in the test-tube as well as within the body . . . . Tissue cells could in principle be accessible to indefinite propagation in a similar manner as bacteria."[31] From 1897 to 1902 he attempted to cultivate tissues *in vitro,* using coagulated blood serum, blood clot, or agar as culture media. When he wrote in 1912 of the "Growth of tissues in culture media and its significance for the analysis of growth phenomena" he admitted, however, that "conditions did not make it possible for [him] at that time to carry [these] experiments sufficiently far."[32]

Plant cells, too, were used in early attempts at isolation experiments. In 1902 Haberlandt tried to culture cells from higher plants — pith cells, palisade cells, stamen hair cells — in Knop's solution, to which had been added dextrose, glucose, peptone, glycerine, asparagine, and so forth. He dissected the

29 S. P. Beebe and J. Ewing, "A study of the biology of tumour cells," *Brit. M. J.,* 1906, 2: 1559–1560.

30 Leo Loeb, "Ueber Regeneration des Epithels," *Roux' Arch. f. Entwcklngs-mechn. d. Organ.,* 1898, 6: 297–364.

31 Leo Loeb, "Growth of tissues in culture media and its significance for the analysis of growth phenomena," *Anat. Rec.,* 1912, 6: 109–120; see p. 109.

32 Leo Loeb, 1912, *op. cit.,* ftn. 31 above, p. 110. He reported some of his early attempts to perform *in vitro* experiments, without specifying their results, in L. Loeb, *Ueber die Entstehung von Bindegewebe, Leukozyten und roten Blutkörperchen aus Epithel und über eine Methode isolierte Gewebsteile zu-züchten,* Chicago: Stern, 1897.

cells free under the microscope, and placed them in hanging drops. The experiments failed, in that the cells did not multiply, but Haberlandt wrote magnificently about what the significance of their outcome would have been, had they succeeded.[33]

How much Harrison knew of the work of these investigators before he performed his own first tissue culture experiments is not entirely clear from the printed record. He did not cite their work in his earliest short papers on tissue culture,[34] but when these appeared in print the fashions for reference to the scientific literature were different than they are now. And in any event, what he cited from the literature in any particular article was no indication of all he knew. He listed Born's 1896 publication in one of his early extensive papers on tissue culture, published in 1910 in the memorial volume for Brooks,[35] but only in connection with the ameboid activity of cells in wound healing. He also discussed some of Leo Loeb's experiments in this paper, but not in another long article published the same year in the Festschrift for Roux.[36] In the paper in the memorial volume for Brooks, he listed among his references the paper by Roux which had described the removal of parts of the chick into warm saline solution, but he referred to it in the text only with respect to Roux' definition of self-differentiation. In neither of the 1910 papers did he write of Haberlandt, although in a lecture delivered in 1927 and published in 1928[37] he gave him full credit for being the first to attempt true cell culture. Harrison may have been influenced in other directions by plant biology, as we shall

33 G. Haberlandt, "Kulturversuche mit isolierten Pflanzenzellen," *Sitzungsber. d. Akad. d. Wissensch. Wien, Math.-naturw. Kl.*, 1902, *111* (Abt. 1): 69–92.

34 Harrison, 1907, *op. cit.*, ftn. 19 above.

35 R. G. Harrison, "The outgrowth of the nerve fiber as a mode of protoplasmic movement," *J. Exper. Zool.*, 1910, *9:* 787–846.

36 R. G. Harrison, "The development of peripheral nerve fibers in altered surroundings," *Roux' Arch. f. Entwcklngsmechn. d. Organ.*, 1910, *30* (Theil II): 15–33.

37 R. G. Harrison, "On the status and significance of tissue culture," *Arch. f. exper. Zellforsch.*, 1928, *6:* 4–27.

see shortly, and Nicholas, the obituarist who knew him best, wrote, when discussing Harrison's first tissue culture experiments: "Harrison had been greatly impressed by the results obtained in growing plant tissues and had read extensively the tissue culture experiments of Haberlandt and Sachs."[38]

But no matter what had been done before his time, and no matter what he did or did not know of it, it was the work of Harrison that began the development of tissue culture as we know it. In a somewhat double-edged introduction to Albert Fischer's monograph on tissue culture, Alexis Carrel said that: "The early technique, which was derived from the beautiful experiments of Harrison . . . , did not allow an accurate analysis of the action of a tissue upon other tissues and upon the humors . . . . The early techniques led to many errors, and had to be profoundly modified before the method of tissue culture could become an instrument of physiological investigation."[39] That there was a technique that could become an instrument of physiological investigation was due to Harrison. In discussing Harrison's contributions to tissue culture Nicholas has called attention to the fact that Harrison "was the first American zoologist to be voted the Nobel Prize" and explained that "since the vote was in 1917, the award was never made";[40] a decision of the Prize Committee not to award him the prize in 1933 is discussed further by Nicholas elsewhere.[41] Although Margaret and Warren Lewis, Albert Fischer, Giuseppe Levi, various workers at the Rockefeller

38 J. S. Nicholas, "Ross Granville Harrison (1870–1959)," *Yr. Book Amer. Philos. Soc.*, 1961, pp. 114–120; see p. 117. Nicholas' reference to Sachs is enigmatic. The latter's pioneering work on the culture of whole plants in artificial media was of great practical and theoretical significance, but I do not know of any experiments he performed that involved culture of parts of plants. Harrison, of course, would have been intrigued by his concept of morphogenetic substances.

39 In Fischer, *Tissue Culture, op. cit.*, ftn. 24 above, p. [7].

40 J. S. Nicholas, "Ross Granville Harrison 1870–1959," *Yale J. Biol. Med.*, 1960, *32:* 407–412; see p. 411.

41 J. S. Nicholas, "Ross Granville Harrison 1870–1959," *Biogr. Mems., Nat. Acad. Sc. U.S.*, 1961, *35:* 132–162; see pp. 148ff.

Institute, and some others began promptly to work in the field of tissue culture, the method was rather slow to become generally adopted. The first Nobel award for work involving the use of tissue culture was to Enders, Robbins, and Weller in 1954. During the past quarter century its use has become increasingly widespread, and great numbers of investigators find it indispensable within widely varied fields of biology and medicine.

Harrison was an exceptionally modest man to whom prizes were of minimal importance, although he received a considerable number.[42] Techniques were also, as we have said, of less importance to him than the problems they were to be used to elucidate. One of the major problems central to Harrison's thinking concerned the nature of the factors instrumental in establishing bilateral symmetry, such as it is, in vertebrates, and the remainder of this essay will devote itself to the possible origins of Harrison's first interest in this problem and to the thought behind his experimental investigation of it.

Harrison was far from being the first embryologist to interest himself in problems concerned with symmetry. Karl Ernst von Baer himself, in the treatise[43] that initiated the development of embryology as an organized science, used varieties of symmetry as the basis for defining what he considered to be the four major developmental types in animals. Later, the first experiments that stimulated the development of the new science of experimental embryology were designed to investigate the origins of bilateral symmetry in the vertebrates: the physiologist Pflüger in 1883[44] tried to test experimentally the effect of gravity on the establishment of the

42 See Nicholas, 1960, *op. cit.*, ftn. 40 above, pp. 411–412, for a list of some of the prizes and honors awarded to Harrison.

43 Karl Ernst von Baer, *Ueber Entwickelungsgeschichte der Thiere. Beobachtung und Reflexion*, Bd. I, 1828; Bd. II, 1837, Königsberg: Bornträger.

44 E. Pflüger, "Ueber den Einfluss der Schwerkraft auf die Theilung der Zellen," *Pflügers f. d. Arch. ges. Physiol.*, 1883, *31*: 311–318.

median plane of symmetry in the frog's egg, and Roux' own first experiments[45] had the same aim, although they were performed by a different method from that used by Pflüger, of whose experiments Roux did not know at the time. Roux' experiments, reported in 1884, did not demonstrate an effect of gravity on the development of bilateral symmetry, but he continued his interest in the problem and soon described results showing that what determines the position of the median plane in the frog's egg is the point of entrance of the spermatozoon and the course of the so-called copulation path followed by the sperm nucleus as it migrates through the egg toward the egg nucleus.[46] The significance with respect to the median plane of egg and embryo of the point of entry of the spermatozoon had in fact already been demonstrated by George Newport in 1854,[47] but Roux did not know of Newport's work when he performed his own experiments.

If, however, Harrison, as in the case of the outgrowth of the axis cylinder, was not the first to be concerned with problems relating to symmetry, and if he may have drawn ideas from his contemporaries and his immediate and less immediate predecessors, he was again truly inventive in devising experiments to test the time at which, and the manner in which, symmetry is established in vertebrate embryos, and

45 Wilhelm Roux, "Beiträge zur Entwickelungsmechanik des Embryo. II. Ueber die Entwickelung der Froscheier bei Aufhebung der richtenden Wirkung der Schwere," *Breslau. ärztl. Ztschr.*, 1884, 22. März, pp. 1–16; also in Roux, *Gesammelte Abhandlungen, op. cit.*, ftn. 22, vol. II, pp. 256–276.

46 Wilhelm Roux, "Beiträge zur Entwickelungsmechanik des Embryo. III. Ueber die Bestimmung der Hauptrichtungen des Froschembryo im Ei und über die erste Teilung des Froscheies. *Breslau. ärztl. Ztschr.*, 1885, Nr. 6–9, vom 28. März an, pp. 1–54; also in Roux, *Gesammelte Abhandlungen, op. cit.*, ftn. 22 above, vol. II, pp. 277–343. Wilhelm Roux, "Beiträge zur Entwickelungsmechanik des Embryo. IV. Die Bestimmung der Medianebene des Froschembryo durch die Copulationsrichtung des Eikernes und des Spermakernes," *Arch. f. mikr. Anat.*, 1887, *29*: 157–211; also in Roux, *Gesammelte Abhandlungen*, vol. II, pp. 344–418.

47 George Newport, "Researches on the impregnation of the ovum in the Amphibia; and on the early stages of development of the embryo," *Philos. Tr. Roy. Soc. London*, 1854, *144*: 229–244.

once more the design of his experiments was such that what had seemed a recondite problem became immediately amenable to simple and controlled manipulative investigation.

Briefly, his experiments were as follows. Using larvae of the spotted salamander, he grafted the disc composed of ectoderm and mesoderm of somatopleuric origin, which later forms the limb, either to the side of origin of the disc or to the opposite side of the body; and he grafted it either in its normal orientation or rotated dorso-ventrally through 180°. The experiments were performed at a tailbud stage. Preliminary reports of the experiments were published in 1916 and 1917;[48] the definitive article appeared in 1921,[49] and the results may be summarized briefly thus: at the stage that Harrison worked with, the antero-posterior axis of the limb was already established, but not the dorso-ventral nor the medio-lateral. Students of Harrison were later to show that in the case of the spotted salamander the antero-posterior axis of the limb is determined as early as the gastrula stage, the earliest stage so far investigated; after the antero-posterior axis is established, the dorso-ventral and medio-lateral axes are determined in turn. Comparable experiments were later performed by Harrison on the inner ear of the spotted salamander,[50] and for this organ, in contrast to the limb, Harrison found stages during which none of the axes are determined; as in the limb, each of the three becomes established in turn.

[48] R. G. Harrison, "On the reversal of laterality in the limbs of Amblystoma embryos," *Anat. Rec.*, 1916, *10:* 197–198 (abstract); "Further experiments on the laterality of transplanted limbs," *Anat. Rec.*, 1917, *11:* 483–484 (abstract).

[49] R. G. Harrison, "On relations of symmetry in transplanted limbs," *J. Exper. Zool.*, 1921, *32:* 1–136.

[50] R. G. Harrison, "Factors concerned in the development of the ear in Amblystoma punctatum," *Anat. Rec.*, 1934, *64 (suppl. 1):* 38–39 (abstract); "Relations of symmetry in the developing ear of Amblystoma punctatum," *Proc. Nat. Acad. Sc.*, *U.S.*, 1936, *22:* 238–247; "Further investigations of the factors concerned in the development of the ear," *Anat. Rec.*, 1938, *70 (Suppl. 3):* 35 (abstract); "Relations of symmetry in the developing embryo," *Tr. Connecticut Acad. Arts & Sc.*, 1945, *36:* 277–330.

We shall come in due time to Harrison's explanation of these results, which leads straight to the heart of modern molecular biology, but since the stated purpose of this essay is to examine the coherence of Harrison's own ideas and their relations to those of his contemporaries and predecessors, let us now examine the relationships of Harrison's limb bud grafts to his earlier studies.

Limbs of amphibians and fins of fishes are comparable structures, and no great leap of the imagination is required to transfer interest from one to the other. We remember that Harrison's first investigations related to the development of the fins of bony fishes. In 1894 he published a paper[51] that looked into the ectodermal versus mesodermal origin of the fin skeleton, and during the academic year 1894–1895 as a teaching substitute for Thomas Hunt Morgan at Bryn Mawr College, he induced a graduate student, Esther Byrnes, to look into the origin of the amphibian limb. It was she who established experimentally that the limb mesoderm arises in the amphibian not from outgrowths of the somites but from the somatopleure.[52] This was a necessary prelude to further experimentation on the amphibian limb; it is hardly possible to manipulate, with understanding, the rudiment of a body constituent before knowing what and where it is.[53]

Harrison's first experiments involving limb transplants were designed to examine the bearing of the experiments on problems relating to the development of nerves; in 1907 alone, the year during which Harrison's first paper presenting results of his tissue culture experiments appeared, he published three

[51] Harrison, "Ectodermal or mesodermal origin of the bones of teleosts?", *op. cit.*, ftn. 3 above.

[52] Esther F. Byrnes, "Experimental studies on the development of limb-muscles in Amphibia," *J. Morphol.*, 1898, *14:* 105-140.

[53] Harrison himself published in 1918 an exhaustive article on the role of the somatopleuric mesoderm in the formation of the salamander limb, demonstrating it to be, in the terminology of the day adopted from Driesch, an equipotential system ("Experiments on the development of the fore limb of Amblystoma, a self-differentiating equipotential system," *J. Exper. Zool.*, 1918, *25:* 413-461).

papers,[54] two of them abstracts, on the limb grafting experiments as related to the development of peripheral nerves. Thus we see that in performing his first limb grafts he was combining what were by then two old interests, the development of the appendage itself, and the mode of the development of the nerve fiber.

His previous experience working with the limb accounted for his ability to recognize that this is a favorable body part in which to study the origins of symmetry. Previous experiments on the inversion of the amphibian ear rudiment reported by Streeter[55] and Spemann[56] had had conflicting results. Harrison stated at the beginning of his 1921 paper on the development of limb symmetry that: "The circumstance that originally suggested the present study was the apparent difference in the results obtained by Streeter ('07) and by Spemann ('10) in their respective experiments with the amphibian ear vesicle."[57] A potential source of error in the experiments of Streeter and Spemann involving inversion of the ear vesicle was the possibility that the inverted vesicle could have righted itself mechanically within the host, undetected since buried below the skin, before the experiments were terminated. Harrison reasoned correctly that comparable experiments on the limb bud would have the advantage that the progress of its differentiation can be observed throughout development by gross inspection in urodele embryos, where it develops on the body surface and is not covered by an operculum as in anurans.

[54] R. G. Harrison, three papers with the same title, as follows: "Experiments in transplanting limbs and their bearing upon the problems of the development of nerves," *J. Exper. Zool.*, 1907, *4*: 239–281; *Anat. Rec.*, 1907, *1*: 58–59 (abstract); *Roux' Arch. f. Entwcklngsmechn. d. Organ.*, 1907, *24*: 673–674 (abstract).

[55] George L. Streeter, "Some factors in the development of the amphibian ear vesicle and further expriments on equilibration," *J. Exper. Zool.*, 1907, *4*: 431–445.

[56] H. Spemann, "Die Entwicklung des invertierten Hörgrübchens zum Labyrinth. Ein kritischer Beitrag zur Strukturlehre der Organanlagen," *Roux' Arch. f. Entwcklngsmechn. d. Organ.*, 1910, *30* (Theil II): 437–458.

[57] Harrison, 1921, *op. cit.*, ftn. 49 above, p. 2.

In fact, however, the record proves that Harrison's interest in problems relating to symmetry was of long standing, antedating by far the performance of Streeter's and Spemann's experiments with ear vesicles. In the mind of an embryologist who studies the morphogenesis of bilaterally symmetrical creatures such as vertebrates, which develop from spherical or near-spherical eggs outwardly radially symmetrical when shed, problems of symmetry are bound up with those of polarity, and polarity was one of Harrison's earliest concerns as an experimentalist. It has been pointed out above that when Harrison performed his first grafting experiments, he was already interested in the regeneration of the tail grafted in reverse position. When a tadpole tail is amputated, he remarked in 1898,[58] a new one grows out, and the "polarity" of the organism is maintained. On the other hand, a severed tail does not regenerate a new trunk and head in the tadpole, as it does in planarians and hydroids. Harrison believed that this might possibly be accounted for by the lack of food-supply to the severed tail, and to test this possibility he joined an amputated tail by its distal end to the body of another larva, on the theory that this would enable its proximal end to develop under optimal conditions. Needless to say, even under optimal conditions the originally proximal end of the amputated amphibian tail does not regenerate a trunk or a head.

But what may have induced him to perform the test as he did? It is not impossible that once again, directly or indirectly, consciously or unconsciously, he may have received a clue from a botanist. We have mentioned earlier Harrison's interest in the work of Haberlandt as it related to tissue culture; now we may mention his evident interest in the work of Hermann Vöchting, the plant grafter who was himself much concerned with problems of polarity. Vöchting was not the first to investigate the polarity of plant grafts; insertion of plant grafts in inverse orientation had been begun at least as early

[58] Harrison, 1898, *op. cit.*, ftn. 7 above, p. 448.

as the time of Pliny, as Vöchting was aware.[59] But it was Vöchting who was the articulate, and in the nineteenth century the modern, botanist who discussed plant grafting in writings influential in his times and accessible to embryologists well-versed in German.

Several times in his 1898 paper Harrison compared his early grafting experiments with those of Vöchting on plants as reported in a book published in 1892,[60] and two of Harrison's references to Vöchting's book relate to experiments involving the reversal of polarity in grafts. Furthermore, Born before him, in 1896, had discussed Vöchting's experiments, which he stated had been drawn to his attention by a member of the audience when he first described his own grafts to the Schlesische Gesellschaft in 1894 in the talk referred to on page 94.

Vöchting's book was entitled *Ueber Transplantation am Pflanzenkörper. Untersuchungen zur Physiologie und Pathologie,* and it dealt, as its title implies, primarily with plants. But it concludes with a short chapter, covering about two pages, on transplantation in animals. This begins with a brief comment on Trembley's, Réaumur's, and Blumenbach's successful attempts to unite two separate heads of *Hydra* of the same or different species. Then in the next paragraph Vöchting performs an imaginary experiment of his own: "The next experiment to undertake will be a repetition of Trembley's experiment, with the variation that the parts should be brought together not in normal but in inverse position."[61] "According to all probability," he continues, "they would repel each other."[62] Born referred to this passage in 1896, but

---

59 See Jane M. Oppenheimer, "William Gilbert: plant grafting and the grand analogy," *J. Hist. Med. & Allied Sci.,* 1953, *8:* 165–176, for a discussion of the early history of inversion of plant grafts and shoots. Reprinted in this volume, pp. 350–365.

60 Hermann Vöchting, *Ueber Transplantation am Pflanzenkörper. Untersuchungen zur Physiologie und Pathologie,* Tübingen: Laupp'sche Buchhandlung, 1892.

61 Vöchting, *ibid.,* p. 160.

62 *Loc. cit.*

in doing so he refined the experiment in his imagination: "Moreover, it would be easy to carry out on the frog larva an experiment analogous to Vöchting's. It would be necessary only to remove a flat oval piece from the belly of a number of larvae, and to replace half of the pieces normally and half abnormally, that is, with the former hind end forward, in order to see whether the healing is equally smooth in the two cases, or whether in the latter case any pathological results ensue."[63] This was very close to the specific experiment that Harrison was to perform with the flat limb disc; since pathological phenomena did not ensue, the experiment was to prove ideal for the analysis of the development of bilateral symmetry.

Interesting as are the backgrounds related to the initiation of these experiments, equally, or perhaps even more so, are those which relate Harrison's ultimate interpretations of the results to his own early ideas and to those of the men whose works he was studying in his early formative years. When he first reported *in extenso* the results of the limb transplantation experiments designed to elucidate the origins of bilateral symmetry, he made an analogy, and he meant it to be no more than that, between the whole developing limb as it established its three axes in turn and the tetrahedral carbon atom.[64] He never did describe definitively the results of his experiments on the ear, but in a preliminary report of them he stated that the transformation from one phase to the next must be associated with "changes in the orientation of ultramicroscopic elements."[65] At the Harvard Tercentenary Conference, where he presented his results on the ear somewhat more fully, his candidates for the ultramicroscopic elements were named as protein molecules.[66] In 1940 Harrison, Astbury, and Rudall[67]

63 Born, 1896, *op. cit.*, ftn. 5 above, p. 601; the English translation is mine.
64 Harrison, 1921, *op. cit.*, ftn. 49 above.
65 Harrison, 1936, *op. cit.*, ftn. 50 above, p. 246.
66 Harrison, 1945, *op. cit.*, ftn. 50 above.
67 R. G. Harrison, W. T. Astbury, and K. M. Rudall, "An attempt at an X-ray analysis of embryonic processes," *J. Exper. Zool.*, 1940, *85*: 339–363.

had to report their results as inconclusive for technical reasons when they attempted to demonstrate polar or other specific orientation of molecules in embryonic tissue by X-ray diffraction studies. Thus an important question remains open, but we may inquire as to how early there arose in Harrison's mind thoughts which culminated in the performance of these truly progressive experiments in molecular biology.

Let us see what he wrote in 1898 in relation to his experiments on heteromorphosis:

Coupled with the occurrence of heteromorphosis is the question of the polarity of the organism. Unfortunately, the term "polarity" is used with many different shades of meaning. Fundamentally, a purely geometrical conception, it signifies more when used by the morphologist, implying not only symmetry, but also an internal cause for that symmetry, by virtue of which every particle of the organism has the same polar relations as the whole.[68]

In a footnote to this paragraph, which uses *Hydra* as an example, Harrison refers as follows to the work of his own mentor Nussbaum:

This is expressed most clearly and categorically in the quoted words of Nussbaum . . . as follows: "Moreover, in order to explain what has happened in our experiments, we must make the assumption that the cells, in their structure as well as their function, are highly differentiated in the composition of their smallest parts; that is to say that inside and outside, fore and hind, have their full meaning not only in the whole individual, but that the axial orientations of the individual are based on the orientations of its smallest parts. Thus in each cell there must be a fore and a hind, an inside and an outside, right and left thus being self-determined . . . [Harrison's ellipsis] and since each cell must be conceived of as further divisible, these axial orientations must be thought to be already present in the smallest parts of the cells."[69]

[68] Harrison, 1898, *op. cit.*, ftn. 7 above, p. 469.
[69] *Loc. cit.*, ftn. 1. Harrison gave the quotation from Nussbaum's paper in German; the English translation is mine. The reference to Nussbaum's paper is: Moritz Nussbaum, "Ueber die Theilbarkeit der lebendigen Materie. II. Mittheilung. Beiträge zur Naturgeschichte des Genus Hydra," *Arch. f. mikr. Anat.*, 1887, *29*: 265–366; see p. 348.

Thus when Harrison first expressed an interest, in print, in polarization and symmetry of subcellular units as related to those of the whole individual, he referred to the work of the man with whom he was working most closely in his early years at Bonn.

But to whom did Nussbaum refer? Immediately after the passage cited by Harrison and translated in the foregoing paragraph of this essay, stands the sentence, in my translation, "This is supported also by the experiments of the botanists," and Nussbaum then refers to a paper by Vöchting published in 1877 in *Pflügers Archiv*.[70]

Harrison, as a distinguished editor of a distinguished periodical, encouraged his contributors to hold their footnotes to a minimum number, but his own in his early papers are enlightening. In the 1898 article, on the page following that on which is found the footnote to Nussbaum just quoted, there is another footnote incorporating one of the references to Vöchting mentioned above on page 111: "Vöchting . . . from his elaborate study of plant grafting comes to the conclusion that the polarity of the vegetable cell is comparable to the polarity of the magnet,"[71] and then he quotes a long German sentence of Vöchting's that it is not necessary to reproduce or to translate here. But if we turn to the page in Vöchting's 1892 monograph in which the sentence quoted by Harrison is originally printed, we find, several short paragraphs below, that Vöchting has written: "I have elsewhere tried to show . . . how in this way we can think of the cytoplasm as composed of polarized molecules or micellae ('polarized' as con-

---

[70] Nussbaum, *loc. cit.* The paper by Vöchting he refers to is "Ueber Theilbarkeit im Pflanzenbereich und die Wirkung innerer und äusserer Kräfte auf Organbildung in Pflanzentheilen," *Pflügers Arch. f. d. ges. Physiol.*, 1877, *15*: 153–190.

[71] Harrison, 1898, *op. cit.*, ftn. 7 above, p. 471. Harrison did not hold with the analogy to the magnet. "Even if it should turn out," he wrote when discussing an experiment in which some of the tails grafted in reverse degenerated, "that the degeneration were due to abnormal position of parts, it cannot be shown that there is any resemblance to magnetic repulsion."

ceived of in the chemical sense)."[72] The protein molecules invoked by Harrison in the Harvard Tercentenary address as responsible for embryonic polarity were polarized, without quotation marks, in the chemical sense.

Harrison's papers on the transplantation of limb buds and ear vesicles did not refer to the ideas of Nussbaum and Born and Vöchting on polarity that had earlier had so much in common with his own. In his 1945 essay based on the Harvard Tercentenary address, he refers to Nussbaum and Born only with respect to germ cell continuity and shifting of the yolk in response to gravity, respectively. He does, in the same essay, refer in a footnote to a number of recent articles on "the importance of molecular configuration and orientation in the organization of protoplasm," but the only early concept he mentions is the micellar theory of Nägeli;[73] — a concept also accredited by Vöchting to Nägeli in the sentence preceding that which we have quoted in the previous paragraph, concerning the micellae or molecules polarized in the chemical sense.

Thus, although in his later papers Harrison does not repeat the references that were important to him when first he discussed polarity in 1898, the evidence would seem to belie Abercrombie's interpretation that: "In interpreting the nature of this quite unexpected polarity [Abercrombie refers to the demonstration in the 1921 paper that the antero-posterior axis of the limb was established at the tailbud stage at which Harrison worked] Harrison seems to have had from the start a strongly held hunch, derived from Driesch."[74]

It is quite true that when, in 1921, Harrison wrote: "In an equipotential system without axial differentiation, it is most natural to assume that the elements themselves are isotropic,"

[72] Vöchting, *op. cit.*, ftn. 60 above, p. 156; the translation of Vöchting's German is mine. The paper he refers to is: H. Vöchting, "Ueber die Regeneration der Marchantieen," *Pringsheims Jahrb. f. wissensch. Botan.*, 1885, *16:* 367–414.

[73] Harrison, 1945, *op. cit.*, ftn. 50 above, p. 297, ftn. 16.

[74] Abercrombie, *op. cit.*, ftn. 1 above, p. 120.

he added a footnote referring to Driesch: "The question whether relations of symmetry of the organism are to be based upon symmetrical relations of the intimate protoplasmic structure is answered in the affirmative by Driesch."[75] But the work of Driesch that he referred to[76] was published in 1908, ten years after Harrison had been reading and writing about comparable ideas of Nussbaum and Vöchting, ten years after Harrison himself had already written: "the term 'polarity' . . . when used by the morphologist [implies] not only symmetry, but also an internal cause for that symmetry, by virtue of which every particle of the organism has the same polar relations as the whole."[77]

Harrison performed a number of experiments other than those reported here and wrote many articles to which this essay has not referred; moreover, some of these pertain directly to the subjects we have taken up. But it is surely apparent from what we have selected for discussion that his interests at the beginning of his career stimulated in his mind ideas that he was to develop logically and consistently throughout his life. Since science can grow only by accretion upon itself, it is to his credit, not to his discredit, that a number of his ideas were intimately related to those of his immediate predecessors and contemporaries. His success grew out of his talent for looking into problems that were of immediate concern in his day in such a way that they could be investigated successfully by experiment and thus brought either to ultimate solution, as in the case of the outgrowth of the axis cylinder, or much nearer to it than they had been hitherto, as in the case of the orientation of ultrastructural substituents of the cytoplasm.

[75] Harrison, 1921, *op. cit.*, ftn. 49 above, p. 88, and p. 88, ftn. 96.
[76] H. Driesch, "Zur Theorie der organischen Symmetrie," *Roux' Arch. f. Entwcklngsmechn. d. Organ.*, 1908, 26: 130–145.
[77] See p. 113 above.

Analysis of Development: Problems, Concepts and Their History*

Is cell-differentiation inherent or induced?

A thoughtful and distinguished naturalist tells us that while the differentiation of the cells which arise from the egg is sometimes inherent in the egg, and sometimes induced by the conditions of development, it is more commonly mixed; but may it not be the mind of the embryologist, and not the natural world, that is mixed? Science does not deal in compromises, but in discoveries. When we say the development of the egg is inherent, must we not also say what are the relations with reference to which it is inherent? When we say it is induced, must we not also say what are the relations with reference to which it is induced? Is there any way to find this out except scientific discovery?

W. K. Brooks ('02, pp. 490–491)

IT is the self-imposed task of the present compendium to review and evaluate the past and present accomplishments of the science of embryology in order more intelligently to facilitate progress into its future. The separate contributions which make up the main body of the volume must necessarily concentrate on particular fields of investigation. It is the

* Written at the Osborn Zoological Laboratory, Yale University, and at Bryn Mawr College. I owe especial gratitude to the Library of the College of Physicians of Philadelphia for the use of their collections and for generous assistance. Reprinted from *Analysis of Development*, edited by Benjamin H. Willier, Paul A. Weiss and Viktor Hamburger, W. B. Saunders Company, Philadelphia, Pa., 1955, pp. 1–24.

purpose, therefore, of the first two chapters to provide a general background against which these more special subjects may be considered. Out of convenience, rather than from logical necessity, these two chapters will concern themselves first with concepts, and secondly with techniques, though the nature of the scientific method is such that these two aspects of the problem are inextricably interrelated. Arbitrarily, too, the topics chosen for discussion will be selective rather than exhaustive; since it is not possible in a few pages to do justice to even a few of the great contributors of the past, only those have been chosen whose writings are most relevant to the sequel, and even of these, many can enjoy only the barest mention.

THE EARLY EMBRYOLOGY OF THE GREEKS: ARISTOTLE

Since it was the Greeks who performed the great *tour de force* of freeing science from magic and elevating it into the realms of pure reason, it is sensible to begin by examining a few of their contributions to embryology. They were early to develop an interest in beginnings; their very word for nature (φύσις, physis) according to some, including Aristotle (*Parts of Animals*, 1945 edition, pp. 74–75), implies growth, genesis or origin (φύεσθαι), and Anaximander, who flourished in the sixth century B.C., spoke of the γό νιμον, the germ or fetus of the world. They recognized early that change was an essence of existence, as we know from Herakleitos' emphasis on flux, and as is evident from their mythological conception of cosmos evolving from chaos. And from the beginning they compared cosmos to the organism, witness Plato (*Timaeus*, [1944] edition, p. 117):

Its composing artificer constituted it from *all* fire, water, air, and earth; leaving no part of any one of these, nor any power external to the world. For by a reasoning process he concluded that it would thus be a whole animal, in the highest degree perfect from perfect parts.

118

But more than this, perhaps even because of it, they were able even as early as the time of Anaximander to conceive of the organism as emergent, and indeed of animals as related to man: a fragment concerning the teachings of Anaximander reads that "living creatures arose from the moist element, as it was evaporated by the sun. Man was like another animal, namely, a fish, in the beginning" (Burnet, '30, p. 70).

No attempt can be made here to enumerate the many Greek philosophers to build upon these beginnings, or to evaluate the contributions of those who did. It will have to be sufficient here to name a few, and the interested reader is referred to Balss ('36) for additional details. Suffice it here to comment that theirs was the task of the first early and perhaps random collection of data, which must precede even the primitive classification which many consider to represent the first stage of scientific inquiry.

Of some, we know only from the meager extant fragments that they recorded what they thought to be observed fact; for instance, from Parmenides a fragment remains implying that males are generated on the right and females on the left. In the case of others, even before Aristotle, it is clear that they believed that around the observed facts they could elaborate theory. Empedokles, for example, believed the fetus to arise partly from male and partly from female semen, the children resembling most the parent who contributed most to the offspring; he spoke of the influence of pictures, statues and so forth in modifying the appearance of the offspring, of twins and triplets as due to "superabundance and division of the semen" (Burnet, '30, p. 244); he knew there was a regular sequence of events in development and spoke of the heart as formed first in development, the nails last, sowing seeds of concepts, which, right or wrong, were destined often to recrudesce in subsequent ages.

A Hippocratic treatise on generation went further in developing theories, formulating an early expression of the doctrine of pangenesis, and, relating to it, what seems to be on *post hoc* reasoning a doctrine of the inheritance of acquired characters. This treatise, before Aristotle, recognized the importance of methodology, and advocated systematic daily observation of chicken eggs: "Take twenty or more eggs and let them be incubated by two or more hens. Then each day from the second to that of hatching remove an egg, break it, and examine it. You will find," continues the writer, illustrating an apparent dependence of concept on method and inferring the great generalization, "exactly as I say, for the nature of the bird can be likened to that of man" (Singer, '22, p. 15).

Aristotle's own accomplishment was none the less impressive, for all he drew on his predecessors and contemporaries. "There was a wealth of natural history before his time; but it belonged to the farmer, the huntsman, and the fisherman — with something over (doubtless) for the schoolboy, the idler and the poet. But Aristotle made it a science, and won a place for it in Philosophy" (Thompson, '40, p. 47). And in establishing it as scientific, he set its standards higher than hitherto by far.

He followed, in embryology, the method of the Hippocratic writer *On Generation,* to perform and record most of the available observations, many in error but also many correct, thus to constitute a collection of knowledge on the development of the chick which became the foundation on which all embryology was to build; and it has been said, with much justice, of his account that "almost two thousand years were to roll by before it was to be equaled or surpassed" (Adelmann, *ed.*, in Fabricius, 1942 edition, p. 38). He concerned himself not only with the development of the chick but also with the generation of many other forms, and elaborated a kind of classification (though not in the modern sense; cf. Thompson, '40) of animal forms according to their mode of reproduction. By so doing, he both established embryology as an independent science, and he fitted embryological knowledge into a pattern larger than its own, with great clarity of vision and imagination.

On the theoretical side, he followed his predecessors by adopting a modified view of pangenesis, and concurred with them in supporting the doctrine of the inheritance of acquired characters. He broke away from his predecessors, however, in developing a new and erroneous yet highly influential concept of the relative roles of male and female in development, postulating the former as providing the form, at once formal, efficient and final cause, and the latter the substance, the material cause, for the new organism.

By thus undervaluing the egg, he paid embryology the obvious immediate disservice; but in formulating his conception of biological form as inseparable from matter he laid the way open for ultimate progress in biological science. The argument is metaphysical to the taste of the modern scientist; but Aristotle will be found not to be the last embryologist to be so tainted. We concur with his intent, after all, every time we speak of "animal forms" as a euphemism for "animal species." And Aristotle, with the natural historian's innate feeling for natural form, by envisioning form as a part of actuality rather than something above it, brought biological material to be directly investigable by the sense organs.

His theories concerning special developmental phenomena, related to his primary philosophy as they were, are deep in much of the embryological and indeed the wider biological thinking both of the past and the present. His description of the heart as the first organ of the embryo to be formed, both in time and in primacy, tied as it was to the conception of the soul as formal and final cause and of vital heat in the blood as the agent of the soul, dominated the notions not only of the developing but also of the adult circulation, and hence all physiology, through to the nineteenth century and the downfall of the phlogiston theory. His concept of organ as related to final cause epitomizes teleology, and with all the weight of

Galen's authority in support still permeates much of the thought of modern biology. Matter with form inseparable from it as opposed to the more material matter postulated by Leucippus' and Democritus' atomic theory, which implied preformation, in a way made possible the whole doctrine of epigenesis, first clearly formulated by Aristotle and still central in all embryological thinking today. Form as inseparable from matter makes possible a conception of pattern emergent, an analogy of development and the *process* of plaiting a net or the *process* of painting a picture; for Plato, the Ideal mesh would have been already woven, the Ideal portrait previously complete. Aristotle (*Generation of Animals*, 1943 edition, pp. 147, 149, 225) could frame the modern question:

How, then, are the other parts formed? Either they are all formed simultaneously — heart, lung, liver, eye, and the rest of them — or successively, as we read in the poems ascribed to Orpheus, where he says that the process by which an animal is formed resembles the plaiting of a net. As for simultaneous formation of the parts, our senses tell us plainly that this does not happen: some of the parts are clearly to be seen present in the embryo while others are not. . . . Since one part, then, comes earlier and another later, is it the case that A fashions B and that it is there on account of B which is next to it, or is it rather the case that B is formed after A? . . .

In the early stages the parts are all traced out in outline; later on they get their various colours and softnesses and hardnesses, for all the world as if a painter were at work on them, the painter being Nature. Painters, as we know, first of all sketch in the figure of the animal in outline, and after that go on to apply the colours.

The metaphor will speak for itself to modern experimental embryologists. Aristotle, however, for all his natural acuity, was strangely double-minded. In his dynamic feeling for form, derived from direct study of living biological material, he was modern, and was to lead eventually straight to the inductive biology of modern times. But his conceptions of the wider Universe, based on pure reason, because statically and structurally interpreted and thus transmitted by medieval commentators, deluded posterity, and it was unfortunately the static Aristotle, the Aristotle of a sterile cosmogony, crystal clear but crystal rigid, who dominated the thought of the Middle Ages. So far as even the embryology was concerned, the Middle Ages transmitted his concepts, and occasionally amplified them, as in the case of Albertus Magnus, but devitalized them and thereby hardly improved them. Appreciation of their dynamic qualities awaited the Renaissance and later ages.

EMBRYOLOGY AND THE RENAISSANCE: FABRICIUS, HARVEY

When the Renaissance came under way it accelerated its course into the new thought by taking strength from the Greek past through all the resources of Humanism; and a "reconstruction of the Greek spirit" (cf. Singer, ['41], p. 166) was an essential part of the rebirth. Even Galileo has been called a "typical Paduan Aristotelian" in method and philosophy at least, if not in physics (Randall, cited by Adelmann, ed., in Fabricius, 1942 edition, p. 55), and Whitehead ('25, p. 17) reminds us that Galileo "owes more to Aristotle than appears on the surface of his *Dialogues:* he owes to him his clear head and his analytic mind." Vesalius' interpretations of his observations were as teleological as those of Galen after which they were modelled (cf. Singer, '44, p. 81, who called him "a disciple of Galen by training, by inclination, and by his whole cast of thought"); his method, however, was also in part that of Aristotle. Copernicus, who was accused by Kepler of interpreting Ptolemy, not nature, at least challenged the Aristotelian cosmogony; Vesalius imitated the method of the Aristotle who is so rarely remembered as having written about an embryological problem (*Generation of Animals,* 1943 edition, pp. 345, 347):

This, then, appears to be the state of affairs . . . so far as theory can take us, supplemented by what are thought to be the facts about their behaviour. But the facts have not been sufficiently ascertained; and if at any future time they are ascertained, then credence must be given to the direct evidence of the senses more than to theories.

The scientist, who customarily characterizes the Renaissance as a movement for freedom with respect to authority, often neglects to remember that it was in part from "authority" that the inspiration to achieve freedom derived.

It was Fabricius, student of Fallopius, himself a student of Vesalius, who first exhaustively applied the rigorous "new" Vesalian method of direct observation to the study of embryos, though he had many predecessors who had made isolated observations on embryonic material (among them Columbus, Fallopius, Eustachius, Arantius, Aldrovandus, Coiter *et al*. Cf. Needham, '34, and Adelmann, *ed*., in Fabricius, 1942 edition, for full discussion; see also Adelmann for full critical treatment of Fabricius himself).

On the observational side, he was the first to publish illustrations based on systematic study of the development of the chick, and this, though he neglected to describe them in detail, was probably his most significant contribution. He made the way easier for the later preformationists by drawing the supposed three and four day chicks much too advanced for their normal chronological age; among his other fallacies, the most notable was his ascription to the chalazae of the role of forming the embryo. Among his improvements to the existing embryological knowledge was his emphasis that the *carina* (whose metaphysics he discussed more completely than its embryological fate) is formed before the heart, controverting Aristotle, and before the liver, taking issue with Galen in both fact and philosophy. He studied the fetal anatomy of various vertebrates, that of many mammals, including man, and presented illustrations of the comparative anatomy of the placenta, showing his special interest in the umbilical and the fetal circulation, though he devoted himself to Galenic principles in his interpretations of these. Even Fabricius, then, as late as the sixteenth century was exemplifying the conflict of the Renaissance between allegiance to authority and confidence in direct personal observations. But though in one sense his position represents an inevitable retreat, even behind the position of Aristotle, in that he emphasized the anatomy of embryos rather than the process of development, yet his work looked forward to the new embryology in the influence it exerted on William Harvey.

Fabricius' name, as Adelmann points out (*op. cit.*, p. 115) begins the first sentence of Harvey's text on generation; and Harvey, too, like his preceptor, looked back to Aristotle in his interpretations, for all that his demonstration of the circulation in method, fact, and conception, was to lead to the whole experimental and analytical biology of the future. Harvey followed Bacon's principle of explaining nature by observation and experiment, and Galileo's of measuring what is measurable and making measurable what is not. Harvey's contemporaries believed, with Fracastorius, that "the motion of the heart was to be understood by God alone" (Harvey, *De motu*, 1931 edition, p. 25). Harvey proved it to be a mechanical function. Yet he could speak of the motion of the blood, after Copernicus, Kepler and Galileo, as "circular in the way that Aristotle says air and rain follow the circular motion of the stars" (*ibid.*, p. 70) and, like a good Aristotelian, he left the vital spirits remaining in the blood. "Whether or not the heart," he wrote, "besides transferring, distributing and giving motion to the blood, adds anything else to it, as heat, spirits, or perfection, may be discussed later and determined on other grounds" (*ibid.*, p. 49). Harvey may have surmised how to treat the organ as a machine, but he was in some ways too Aristotelian to appreciate the implications of his own advanced experiment.

He was not so bound by authority, however, as to be unable to free himself from some of the old embryological errors. He refuted on an observational basis, for instance, the notion that right and left represent maleness and femaleness, and he corrected the idea of Fabricius concerning the role of the chalazae by demonstrating the *cicatricula* (our blastoderm) as the source of the embryo; he corrected, too, various specific observational errors of Aristotle. Most important, he abolished for all time the Aristotelian conception of female as substance and male as form. Galen to be sure had seemed to localize both material and efficient causes in both male and female semen, as had Fabricius after him in a confused sort of way; but it was Harvey, for all his fanciful speculation concerning the significance of fertilization, who finally elevated the egg to its full and ultimate dignity. The processes of development can obviously hardly be investigated before the object that is developing is at least defined as their residence, and Harvey's contribution here was therefore a significant one.

It is abundantly clear, however, that by egg Harvey meant something different than we do. He knew there was necessary for development a double contribution, deriving from both male and female parent:

> The *egge* is a certain Conception proceeding from Male and Female, qualified with the power of both: and out of it being One, one *Animal* is constituted. . . . An *egge* can no more be made without the assistance of the *Cock* and *Henne,* then the *fruit* can be made without the *Trees* aid. . . . For without a *Cock* it cannot be *fruitfull,* without a *Henne* it cannot be at all (1653, pp. 136, 157, 155).

Yet even in the case of the chick this is not the egg to Harvey that is the visible entity of the laboratory or kitchen:

> And though it be a known thing, subscribed by all, that the *foetus* assumes its original and birth from the Male and Female, and consequently that the Egge is produced by the Cock and Henne, and the Chicken out of the Egge: yet neither the School of Physitians, nor *Aristotles* discerning Brain, have disclosed the manner, how the Cock and its seed, doth mint and coine the Chicken out of the Egge. . . . But that neither the *Hen* doth emit any Seed in *coition,* nor poure forth

any blood at that time into the cavity of the *Uterus;* as also that the egge is not formed after *Aristotles* way; nor yet (as *Physitians* suppose) by the commixture of Seeds, and likewise that the *Cocks* seed doth not penetrate into the hollow of the *womb,* nor yet is attracted thither, is most manifest, from this one Observation, namely, *That after coition there is nothing at all to be found in the* Uterus, *more then there was before (ibid.,* pp. 250, 199).

He met the same failure in a vain examination of the uterus of the mammal, and was driven therefore to resolve his dilemma by a poor analogy:

The *Egge* is . . . a kind of an *exposed Womb,* and place where the *Foetus* is formed: for it executes the office of the *Matrix,* and shelters the *Chicken* till its just time of *Birth.* . . . *Oviparous creatures* are therefore not distinguished from *Viviparous,* in this, that these bring forth their *Foetus* alive, but they do not; . . . but their maine difference consists in the *manner* of *Generation;* namely, in that *Viviparous* creatures continue their *Womb* within them, in which the *Foetus* is fashioned, cherished, and compleated: *but Oviparous* expose their *Egge* or *Matrix* without: yet nevertheless they do ripen and cherish it as much by *Incubation,* as if they did reserve it within their *bowels (ibid.,* p. 127).

Martin Llewellyn put it more succinctly, if less elegantly, in his poem "To the Incomparable Dr. Harvey, On his Books of the Motion of the Heart and Blood, and of the Generation of Animals," when he wrote *(ibid.,* n.p.):

That both the *Hen* and *Houswife* are so matcht,
That her Son *Born,* is only her Son *Hatcht.*

Harvey began his embryology from an Aristotelian metaphysical preconception: "All perfect science depends upon the knowledge of all causes: and therefore to the plenary comprehension of Generation, we must ascend from the last and lowest efficient to the very *first* and *most supreme,* and know them all" *(ibid.,* p. 259). Frustrated by the inability of his own senses to find the physical reality he sought, he took solace in a metaphysical conception of his own, at a different level, and envisioned a metaphysical egg:

127

The Egge ... seemes to be a kinde of *Medium;* not onely as it is the *Principium,* and the *Finis,* but as it is the Common work or production of both Sexes, and compounded of both. . . . It is also a *Medium,* or thing between an *Animate* and an *Inanimate* creature; being neither absolutely impowered with life, nor absolutely without it. It is a Midway or Passage between the *Parents* and the *Children;* between those that were, and those that are to come. . . . It is the *Terminus à quo,* the Point or Original from which all the *Cocks* and *Hennes* in the world do arise and spring: and it is also the *Terminus ad quem,* the Aim and End proposed by nature, to which they direct themselves all their life long. By which it comes to pass, that all *Individuals,* while to supply their *Species* they beget their Like, do continue and perpetuate their duration. The *Egge* is at were [*sic*] the Period of this Eternity (*ibid.,* p. 137).

But though Harvey necessarily ended as he began in metaphysics, he had shown the embryologists to follow him where to begin their physical investigations. His transmission, therefore, of Aristotle's notions of epigenesis takes on a new meaning, since his epigenesis takes place in an egg which to embryologists succeeding him was the visible egg of reality, the egg which he searched for even though he failed to find it. His description of epigenesis, in which

All . . . parts are not constituted at once, but successively, & in *Order.* . . . *Nature* doth feed and enlarge all the Parts, out of the self same Nutriment, whereof the [*sic*] *first* did frame them . . . and like a *potter,* first she divides her *materials,* and she allots to the *Trunk,* the *Head,* and the *Limbs,* every one their *share* or *cantlin:* as *Painters* do, who first draw the *Lineaments,* and then lay on the *Colours* (*ibid.,* pp. 225, 331),

is a description significant for the modern embryologist in more ways than by the repetition of Aristotle's metaphor.

The fairly common delusion, however, that Harvey championed the cause of epigenesis to the exclusion of others has little basis in fact. Harvey was more cautious than many more modern investigators in emphasizing that "the *principles* of divers *Animals* being also diverse . . . the manner of the generation of *Animals* is diverse likewise" (*ibid.*, p. 384), and while he considered some animals to be "perfected by a *succession* of *parts*" (*ibid.*, p. 344), he knew others to be "made intire at once" (*loc. cit.*), "formed and transfigured, out of *matter* already concocted and grown" (*ibid.*, p. 222). "The form ariseth *ex potentiâ materiae praeexistentis,* out of the power or potentiality of the pre-existent matter; and the *matter* is rather the first cause of the *Generation,* then any *external Efficient*" (*ibid.*, p. 223).

This resounds strongly of preformationism, and indeed in the modern rather than the old-fashioned sense. There are those who claim that Harvey's work on generation was of little historical moment because of its relative obscurity at the time of its publication. Malpighi, however, knew it, and he knew because of it to start his studies with the blastoderm; indeed, Harvey is mentioned on the first page of Malpighi's text, a notation which may bear witness to the fact that the ideas of preformation may themselves have been fostered as least in part by the inadequacies of the early epigenetic postulate.

EMBRYOLOGY AND THE NEW MICROSCOPE: PREFORMATION AND MALPIGHI; EPIGENESIS AND WOLFF

Harvey's failure which drove him back to the metaphysics from which he started we have called a physical one related to the inadequacy of his senses. Malpighi here had the advantage over him, with the use of the microscope as a new tool, and with it he overstepped the old limitations to enter what might seem in some ways a new conceptual realm, namely that of preformationism.

This doctrine of preformation, however, was no clear and strong new reply to an old question by a new science. It was a principle deeply intrenched in ancient philosophy and destined to outlast for many years the validity of the scientific evidence once seeming to favor it. It remained, indeed, a philosophical dogma rather than a scientific principle even after long being discussed on a scientific basis; its most ardent biological champion, Bonnet, was to betray the preponderance of its philosophical over its scientific weight by calling it "one of the greatest triumphs of rational over sensual conviction" (cited by Needham, '34, p. 191).

The concept roots, on the philosophical side, at least as remotely into antiquity as the times of Leucippus and Demo-critus, whom Aristotle so strongly opposed, and the implications of preformation inherent in the ancient materialistic doctrines were clearly realized by Lucretius (*De rerum natura*, Bk. I, lines 159–214). Seneca wrote as early as the first century (cited by Needham, '34, p. 48):

> In the seed are enclosed all the parts of the body of the man that shall be formed. The infant that is borne in his mother's wombe hath the rootes of the beard and hair that he shall weare one day. In this little masse likewise are all the lineaments of the bodie and all that which Posterity shall discover in him.

When the formed element is present *ab initio*, the end and the beginning are the same, and the principle of *emboîtement* becomes difficult to escape. It too was recognized early; a theory of *emboîtement* expressed by Saint Augustine is quoted by Wheeler (1898). Nearer to the time of Malpighi (for the early and intervening development of the concepts see Cole, '30; Meyer, '39; and Needham, '34), Joseph of Aromatari (1625) reiterated an old idea of Empedokles that the plant is present in the ungerminated seed and said that "the chick is formed before the hen broods upon it" (Meyer, '39, p. 63).

It was Malpighi, however, who in 1673 reported the observations which were to endow the theory with new vigor. He studied with the new microscope what he thought to be the unincubated egg, to see in its blastoderm the structures so magnificently portrayed in the familiar plates, and to interpret them to signify that the parts of the animal may pre-exist in the egg. He indulged in less dogmatism in his claims, however, than posterity customarily attributes to him, as is emphasized in analysis of his work by Adelmann currently in progress. Malpighi organized no formal and systematic theory of development; he did not himself use the word preformation, and there is some question, according to Adelmann, as to what he meant by the pre-existence of the animal in the egg. He expressed his notions only tentatively, and he was, in fact, uncertain whether new structures existed before he observed them: "Nam primum ortum non assequuti, emergentem successive partium manifestationem expectare cogimur" (1685 edition, p. 577). In sum, according to Adelmann's interpretation, he can justly be called a preformationist only with considerable qualification.

As Maître-Jan was to point out and explain in 1722, the egg examined by Malpighi was not what he had considered it — an egg studied after exposure to the heat of the August sun in Bologna is "unincubated" only with reference to the hen — but the work was no less influential than had it been founded on a different premise. Malpighi's primary contribution was his successful presentation for the first time of visible evidence on the detailed constitution of the young embryo. And evidence adduced by one of the new tools was as certain in the seventeenth as in the twentieth century to draw popular enthusiasm.

It was a function of his times that such evidence could be construed as support for embryological theory. What Malpighi saw and figured could be interpreted according to postulates compatible with Descartes' hypothesis of the infinite divisibility of matter; what he figured could be generalized into theories implying the embryo to be the same kind of "earthly machine" as Descartes' adult, and the concepts which were to incorporate his observations into the doctrine of preformation were crystallizing in many minds. Malpighi was no lone prophet of the new embryology. His contemporaries were going far to cry physical facts to fit a philosophical pattern. Croone, at much the same time, was making somewhat similar claims for the pre-existence of the chick in the egg, on the basis of a fantastically egregious error, mistaking a fragment of vitelline membrane for the embryo (Cole, '44). Swammerdam had in 1672 expressed a somewhat comparable concept for the egg of the frog, and Grew an analogous one for plants the same year. Malebranche, on the basis of observations as well as speculation, was expressing similar conclusions and generalizing the doctrine for plants and animals on a strong philosophical foundation (Schrecker, '38). For Leibniz, preformation was not only a metaphysical but also a strictly biological postulate which he related to his concept of the fixity of species. Bonnet, after his discovery of parthenogenesis in aphids, made preformation the basis for all his biological and philosophical speculations; the theory was supported by all the weighty authority of Haller, and even by such advanced experimentalists as Spallanzani and Réaumur.

Vallisnieri's speculations on the possibility that not only the whole human race but also all human parasites were represented in the ovaries of Eve, and Hartsoeker's calculation of the necessary size of a rabbit large enough to enclose all rabbits from the beginning of time; Dalenpatius' absurd claims to have seen the homunculus in the spermatozoon, and all the foolish arguments between ovists and animalculists exemplified the extremes to which the doctrine was led; and such ridiculous claims served primarily to overburden it until it was close to collapse under its own weight. But it also fell, as it rose, on the basis of more serious philosophical principles; again a philosophical need had created a demand which again an observational embryologist — this time Caspar Friedrich Wolff — was to fulfill.

Wolff started out with a full appreciation of the philosophical limitations to embryological progress implied by the preformation doctrine: "Qui igitur systemata praedelineationis tradunt, generationem non explicant, sed, eam non dari, affirmant" (1759; cited from 1774 edition, p. xxi); those who adopt the systems of predelineation do not explain generation but affirm that it does not occur. He was to launch his own attack from two sides, from the philosopher's and the observer's, but he started from the former's position "Verum explicat generationem, qui ex traditis principiis & legibus partes corporis & modum compositionis deducit. . . . Et absoluit theoriam generationis, qui totum corpus generatum ex principiis & legibus illis eo modo deducit" (*ibid.,* pp. xii, xiii).

Deducing the body from principles and laws is the philosopher's way, not the embryologist's; but Wolff's virtue was that he felt compelled to supplement his abstruse reasoning by examination of his material and he was thus able to substantiate his theory. Aristotle, as a Greek, had experienced no such compulsion; Harvey had had the will but not the way; Wolff had not only the desire, but also the good fortune and the good skill to be both philosophically and observationally accurate within closer limits than his predecessors, and posterity concurs in von Baer's evaluation of some of his work as at that time "die grösste Meisterarbeit, die wir aus dem Felde der beobachtenden Naturwissenschaften kennen" (1837, II, 12).

Starting from highly abstract speculations concerning growth and nourishment in their relation to what we should call differentiation, he took up in particular detail (to be sure, some years before Goethe, but also, well over a millennium later than Theophrastus) the metamorphosis of plants, pointing out that the rudiments of leaves are basically similar to those of the parts of the flower and that the rudiments of both alike are derived from essentially undifferentiated tissue. This was to lead to his fundamental premise that in animals as well as plants development proceeds by gradual differentiation of originally homogeneous material.

There is importance in the fact that he considered the undifferentiated material to be comparable in plants and animals. But though his emphasis on this similarity of construction of material in plant and animal may, as Sachs and Huxley realized though later generations have forgotten, have had effect on the development of the doctrines implying universality of cell and protoplasm, it was primarily his emphasis on its early undifferentiatedness that was of more immediate import.

It has been said of Wolff, as of Harvey, that he was without influence in his own day, his writings neglected and without effect until after their translation into German by Meckel in 1812. This is inaccurate. Haller knew his work, and certainly the biological world was kept plentifully and liberally informed of what Haller was thinking; Kant knew of the concept via Blumenbach (cf. *Critique of Judgment*, §81) and from the beginning Kant had the attention of the scientists. Diderot could affirm with confidence, as early as 1769, when writing about "germes préexistants," that

Cela est contre l'expérience et la raison: contre l'expérience qui chercherait inutilement ces germes dans l'oeuf et dans la plupart des animaux avant un certain âge; contre la raison qui nous apprend que la divisibilité de la matière a un terme dans la nature, quoiqu'elle n'en ait aucun dans l'entendement (*Entretien entre D'Alembert et Diderot;* written 1769, first published 1830; cited from 1875 edition, II, 110).

Diderot was no technical embryologist; while it is possible, it is hardly probable that he had read the *Theoria generationis*. It is far more likely that he was expressing for political reasons an appropriate scientific concept which was already sufficiently widely disseminated to have reached his admittedly universal ear.

May not this be the clue to Wolff's success where Malpighi had failed? The new century had brought new thinking with it, a new thinking in terms of change. Social and political change were soon to grow out of it: revolution and evolution had a common philosophical background; it was eventually, with Hegel, to reach full fruition as the central doctrine of a specific philosophical system. Wolff's work was an early expression of this tendency. It is no accidental coincidence that the Christian Wolff who taught philosophy to Caspar Friedrich Wolff, the originator of a biology of change, was a popularizer of Leibniz who had invented a calculus as a mathematics of change. Without this background, it is as unlikely that Wolff would have found a homogeneous blastoderm under his microscope as it was inevitable that Malpighi should have denied one a century before.

But Wolff's thinking typified too another kind of thought that was soon to broaden more generally. Wolff was prone to generalize from plant to animal (cf. "a bat is a perfect leaf . . . for the mode of origin of the two is the same"; from *Theorie der Generation*, 1764, §64, unavailable to me; cited by Huxley, 1853b, p. 293). His first proof of epigenesis in the chick came from his demonstration that the blood vessels of the chick blastoderm are not present from the beginning; he was probably led to the investigation by his false and far-fetched analogy between the vessels of the animal and those of the plant whose development he had already studied. Certainly if semantics gives any indication, his preoccupation with plants colored his later interpretations of observation on animal development. When he demonstrated that animal organs — the intestine and probably the central nervous system — are formed by the folding of homogeneous layers into tubes he called them by the name for leaf.

This is a strong hint, as is his "tracing of the body from principles and laws," of the *Naturphilosophie* to come, and it is curious, from his own point of view, that the emphasis laid by history on his accomplishment is centered so strongly on his microscopic discovery of what was not there. In his time, what influence he had probably spoke more positively in the direction of transcendentalism. Upon his concept of epigenesis and change and upon his intimations of layering in the embryo — both concepts to which Wolff was led by his tendencies towards *Naturphilosophie* — embryology was to follow with its whole momentous sequel, but only after a serious delay during which concepts were to arise which in many ways negated the concept of change which Wolff originated, concepts paradoxically enough also derived on a basis of *Naturphilosophie*.

EMBRYOLOGY AND NATURPHILOSOPHIE: GOETHE AND VON BAER

But why now *Naturphilosophie*, whose influence on embryology was to grow so strong that its domination is not yet now completely outworn? It was certainly at least in part the clear and inevitable reaction against Cartesianism and against the instillation of the analytical order and system of seventeenth century mechanics into the study of animate nature. Goethe, one of its warmest partisans, has spoken specifically to this point in his *Geschichte meines botanischen Studiums* (*Gedanken und Aufsätze,* 1944 edition, XII, 314):

> Vorläufig . . . will ich bekennen, dass nach *Shakespeare* und *Spinoza* auf mich die grösste Wirkung von *Linné* ausgegangen, und zwar gerade durch den Widerstreit, zu welchem er mich aufforderte. Denn indem ich sein scharfes, geistreiches Absondern, seine treffenden, zweckmässigen, oft aber willkürlichen Gesetze in mich aufzunehmen versuchte, ging in meinem Innern ein Zwiespalt vor: Das, was er mit Gewalt auseinanderzuhalten suchte, musste, nach dem innersten Bedürfnis meines Wesens, zur Vereinigung anstreben.

Goethe is as good an example as any with whom to continue the discussion, not only because he originated the concept of morphology in our modern and dynamic sense, but also especially because he was so vividly articulate in describing what went on in his own mind during the process of it. His own studies on the metamorphosis of plants and on the vertebral constitution of the skull, emphasizing the unity of type, and what he thought was his discovery of the intermaxillary bone in the human fetus, suggesting that the uniformity of anatomical plan is based on the existence of a developmental archetype, typify the new *Naturphilosophie.* Natural phenomena represent modifications of an Idea in the Mind of the Creator: here is a new Idealism, less important in that it revivified Plato than that it again lost sight of Aristotle, with as disastrous delaying consequences as in the Middle Ages: Agassiz, as late as 1857, could still answer with an unequivocal affirmative his self-addressed question as to whether the taxonomic divisions of the animal kingdom have "been instituted by the Divine Intelligence as the categories of his mode of thinking" (1857, p. 8).

This must inevitably appeal, with all of its implications of beauty in nature, to Goethe the poet, who is said to have soothed himself to sleep visualizing a seed growing into a plant. Its mysticism, quite in the neo-Platonic tradition, should have been opprobrious to the scientist; but this was the moment in history when the scientist turned romantic, to his own loss. The Middle Ages, for all the weaknesses of scholasticism, maintained the firm conviction that the Universe was capable of being understood by human reason; and, as Whitehead ('25) reminds us, it is to medieval scholasticism that we are indebted for our habits of exact thought. The *Naturphilosophen,* at their most emotional extremes, grew away from reason in its best sense, and their thought was hardly precise in the sense of modern science. Whitehead stresses too the high standard of objectivity set by the ancient and medieval worlds, with its obvious advantage for science. Its loss was part of the price paid for the developing individuality emerging from the philosophy of the late eighteenth and early nineteenth centuries, and this was a debt whose payment nearly bankrupted the intellectual economy of the *Naturphilosophen.*

The movement had its philosophical support from Kant,

who, like Leibniz before him, laid emphasis on the meta-physical, and who put a premium on transcendentalism; Kant's categories, after all, were given in advance of experience and the *Ding-an-sich* was beyond it. Goethe, however, was independent of Kant. "Meine 'Metamorphose der Pflanzen,'" he told Eckermann, "habe ich geschrieben, ehe ich etwas von Kant wusste, und doch ist sie ganz im Sinne seiner Lehre" (Eckermann, 1905 edition, I, 310.) It might have been better if he, and the other *Naturphilosophen*, had known Kant better. Kant, as Rádl ('30, p. 369) has pointed out, "had declared that the Absolute is never known and can never be known; yet his followers," to continue with Rádl, "— the Romantic Phil-osophers — made this Absolute the basis of their philosophy, the only real thing left in the Universe."

For biology, it was this confusion between the Idea and its representation in the organism, the Absolute and the know-able, that was dangerous. Goethe typifies this, too. He could coolly dictate the rules for observing scientific objectivity (*Ge-danken und Aufsätze,* 1944 edition, XII, 93):

Jeder Forscher muss sich durchaus ansehen als einer, der zu einer Jury berufen ist. Er hat nur darauf zu achten, inwiefern der Vortrag vollständig sei und durch klare Belege auseinandergesetzt. Er fasst hiernach seine Ueberzeugung zusammen und gibt seine Stimme, es sei nun, dass seine Meinung mit der des Referenten übereintreffe oder nicht.

"Sobald man in der Wissenschaft einer gewissen beschränk-ten Konfession angehört," he said to Eckermann, "ist sogleich jede unbefangene treue Auffassung dahin. . . . Es gehört zur Naturbeobachtung eine gewisse ruhige Reinheit des Innern, das von gar nichts gestört und präokkupiert ist" (Eckermann, 1905 edition, II, 218, 220).

He could, however, as sublimely ignore his own precepts. Where was his inner purity without preoccupation, where was his independence of a particular confession, when Eckermann came in to him with news of the July Revolution to have him cry (*ibid.,* II, 473):

Nun . . . was denken Sie von dieser grossen Begebenheit? Der Vulkan ist zum Ausbruch gekommen; alles steht in Flammen, und es ist nicht ferner eine Verhandlung bei geschlossenen Thüren,

and heard him reply, when Eckermann spoke of ministers and royal family (*ibid.*, II, 474–475):

Ich rede gar nicht von jenen Leuten; es handelt sich bei mir um ganz andere Dinge. Ich rede von dem in der Akademie zum öffentlichen Ausbruch gekommenen, für die Wissenschaft so höchst bedeutenden Streit zwischen *Cuvier* und *Geoffroy de Saint-Hilaire!* . . . Die Sache ist von der höchsten Bedeutung. . . . Wir haben jetzt an Geoffroy de Saint Hilaire einen mächtigen Alliierten auf die Dauer. . . . Das Beste . . . ist, dass die von Geoffroy in Frankreich eingeführte synthetische Behandlungsweise der Natur jetzt nicht mehr rückgängig zu machen ist. . . . Von nun an wird auch in Frankreich bei der Naturforschung der Geist herrschen und über die Materie Herr sein. Man wird Blicke in grosse Schöpfungsmaximen thun, in die geheimnisvolle Werkstatt Gottes! — Was ist auch im Grunde aller Verkehr mit der Natur, wenn wir auf analytischem Wege bloss mit einzelnen materiellen Teilen uns zu schaffen machen, und wir nicht das Atmen des Geistes empfinden, der jedem Teile die Richtung vorschreibt und jede Ausschweifung durch ein innewohnendes Gesetz bändigt oder sanktioniert!

Here is the romantic fallacy that lies at the hollow core of *Naturphilosophie;* here it is that the *Naturphilosophen* separate from Kant. Kant did not question the validity of natural science in its own realm; indeed, he justified it. He simply defined the regions in which it could operate, while the *Naturphilosophen* with their zeal for synthesis and their preoccupation with the spirit as the synthesizing element related the real to the transcendent in such a confused way that they could think clearly on neither.

Idealism for the philosopher is one thing: Kant felt that science could be accurate only when mathematically expressed, which is one kind of idealism. Huxley had the same intuition; in a paper on the Mollusca he wrote (1853a, p. 50):

From all that has been stated, I think that it is now possible to form a notion of the archetype of the Cephalous Mollusca, and I beg it to be understood that in using this term, I make no reference to any real or imaginary "ideas" upon which animal forms are modelled. All that I mean is the conception of a form embodying the most general propositions that can be affirmed respecting the Cephalous Mollusca, standing in the same relation to them as the diagram to the geometrical theorem, and like it, at once imaginary and true.

Boyle had presented the problem earlier to the physical scientist. His law was set for the ideal gas, and it became the task of the scientist to check experimentally the behavior of the real gas against that postulated for the ideal. Such a conception lacks meaning to the biologist; no such experiment is possible for him in relating the real to the ideal set up by the *Naturphilosophen*. Neither Boyle's kind of idealism, nor Huxley's, is that of the *Naturphilosophen*, whose weakness was not so much that it left no room for the experiment as that it closed their minds to whole systems of possible interpretations of the observed phenomena which they collected to gain credence for their fancies.

The weakness of the *Naturphilosophen* by and large was that they tried to force a rigid and fixed and obvious structure out of Spinoza's deeper and more fluid and subtle pantheism. Goethe, with more strength and with more sensitivity, could like Herder pass beyond them to be carried away by the dynamic wholeness of nature which to him was alive in the sense of the new morphology which was to follow later. Goethe, too, could grow beyond the romantic in other realms of thought than the scientific; but the professional biologists largely lacked his profundity and maturity and remained at the static phase too long. While Goethe's significance as a prophet for *Naturphilosophie* is hardly to be minimized, there were others who were to bear the responsibility for working out the biological details and who carried the doctrine to the illogical extremes which were so to retard the progress of biology proper: Goethe's friend, Nees von Esenbeck, who considered the entire vegetable world a leaf; Goethe's hero

Étienne Geoffroy Saint-Hilaire; and Serres, who said, as Oken was saying too, that the entire animal kingdom was a single organism; Oken was going so far as to compare the parts of a plant to fire, water, earth and air.

Yet it was against this dark background that the students of the natural philosopher Döllinger (cf. Temkin, '50) at Würzburg were to begin to build constructively upon Wolff's concepts; and the fact that they could start to do so is related probably to Wolff's own compatibility with *Naturphilosophie*. Wolff's epigenesis had started as conceptual; his concept, and the results of his own microscopic examinations, led those who were to follow him to the material where they could build upon what he had postulated and demonstrate a mechanism of the process of change he had postulated.

The group consisted of Pander, who first demonstrated the existence of the three primary germ layers in the embryo of the chick; of Goethe's friend D'Alton, who acted as artist; and of von Baer, who generalized Pander's germ layers for other animals and who in so doing generalized the science of embryology itself.

Pander's advance was a great one, in a way, in terms of independence of thought; and his achievement, in an environment of overgeneralization, in being able to concentrate on describing specific processes of development in a single form without drawing far-fetched analogies, was considerable. But Pander could not, or did not, carry through, and it was left to von Baer, or rather, von Baer took it upon himself, to broaden the base by the examination of more varied material.

With his inspiration from the romantics, he looked at the diverse material with a question in his mind as to its comparability; and he came away from it with the conviction that the comparability was there, in terms of origin (hence the discovery of the mammalian egg), and in terms of process in the similarity of the formation of the germ layers and in the derivation of similar organs from comparable layers in the different vertebrate forms. He demonstrated development to be at once from homogeneous to heterogeneous, from general to special, in all the forms that he studied. Though his feat was an overwhelmingly intellectual, not technical, achievement, his great advance was the extent to which he based his conclusions on the zealous and accurate and untiringly meticulous miscroscopic observations on a wide variety of animal material: *Beobachtung* preceded *Reflexion* in his title.

His emphasis on comparability involved, to be sure, as did that of the other *Naturphilosophen,* an emphasis on Type: "Zufrieden würde ich seyn," he wrote, "wenn man es als meinen Antheil betrachtet, nachgewiesen zu haben, dass der Typus der Organisation die Entwickelungsweise bedingt" (1828, I, xxii). But he meant by Type something different than the others:

Vor allen Dingen mache ich darauf aufmerksam, dass man den Grad der Ausbildung des thierischen Körpers und den Typus der Organisation unterscheiden muss. *Der Grad der Ausbildung des thierischen Körpers* besteht in einem grössern oder geringern Maasse der Heterogenität der Elementartheile und der einzelnen Abschnitte eines zusammengesetzten Apparates, mit einem Worte, *in der grössern histologischen und morphologischen Sonderung. . . . Typus* nenne ich das Lagerungsverhältniss der organischen Elemente und der Organe (1828, I, 207–208).

Our persuasion, that the grades of development must be distinguished from the types of organization, is founded upon the following considerations: — We know that all the functions of the perfect animal body contribute to a general result, — to the life of the animal; but also that the general mass manifests the total life (for animal life is always a totality). . . . With a greater separation and more complete independence of these functions is combined a greater differentiation of the body into organic systems, and of these systems again into separate more individualized sections. In this consists the higher development of the animal body.

But the mode in which these organs of the animal body are united together, is a wholly distinct matter. And it is to this manner in which the organic elements are combined that we give the name of *Type*. Every type may be manifested in higher and lower degrees of organization; the type and the grade of development together determine the special forms (1826; cited from 1853 edition, pp. 178–179).

Here there is an implication still of the Type and Archetype of the *Naturphilosophen,* but it is becoming more Type in common with Aristotle's form in the sense of potentiality. While von Baer has adopted a concept from *Naturphilosophie,* he has developed it further; for von Baer, it is the embryo, not the Idea, that is becoming the type. It is irrelevant for our purposes that he considered the primary types to be those of the vertebrate, the annulate, the radiate and the mollusk (the double symmetrical, the longitudinal, the radiate and the spiral; polarity and symmetry were a central idea, both problem and metaphysical reply to it, for the *Naturphilosophen* as for modern biologists). What is significant is that he could regard them, rightly or wrongly, as separate types of extant, visible, dissectable and observable animals perceived by his sense organs. This is phenomenological type, type not in an Idea but present as structure in an adult organism, and if masked there, sometimes discernible in the structure of the embryo; and thereby the relationship of embryology to comparative anatomy becomes fixed for all time.

The extent to which he could emancipate himself from the tendency to overgeneralize of the *Naturphilosophen* is probably nowhere made clearer than in his refusal to accept the "law" of parallelism most clearly expressed before his time by Meckel (for discussion of earlier contributors to the development of this concept see especially Needham, '34, and Meyer, '35; there are those who consider the doctrine to be foreshadowed even by Aristotle and Harvey, an interpretation which Meyer quite justly disputes):

Dass der Embryo höherer Thiere, ehe er seine vollkommne Ausbildung erreicht, mehrere Stufen durchläuft, wurde schon oben bemerkt; hier ist nachzuweisen, dass diese verschiednen Stufen denen entsprechen, auf welchen tiefer stehende Thiere das ganze Leben hindurch gehemmt erscheinen (Meckel, 1821, I, 396–397).

Von Baer, in contrast, with his emphasis on difference in adult type, denies the validity of Meckel's "Law" (1828, I, 220):

Dadurch ist aber nicht erwiesen, dass jeder Embryo einer höhern Thierform allmählig die niedern Thierformen durchlaufe. Vielmehr scheint sich der Typus jedes Thiers gleich anfangs im Embryo zu fixiren und die ganze Entwickelung zu beherrschen. . . . *Der Embryo des Wirbelthiers ist schon anfangs ein Wirbelthier. . . . Mithin durchlaufen die Embryonen der Wirbelthiere in ihrer Entwickelung gar keine (bekannten) bleibenden Thierformen.*

Frequent misconceptions have been expressed concerning von Baer's relationship to the formulation of the biogenetic law which have been well clarified by Meyer ('35); misconceptions which have arisen probably at least in part because of Darwin's quotation, in later editions of the *Origin of Species,* of von Baer's passage accentuating, in line with his stress on development from the general to the special, the likeness of young vertebrate embryos:

The embryos of mammalia, of birds, lizards, and snakes, probably also of chelonia are in their earliest states exceedingly like one another, both as a whole and in the mode of development of their parts; so much so, in fact, that we can often distinguish the embryos only by their size. In my possession are two little embryos in spirit, whose names I have omitted to attach, and at present I am quite unable to say to what class they belong (Darwin, 1902 edition, II, 241),

and his stress was exclusively on resemblances between embryos rather than between adults of one group and embryos of another.

Darwin might have made von Baer's position clearer had he cited the delightful passage from the Fifth Scholion (1828, I, 203–204; cited here from 1853 edition, p. 191):

Let it be imagined that Birds had studied development, and that it was they who in turn investigated the structure of the adult Mammal and of Man. Should we not find something of this sort in their physiological handbooks? "Those four-legged and two-legged animals have much resemblance to embryonic forms, for their cranial bones are separated, and they have no beak, just like us during the first five or six days of incubation: their extremities are a good deal alike, as ours are for about the same period; there is not a single true feather over their whole body, but only delicate feather-shafts, so that we, as fledgelings, are more advanced than ever they are; their bones are hardly at all brittle, and like ours during youth contain no air at all; they have no trace of air-sacs, and their lungs are not adherent, like ours at the earliest period; they have no crop; their proventiculus and gizzard are more or less compounded into a single sac; evidently arrangements which in us are only transitory, and the nails are in most of them as clumsily broad as in us before we break the shell; the Bats alone — seemingly the most perfect among them — have any power of flight, which is quite absent in the rest. And these Mammals, which for so long a period after birth cannot find their own food, and which are unable to raise themselves from the earth, must pretend forsooth that they are more highly organized than we!"

It must be granted that von Baer himself sometimes indulged in flights of fancy comparable to those of the other *Naturphilosophen.* "Dass nämlich Kiefern und Extremitäten Modificationen eines Grundtypus sind," he wrote, "ist augenscheinlich. . . . Die Kiefern aber nähern sich so sehr der Natur der Rippen, dass man von ihnen einen Grund hernehmen kann, auch die Extremität des Rumpfes für verstärkte Rippen anzusehen" (1828, I, 192). His theories of fertilization, and of the significance of symmetry with regard to type, were as foolish as those of his contemporaries; but his strength in being so frequently able to overcome such temptation was more remarkable than the occasional symptoms of his succumbing to it.

He had on the whole a particularly clear appreciation of his contemporaries' confusion between fact and idea: he stated it explicitly in one of his criticisms of the theory of parallelism: "Man lernte allmählig die verschiedenen Thierformen als aus einander entwickelt sich denken — und schien dann, von einigen Seiten wenigstens, vergessen zu wollen, dass die Metamorphose nur eine Vorstellungsart sey" (*ibid.,* I, 200).

Von Baer's own embryology, for the first time, for all of

its emphasis on the relationship of the special to the general, was an embryology in which the metaphysical became subordinate to the biological in the sense of modern embryology, and became an embryology which proceeded from embryological facts and phenomena towards embryological concepts, rather than in the reverse direction; and von Baer, in accomplishing this feat, made one of the greatest advances in all biological history. His force of intellect, his consequent self-mastery and ability to free himself to develop beyond the thought in which he was trained, are unmatched in biological progress. He could emancipate himself from the thinking of his times more than Vesalius, more than Harvey before him; more than Darwin after him, and though perhaps not in an analytical sense, yet in a synthetic sense more than Mendel to follow.

His courage to maintain his own independence of thought may have been fed by his century's new kind of awareness of the individual, with its philosophical background from Leibniz and Kant, developed by Fichte and Schelling and Hegel, and its translation during the eighteenth century into more widespread acceptance than ever before of the significance of freedom of individual action. Von Baer absorbed the concept of independence: "Deswegen ist auch das wesentlichste Resultat der Entwickelung, wenn wir sie im Ganzen übersehen, die *zunehmende Selbstständigkeit* des werdenden Thiers" *(ibid.,* I, 148), he wrote, and he concentrated on the individual. *Wesenheit* was all: "Die Wesenheit des Thiers beherrscht die Ausbildung. . . . Die Wesenheit . . . der zeugenden Thierform beherrscht die Entwickelung der Frucht" *(ibid.,* I, 147–148).

But like Aristotle and Goethe, von Baer was obsessed with the dynamic and functional qualities of the organism as a whole. "We know that all the functions of the perfect animal body contribute to a general result — to the life of the animal," we have already quoted, "but also that the general mass manifests the total life (for animal life is always a totality)." "Die Entwickelungsgeschichte des Individuums ist die Geschichte der wachsenden Individualität in jeglicher Beziehung" (*ibid.*, I, 263), he wrote too; and he thought of the growing individual too, like Goethe, in respect to a larger whole; to him the palm, "dem es vorbehalten ist, die bildenden Kräfte des thierischen Körpers auf die allgemeinen Kräfte oder Lebensrichtungen des Weltganzen zurückzuführen" (*ibid.*, I, xxii).

Like Goethe, he could say, and in almost the same figure of speech, that "die *Geschichte der Natur* ist nur *die Geschichte fortschreitender Siege des Geistes über den Stoff*" (1864, pp. 71–72), but he meant it in a different context (1828, I, 263–264):

Hat aber das eben ausgesprochene allgemeinste Resultat Wahrheit und Inhalt, so ist es *Ein* Grundgedanke, der durch alle Formen und Stufen der thierischen Entwickelung geht und alle einzelnen Verhältnisse beherrscht. Derselbe Gedanke ist es, der im Weltraume die vertheilte Masse in Sphären sammelte und diese zu Sonnensystemen verband, derselbe, der den verwitterten Staub an der Oberfläche des metallischen Planeten in lebendigen Formen hervorwachsen liess. Dieser Gedanke ist aber nichts als das Leben selbst, und die Worte und Sylben, in welchen er sich ausspricht, sind die verschiedenen Formen des Lebendigen.

But if von Baer's outlook, like Goethe's, was cosmic in scope, his inspiration was the detailed and specific study of the developing form of the individual living embryo. Like Aristotle, he accepted form as inseparable from the formed. The advantage of refinement bestowed by time to his philosophical and technical method, as compared with Aristotle's, enabled him to concentrate more on the formed, which was biological material, than on form as such and metaphysical; and in so advancing he became the true synthetic genius which Goethe had aspired to be, "der grösste unter uns in Vergangenheit, Gegenwart und weiter Zukunft" (Roux, 1889; cited from Roux, 1895b, II, 25).

EMBRYOLOGY AND EVOLUTION:
DARWIN AND HAECKEL

It has been said that all biology since Darwin has been a commentary on the *Origin of Species*. Embryology would be in a more advanced position than its present one if one could claim that all embryology after von Baer represented a commentary on his great treatise. It is true that immediately following his time, even during it, great strides were made in the amplification and refinement of his teachings. Rathke, in particular, whose quality of mind was in many ways like that of von Baer, made particular advances in demonstrating the existence of the germ layers in invertebrates as well as vertebrates and in discovering the presence of gill slits in the mammalian embryo. The universality of the germ layers was given new meaning with the enunciation of the doctrines of universality of protoplasm and of cells when von Kölliker and Remak and others brought together the results of these with the results of the germ layer doctrine. Had these continued as the main trends of embryology, von Baer's synthetic scheme would have been broadened in the fashion it deserved. Instead, a return to the overgeneralization of *Naturphilosophie* once more delayed its progress into the future.

One symptom of this was the continued emphasis, in spite of von Baer's warnings, on the comparability of embryos of "higher" forms to the adults of "lower," and such false analogy was carried over even into the germ layers, von Baer's own territory, thus seeming to be supported by his facts though he had so explicitly denied the concept. Huxley, in 1849 (p. 426), described the Medusae as constructed of two membranes "which appear to bear the same physiological relation to one another as do the serous and mucous layer of the germ," opening the way for the ultimate generalization. When, therefore, shortly after the publication of the *Origin of Species*, Kowalewski found that invertebrate and vertebrate embryos

alike formed from a bilaminar sac, that in the most varied
material — Psolinus, Amphioxus, Phoronis, Limnaeus, Ophiura, Echinus, Asteracanthion, Sagitta, Ascidia, Escholtzia, Sepiola as well as birds, mammals and turtles —

... bei allen von mir hier erwähnten Embryonen geht die Bildung der
beiden erwähnten Schichten oder Blätter (der äusseren und inneren)
ganz auf dieselbe Weise vor sich. . . . Also wäre die erste Bildung des
Embryo für alle diese verschiedenen Thiere ganz übereinstimmend;
nur in den weiteren Veränderungen sehen wir die Unterschiede auftre-
ten, welche jeden einzelnen Typus bezeichnen (1867, p. 5),

the decision was sealed. He ended on the same note of caution
as von Baer, but his voice too was drowned out by the clamor
originating from a new cry of transcendentalism that surpassed
anything the earlier *Naturphilosophen* would have dreamed
possible. The difference, of course, was that meantime the
Origin of Species had appeared.

The compulsion to synthesize all of animate nature into a
single grandiose scheme which the false analogies of the earlier
transcendentalism had formerly satisfied was now to be as-
suaged by the evolution doctrine, which represented a synthesis on another basis; in the new scheme, common descent replaced the archetype as the primary synthesizing factor.

It has been said that it was Darwin who "dragged [organ-
isms] down from . . . metaphysical regions into daily life, and
examined their immediate purpose in relation to the whole
environment of the living organism" (Rádl, '30, p. 381). But
Darwin in some ways advanced no more abruptly in respect to
the descent from metaphysics than had von Baer, and the
structure of thought he created was in many ways as metaphysical as that of his predecessors. The influence of the environment alone was no new concept; philosophy had been
worrying about this problem at least since the time of Leibniz.
The species concept, from which Darwin started, was so
highly metaphysical that even now the term defies adequate
biological definition. Darwin's system was a metaphysical one,

too, in that his concern for the individual organism was subordinate to his interest in the interdependence of organisms; his clue to the nature of their relationships came equally from the organisms themselves and from wider areas of thought: from generalizations invented for the fields of geology and economics, and indeed, in a way from his whole century's mood for "Progress."

One of the primary contributions of Darwin, however — indeed of all those concerned with the new doctrine of evolution: Buffon, Erasmus Darwin, Lamarck, John Hunter, Wallace and the many others — was the refocussing once more of attention on the organism as a whole. The key to evolution had come from consideration of the whole living animal, not its parts; evolution was inferred from natural history, not deduced from the preparations in the cabinets of the anatomists where the evidence had been awaiting for centuries the interpretations which the fixity and the tenacity of the notions of unity of type had excluded from coming into being.

It is one of the more curious ironies of history that while before Darwin, transcendentalism had closed the minds of investigators to the possibility of explanation of resemblances between parts of organisms and between whole organisms on the basis of common descent, yet after him the combination of the doctrines was to lead to extremes of exaggeration that were attained separately by neither. There were many who were to contribute to this: Kleinenberg in Germany and Lankester in England made an early start by relating phylogeny to ontogeny on the basis of comparability of the germ layers (for fuller treatment see Oppenheimer, '40), but their views were relatively mild compared to those of many who followed them. The culmination was the work of Haeckel, the greatest revisionist of them all.

The most extreme example of his immoderation was perhaps his naming, on the basis of the "similarity, or *homology*, of the gastrula in all classes of compound animals" (concept originally expressed in monograph on the *Kalkschwämme*, 1872; cited here from Haeckel, [1900], p. 61), in the stead of the coelenterates formerly nominated for the position by Kleinenberg, the imaginary gastraea as the progenitor of all multicellular forms. His figuring of a section through an animal that never existed on the same page (1891, p. 161) that illustrates Kowalewski's gastrulae of Sagitta and Amphioxus and Carl Rabl's of Limnaeus, with no comment in the label to signify that the "Gastrula eines einfachsten Pflanzenthieres, einer Gastraeade (*Gastrophysema*, Haeckel)" is any less real than the others — where is there a handsomer example in all biological or scientific history of what Whitehead has called the "Fallacy of Misplaced Concreteness"?

Such a silly invention as the gastraea, that "magere Tiergespenst," as Kleinenberg (1886, p. 2) called it, as an isolated case might probably have proved of little influence; and its significance is as a symptom (a word used advisedly for its pathological connotations) of Haeckel's basic trouble. What was damaging to science was Haeckel's fervency to oversystematize all morphology through his biogenetic law that "die Ontogenie ist eine Recapitulation der Phylogenie" (1891, p. 7).

In formulating it, he returned to the law of parallelism of Tiedemann, Meckel and Serres, quite by-passing von Baer's more temperate statements. He was influenced to do so of course in part by Fritz Müller, who had earlier (*Für Darwin*, 1864) pointed out on the basis of the study of crustacean larvae that individual development provides a clue to ancestral history. But he misinterpreted Müller as have many more modern readers (cf. Meyer, '35). While Müller was supporting Darwin — indeed, as Meyer says ('35, p. 392), "his main conclusion was that his studies on the development of crustacea confirmed Darwin's idea of evolution" — he yet was formulating no such dogma as Haeckel's concerning the causal relationships between evolution and individual development.

Sir John Lubbock, too, was early considering the relationships of evolution and individual development in support of Darwin; but when he questioned whether insects during the course of metamorphosis pass through their ancestral stages he felt forced to a negative reply in the absence of evidence that a caterpillar ever existed as a fully developed organism. Rádl has commented ('30, p. 140) concerning the biogenetic law that "everything important that has ever been cited against the theory was known when the theory was first put forward; nevertheless it was widely accepted." Lubbock's reservation is an example. But his exception, and all the other exceptions, seemed to lack the dramatic appeal of the false generalization, and the biogenetic law was acclaimed with the same rapt enthusiasm that had greeted the earlier theories of preformation and of unity of type.

Investigators in widely varied fields of interest rapidly carried over the theory into their own territories. Bunge applied it to physiology:

The amount of common salt in the organism corresponds with the amount in the environment. . . . Many plants contain only traces of sodium; those which are rich in it are only the sea-weeds and the plants which grow on the sea-shore, and on the salt-steppes which are dried-up sea-basins. . . .

This is also the case with invertebrate animals; only those which live in the sea, and those nearest allied to them on land, contain much salt. . . .

The land vertebrates are all remarkably rich in salt, in spite of the scanty supply around them. But even these are only apparent exceptions. We need but remember the fact that the first vertebrates on our planet all lived in the sea. Is not the large amount of chlorid of sodium found in the present inhabitants of dry land another proof of the genealogical connection we are forced to accept from morphological facts? . . .

If this interpretation is correct, we should expect that the younger the vertebrates are in their individual development, the more salt they would possess. This is in fact the case. I have convinced myself by numerous experiments that an embryo of a mammal contains more salt than a new-born animal, and that it gradually becomes, after birth, poorer in chlorin and sodium as it develops. Cartilage contains the most sodium of any tissue in our bodies, besides being also the tissue of greatest antiquity. . . . This phenomenon . . . can only be explained by the theory of evolution ('02, pp. 101–103).

Workers in other fields than biology, too, adopted the theory with as much warmth. Preyer, a colleague of Haeckel's at Jena, formulated his conceptions of child phychology with reference to Haeckel's law; Herbart and Ziller before him had held that the individual repeats in his development the stages of cultural development through which the human race has passed. And in our own times, Jung, following Nietzsche and Freud among others, with all his immeasurable influence on modern psychology and literature, has erected the superstructure of his *Psychology of the Unconscious* on the acceptance of Haeckel's premise as though this were the immutable truth that Haeckel in his own day had hoped it:

All this experience suggests to us that we draw a parallel between the phantastical, mythological thinking of antiquity and the similar thinking of children, between the lower human races and dreams. This train of thought is not a strange one for us, but quite familiar through our knowledge of comparative anatomy and the history of development, which show us how the structure and function of the human body are the results of a series of embryonic changes which correspond to similar changes in the history of the race. Therefore, the supposition is justified that ontogenesis corresponds in psychology to phylogenesis. Consequently, it would be true, as well, that the state of infantile thinking in the child's psychic life, as well as in dreams, is nothing but a re-echo of the prehistoric and the ancient ('27, pp. 27–28).

But the blind adoption of Haeckel's doctrines by such workers in bordering fields, and their infection with his faith that "development is now the magic word by means of which we shall solve the riddles by which we are surrounded" (cited from Rádl, '30, pp. 126–127), is less reprehensible than their uncritical acceptance by the professional embryologists, who swallowed them with as much gullibility, and who remained utterly unperturbed by the fact that Haeckel himself was never in any sense a professional embryologist. The seduction of embryology by a fanatic who expressed himself even metaphorically in terms of magic represents a darker chapter in its history than any of its earlier or later retreats to mere metaphysics lacking such taint of the mystic.

Deplorably enough, the record of many of our "modern" textbooks is none too pure with respect to the biogenetic law. But there is no space here for a modern critique of the doctrine (for brief statements of the modern position see Shumway, '32, and de Beer, '51); what is relevant here at the moment is not so much Haeckel's rightness or wrongness as the magnitude of his influence. It was considerable, and acted as a delaying rather than an activating force; and it was stifling to immediate progress, since embryologists were for many years after to examine embryos primarily to establish evidence of phylogenetic relationship. This was not wholly detrimental, of course; like the earlier transcendentalism this gave a strong incentive for looking at embryos, and many accurate observational data were collected which were later to stand embryology in good stead; but progress in terms of new concepts was necessarily impeded. Balfour specified the task, prescribed the fashion, set the standard (1880, I, 4–5):

To test how far Comparative Embryology brings to light ancestral forms common to the whole of the Metazoa. . . .

How far . . . larval forms may be interpreted as the ancestral type. . . .

How far such forms agree with living or fossil forms in the adult state. . . .

How far organs appear in the embryo or larva which either atrophy or become functionless in the adult state, and which persist permanently in members of some other group or in lower members of the same group. . . .

How far organs pass in the course of their development through a condition permanent in some lower form. . . .

Balfour himself acknowledged another department of embryology concerned with the origin of organs and germ layers and tissues, but to this he devoted only a quarter of his great treatise; many of his contemporaries more fully ignored it, and advance had to wait until the furor over Darwin and recapitulation had subsided. The degree to which evolutionary relationships dominated embryology is nowhere better shown than by the results of the few cases where investigators attempted to pursue other paths, and failed in influence.

Leuckart and Bergmann had, in fact, several years before the publication of the *Origin of Species,* already set the program for a new embryology (1851; cited from 1855, p. 36):

Ebenso wie man gegenwärtig strebt, die Combination von Wirkungen zu ermitteln, auf welcher eine bestimmte Krystallform oder die Bildung und Umbildung der Zelle beruht, so wird man sich auch Wege zu eröffnen suchen, um die bewirkenden Ursachen der Anordnung der Organe zu ermitteln: man wird *eine Physiologie der Plastik* dereinst anstreben.

But the few who had the originality, during the nineteenth century, to attempt to work out a "physiology of the plastic" were doomed to failure. Lereboullet made an attempt to do so, in France (cf. Oppenheimer, '36), where he could do so in part because of the dominating spirit of Cuvier, who, like von Baer, emphasized animals rather than relationships and their structure rather than their metaphysics. In part because of Cuvier's strength of mind, Darwin never attained the same heights of scientific popularity in France as in Germany and England; and if Lereboullet was not of such intellectual caliber as to take full advantage of this for embryology, French science still benefited from it in the persons of Pasteur and Claude Bernard. In Germany, Wilhelm His in 1874, Goette in 1875, and Rauber in 1880 attempted mechanical explanations of development, working towards a "physiology of the plastic"; they attracted a few strong disciples such as von Kölliker, but on the whole they cried in the wilderness. His' cry was the most explicit, perhaps, certainly one of the most violent against Haeckel; and quite the obverse, in many ways, of what Balfour was later to declaim (1874, pp. 161, 171–172, 174–175):

Gegenstand und Methode der phylogenetischen Forschung . . . sind durchaus andere als diejenigen der von mir bearbeiteten physiologischen Entwicklungsgeschichte des Individuums. . . . Das nächste Interesse für uns liegt in der . . . formulirten Frage: in wie weit die phylogenetische Geschichte einer Form zugleich als deren Erklärung gelten darf, und wie sich ihre eventuelle Erklärung verhält zur physiologischen Erklärung? . . .

Ich behaupte nun, die Körperform ist eine unmittelbare Folge des Keimwachsthums, und bei gegebener Anfangsform des Keimes aus dem Gesetze des Wachsthums abzuleiten. . . .

Weiterhin ist aber das Keimwachsthum eine Folge der Eigenschaften des eben befruchteten Keimprotoplasmas. Diese sind eine Folge von den Eigenschaften der elterlichen Keimstoffe und der Art ihres Zusammentreffens u.s.w. Wir bekommen somit folgende Reihenfolge zu leistender Erklärungen:

1) Erklärung der Körperform aus dem Wachsthum des Keimes;

2) Erklärung des Keimswachsthums aus den Eigenschaften des befruchteten Keimprotoplasmas und aus den Bedingungen seiner Entwickelung (Temperatur, Ernährungsbedingungen u.s.w.).

3) Erklärung der Eigenschaften des befruchteten Keimprotoplasmas aus den Eigenschaften der elterlichen Keimstoffe und der besonderen Bedingungen ihres Zusammentreffens;

4) Erklärung der Eigenschaften der Keimstoffe aus dem Gange der elterlichen Körperentwickelung;

5) Erklärung der besonderen Bedingungen der Befruchtung aus den Lebensverhältnissen der beiden Erzeuger und so fort.

Erst mit Nr. 5 der obigen Kette beginnt das Gebiet der phylogenetischen Erklärung, und es erstreckt sich von da in periodischer Wiederkehr ins Unermessliche nach rückwärts.

But to no immediate avail did His attempt to remove explanation from the level of the transcendental and ideal, and from the level of metaphysical relationships between organisms, to the level of the embryo itself; Haeckel spoke too strongly in opposition. Haeckel's greatest disservice, after all, was not his simple ignorance of the morphological exceptions to his law as a descriptive statement, but his emphasis on it

156

as an irrefutable explanation of causal relationships. Transcendentalism of Haeckel's variety was as fundamentally incompatible as had been the other kind with any concept of *process*. "Die Phylogenie," he insisted, "ist die mechanische Ursache der Ontogenese" (1891, p. 7), not only distracting to other areas the many who might have otherwise become interested in true mechanical explanations, but refuting, as he thought, irrevocably those who were already involved in developing such interests. He felt His a particular foe, as well he might have; and his polemics against him, since they were inadequate to combat His on his own grounds, descended to ridicule of the most inane sort:

... [Es] lässt sich aus dem Studium der ontogenetischen Arbeiten von His bald erkennen, dass in seiner Vorstellung die bildende "Mutter Natur" weiter Nichts als eine geschickte *Kleidermacherin* ist. Durch verschiedenartiges Zuschneiden der Keimblätter, Krümmen und Falten, Zerren und Spalten derselben gelingt es der genialen Schneiderin leicht, alle die mannichfaltigen Formen der Thierarten durch "Entwickelung" (!) zu Stande zu bringen. Vor Allem spielen die Krümmungen und Faltungen in dieser *Schneider-Theorie* die wichstigste Rolle. . . . Am possirlichsten ist, wie die Schneiderin bei Fabrication der zwei Paar Gliedmassen verfährt . . . . Doch wird diese herrliche "Briefcouvert-Theorie" der Wirbelthier-Beine noch übertroffen durch die "Höllen-lappen-Theorie," welche His von der Entstehung der *rudimentären Organe* giebt. . . . Hier wirft also die schneidernde Natur die überflüssigen Gewebslappen hinter den Ofen, in die "Hölle"! (1891, pp. 53–54).

Haeckel, however, can hardly have been expected to accept His' whole cloth. Whitehead has spoken, in connection with his Fallacy of Misplaced Concreteness, and thinking surely of precisely such mentalities as Haeckel's, of those "clear-cut trenchant intellects, immovably encased in a hard shell of abstractions [who] hold you to their abstractions by the sheer grip of personality" ('25, p. 82). But it was not mere personality that won for Haeckel his felicitous reception. His personality may have made him think as he did; but it was the eagerness of his contemporaries for oversystematization, in terms of just such abstractions as his, that was responsible for the success of his doctrine. Its supplanting had therefore to wait until a new period demanded a different kind of thought, and until Wilhelm Roux could succeed where Leuckart and Bergmann and His had apparently failed.

The attempts at mechanical explanations of development begun by His and the others in the 1870's were surely an outgrowth of the whole philosophy of materialism that pervaded the thinking of the 19th century. But the 19th century was also a strongly romantic century in many ways, perhaps again specifically in reaction against materialism. It is a curious paradox that the Haeckelian doctrines, steeped in romantic idealism, emanated from the impersonal and objective doctrines of Darwin. But they did, and in doing so, flourished with sufficient strength to repress the mechanical theories of development really so much more compatible with the doctrines of evolution; and it is ironical that therefore the success of the new embryological theories had to await a waning of interest in Darwinism.

It must be admitted, however, that although evolution had delayed the new movement in one way, it is also true, in another, that it fostered it. The new interest in the new embryology came again from a new attack on the problem of epigenesis versus preformation, and this derived its origin from the absorption of the evolution doctrine into everyday thinking. The process of evolution implies epigenesis, in that change is the essence of both, and a gradual process from step to step. A generation habituated to thinking about change building on change in evolution could more easily than its fathers accept the concept of epigenesis with its causal connotations. Embryologists have been familiar with chain reactions for centuries; the significance of progressive differentiation in ontogeny had been made explicit in the modern sense by Leuckart and Bergmann, and through His, who though his "organbildende Keimbezirke" are usually accredited for heralding neo-preformation, yet inferred the causal relationships implicit in neo-epigenesis (1874, p. 2):

Die Entwicklungsgeschichte ist ihrem Wesen nach eine physiologische Wissenschaft, sie hat den Aufbau jeder einzelnen Form aus dem Ei nach den verschiedenen Phasen nicht allein zu beschreiben, sondern derart abzuleiten, dass jede Entwicklungsstufe mit allen ihren Besonderheiten als nothwendige Folge der unmittelbar vorangegangenen erscheint.

Roux himself, who was a student of Haeckel's, and felt himself his disciple, very definitely acted as intermediator between Darwinism and the new causal analytical embryology. His "Kampf der Theile im Organismen," though written before his great concentration of interest on embryological problems, was consummately important in this respect. By striking an analogy between the struggle for existence among organisms on the one hand, and that between the parts of an organism on the other, Roux pointed up for the first time in a new way the possible significance for differentiation of interrelationships between tissues, and suggested the possibility already in that communication of the "Hervorbildung des chemisch und morphologisch Differenzirteren aus dem Einfacheren ohne differenzirende äussere Einwirkungen," as opposed to the conditions where "andere Gewebe . . . secundär durch Einwirkung seitens der ersteren aus dem embryonalen Blastem differenzirt werden" (1881; cited from Roux, 1895a, I, 332–333). But are not these clearly Haeckel's *innere* and *äussere Bildungstriebe* — words and concepts borrowed by him deliberately from Goethe? And Haeckel, for all his faults, was infected by Goethe with an enthusiasm for the dynamic wholeness of the organism and its environment, which he passed on to Roux who made use of it as Haeckel never could. Spemann was to be moved by it too. He mentioned in his autobiography having known Martin Donndorf who had seen Eckermann, and commented that "man wird nicht mehr leicht jemand begegnen, der in

Augen geblickt hat, welche Goethe gesehen haben" (['43],
p. 86). His own intellectual distance from Goethe was, like
Roux', diminished by the intermediacy of Haeckel.

Im Lager fiel mir das Buch von Wilhelm Preyer über die Seele des
Kindes in die Hand; mit schlechtem Gewissen, wie ein Schuljunge
mit einem Buch unter der Bank, sass ich damit in einer dunklen Ecke.
Das kam aus der Gegend von Ernst Haeckel, der so manchen jungen
Mann meiner und der vorhergehenden Generation zur Biologie geführt
hatte. Dort begegnete ich auch zum erstenmal, soviel ich mich erinnere,
dem Begriff der Biologie als einer umfassenden Wissenschaft vom
Leben, mit all ihren aufwühlenden Lehren über seine letzte Tiefe
(*ibid.*, p. 116).

But if Roux began his work against the natural philosophical background of Haeckel, from whom he also inherited his
predilection for setting up his concepts in a strongly theoretical framework, he was later to grow far beyond Haeckel's
romanticism. Haeckel's own strong predilection for monism
may have exerted its influence in this respect. But Roux had
studied also with Goette. Particularly, also, he was influenced
in the direction of the new preformationism by Weismann.
For the new embryology, strangely enough, received a strong
impetus from the old preformation as this was revived in a
new form. Rádl ('30, p. 263) has made the clever comment,
and justly so, that "Haeckel silenced von Baer, the embryologist, and returned to the ideas of Meckel. Weismann ignored
[von] Baer, the epigeneticist, and went back to the ideas of the
tedious and insipid Bonnet." Roux derived his parentage
from them both; and Weismann himself had been, after all,
a student of Leuckart's.

It is always tempting to contrast Roux' mechanistic preformationist tendencies with the vitalistic and epigenetic interpretations of Driesch, and to assume the enthusiasm for the
new experimental embryology as arising out of the clear-cut
difference between them, and as demanding the collection of
new evidence to justify the choice between them. But what

was more influential in starting the new experimental embryology on its way was not the opposition of results and interpretations of Roux and Driesch so much as the desire to verify or refute the Roux-Weismann hypothesis that the qualitative distribution of nuclear material is responsible for the mosaic sort of differentiation which Roux thought he could demonstrate; and the attack begun on it by Driesch and Hertwig in 1892 not only represented the beginning of all the active experimentation to follow, but led directly to the constriction experiments of Spemann which were destined to have such momentous results.

In the same measure as Weismann was indirectly responsible for the new embryology to follow, nineteenth century materialism lay behind it. Weismann was no freer than any other from the influence of his times; his idioplasm is a modification of that of Nägeli which was "like a microscopic picture of the macroscopic individual" (cited from Rádl, '30, p. 226). Atomicity, as elucidated by Dalton for chemistry, was implicit in the biological ideas of Mendel and Pasteur, and equally in the determinants postulated by Weismann. Weismann's contribution, like that of so many influential figures in the history of science, was the expression of his doctrine to a century philosophically ripe for its acceptance.

And once more a new tool could be exploited to make visibly manifest concrete evidence of a theory bound to become popular because of its appropriateness to the demands of its times. Now, it was the improved achromatic lens, which brought out the cytological details of nuclear behavior during mitosis and meiosis and fertilization, and which gave new meaning to the relationship between cellular inclusions and cellular differentiation, and thus evoked a new interest in the old preformation. This had its effect not only on Roux among the embryologists. In a way, the work of Whitman and all his disciples who devoted themselves to the study of cell lineage in eggs with determinate cleavage grew out of the same

161

background as Weismann's, and came in a different way to setting up the premises for a new kind of preformation (see especially Whitman, 1894a, 1894b, and Wheeler, 1898, for brilliant expositions of the *fin de siècle* position against the older historical background). It led too to the magnificent work of Boveri, who on a purely embryological basis established as soundly as the geneticists later the role of qualitative and quantitative distribution of the chromosomes.

Weismann, however, and the new materialism and the new preformationism, and Goette and His and Haeckel were not the only influences to culminate in Roux. He had his ideas from the botanists, too, and not only indirectly as in the case of Nägeli's idioplasm adopted by Weismann. Sachs, who was also greatly influenced by Nägeli, had been experimentalizing plant biology as Roux was to do with embryology; with the physiologists' primary interest in irritability he worked out the basis of what was later to culminate with Loeb in the theory of tropisms, a concept which the embryologists adopted as soon as the physiologists, and perhaps with even greater fruit. Roux, in the first paper, after the introduction, published in the new *Archiv* (1895d), took it over in his use of "cytotaxis" and "cytotropism" as explanatory of the relationships of amphibian blastomeres to one another. And Roux was not the only one to employ it: Driesch called in "taktische Reizbarkeit" to explain certain behavior of the mesenchyme cells in the echinoderm embryo. Herbst elaborated it further for embryology, even going so far, in his *Formative Reize in der tierischen Ontogenese,* as to postulate on a theoretical basis the dependence of the development of the vertebrate lens on the optic cup, the very year that Spemann (who had himself learned botany from Sachs) was to perform his first experiment demonstrating it (though independent of Spemann; cf. Spemann, '03, p. 566). The ideas of progressive differentiation which had been developing since Aristotle were thus to come to final fruition; Spemann's precision of thought and performance, and his supreme intellectual power, instigated their analysis in a new way, doing more than full justice to the causal-analytical motive of Roux.

For if in Roux many influences converge and if from him many new trends begin, and if in embryology after his time as directly before it, it is not always easy to follow a single guiding motive, yet there stems from him the single modern approach, the *experiment*, and this we owe to him alone. It is true, as so often, that before he was to perform the experiment which was to start the new trend, there had been a gradual preparation for its acceptance on the conceptual side: biological science, like physical, had finally become generally experimentalized; it was no accident that Pasteur and Claude Bernard preceded Wilhelm Roux in time. But Chun had previously performed a similar experiment with as striking results if not as momentous influence; and Roux not only performed the experiment but generalized its significance. His ability to mobilize thought around it was due to his own qualities of mind and person.

Driesch, in a different way than Chun, represents the contrast against which the contribution of Roux becomes more capable of evaluation. Roux had the perspicacity to appreciate that the embryo could be grappled with experimentally; Driesch, though he made a great experimental contribution to embryology, lacked it, and was so steeped in metaphysics that he finally made his option for philosophy proper.

The comparison of their interpretations of what they thought a single comparable experiment illustrates the strength and weakness of both. Roux believed he freed one blastomere in the two-celled amphibian egg from the influence of another by killing the latter, and thought he demonstrated thereby the independent differentiation of the surviving cell. Driesch found a single isolated blastomere of the two-cell echinoderm egg able to form a whole embryo and believed he could prove the differentiation of a cell to be dependent on its position with respect to the whole. Both experiments were subject to critical errors, as we now know, and for both eggs both explanations are partially correct and partially inadequate.

But this was not the only issue between them, nor the fundamental one. Roux interpreted the egg for the first time as a mechanism mechanically analyzable by outside interference; Driesch envisioned it as ruled by an entelechy as spiritual as any *deus ex machina* must be. This difference was within them, and not dictated by their times. Though the spirit of particular times may facilitate choosing one view or the other, there have been mechanists and vitalists at all ages. But those differences in Roux' and Driesch's interpretations were here determined by their own casts of mind, and the fact is that Roux, by his choice, brought the embryo to become experimentally attackable by exact investigation. Roux set the whole program for experimental embryology, and this is his importance, not the fact that he performed an experiment which by 1910 had been proved to be erroneously conceived and interpreted.

Roux' importance, however, is not only in terms of presenting a method of solving problems, but of setting them, and this is pertinent. He could perform an experiment on an embryo because he could ask a question of the embryo that was experimentally answerable, at least within limits. His opposition of *differentiatio sui* and *differentiatio ex alio* answers the warning raised by Brooks (cf. rubric heading this essay) that points of reference must be specified. The choice between them could be made in a limited way by his own method of isolation; the necessity of a more crucial method to certify the choice led to the development of the transplantation technique by Born, Harrison and Spemann. And Roux' experimental program, carried to its logical outcome by the addition of the transplantation methods, in a way implied by it, has led straight to the modern embryology which incorporates the valid features of both epigenetic and preformationistic concepts. Every embryologist, whether concerned with the development of enzyme systems, or the cleavage of so-called determinative eggs, or with fields and gradients in a regulative egg, or whatever, is still concerning himself with the degree to which his material at a particular moment in development is answering to Roux' description of *differentiatio sui* or *differentiatio ex alio*.

Roux' own primary interest was in a theoretical and philosophical problem, that he called the *Causalnexus* of events. But his gift was that he could address his problem in such a way to the embryo that the embryo reacted in what Roux believed an intelligible way to laboratory interference.

The degree of intelligibility of the reaction of the embryo to interference is a problem to which we shall return in the next section. But it may be commented here that Roux, like von Baer, has made a greater advance than Darwin in the descent from metaphysics to the level of the organism; as a result of Roux' program, after all, hypotheses can be tested by exact investigation — and the investigator need only to read any single paper by Spemann or Harrison to know how exact — in an experimental laboratory.

* * * * * * *

This section was started, it may be remembered, from the premise that a backward look might give a clue as to how to proceed in the future for the best progress of embryology. The primary trend that emerges from the survey has seemed the gradual transition from the metaphysical to the physical that characterizes the progress of all developing science. What help may we derive, then, from the embryologists who have made the greatest progress in this respect?

The one valid generalization that can be drawn is that the great progressive minds of embryology — those of Aristotle, Wolff, von Baer, and Roux — and in our own times those of

Spemann and Harrison — have been those of the investigators who have learned to address the embryo by the right question; and these are the men who have derived their intuitions primarily from the study of the embryo itself. The investigators who have derived their ideas from the philosophical side, and examined their embryos to fit their observations into philosophical patterns already set and rigid — Goethe, St. Hilaire, Haeckel, Driesch — were the minds whose philosophical patterns delayed rather than accelerated the course of embryological progress. Aristotle and Wolff and von Baer and Roux started out too from philosophical and theoretical premises, but in such a way that they relegated the initiative of answering their problems to the embryo itself; they could do so only because it was the embryo that gave them their clues as to how to ask their questions. The others had been more interested in the ideas than the embryos, and had become captured by them to the detriment both of themselves and science.

Examining the problem from another aspect, we may say that the greatest delaying influences on embryology have been first the acceptance of the seventeenth century preformation doctrine, then the doctrines of Unity of Type, later the recapitulation doctrine, all concepts whose philosophical rather than their embryological content insured their success. Are we in the course of undergoing a similar delay? Are we too indulging in too high a degree of metaphysical speculation, pushing back what we cannot understand into concepts of fields and gradients which still have only metaphysical reality and into invisible realms what visible structure only inadequately explains? Is our present emphasis on the biochemical and biophysical constitution of the embryo a reaction against this? It is now again beginning to be admitted (cf. many authors in Parpart, *ed.*, '49) that the new biochemistry is insufficient to answer our fundamental problem of organization. We can not safely underestimate the complexity of the problem we attempt to solve, to borrow phraseology from Wheeler

(1898). In biological science, structure is inadequate to explain process. As biologists, we are bound to fail when we use methods applicable only to the study of structure for the analysis of processes functioning in time. The problem of modern embryology as stated above was crudely summed up as the problem of determining the degree to which particular material answers to Roux' description of *differentiatio sui* or *differentiatio ex alio* at any *one moment*. We have no methods as yet to deal with analyzing the transition from one moment to the next. Here the problem is simpler for the classical physiologist, and it is because of this that the progress of the embryologist has followed rather than preceded his.

Another trouble has been, historically speaking, our constant opposition of the metaphysical to the physical; there may be a biological level, too, at which one might work without retreating to the camp of the spiritualists and vitalists, and this is where our imagination has been and still is at its weakest. Roux saw the dilemma, as have so many others (1895c, p. 23):

Für den Forscher auf dem Gebiete der Entwickelungsmechanik gilt in hohem Masse das Wort:

"Incidit in scyllam, qui vult vitare charybdim."

Die zu *einfach mechanische* und die *metaphysische Auffassung* repräsentiren die Scylla und die Charybdis, zwischen welchen dahin zu segeln in der That schwer und bis jetzt nur Wenigen gelungen ist.

Some of the limitations of the too simply mechanical conception will be entered into further in the section to follow; suffice it to conclude here with a few more words about the metaphysical. Modern science considers respect for it a fault, which in many ways it is. But modern science must remember, as Whitehead reminds us, that all thought is abstract, and that intellectual induction at least presupposes metaphysics. And primary success in dealing with the embryo, because of its complexity, must derive from the inductive rather than the deductive process. No scientific progress has ever been made without reflection and speculation; and it must be remembered that both imply holding a mirror to nature, and that the surfaces must be held true.

Woodger ('48), as a matter of fact, in a most interesting theoretical paper, "Obervations on the present state of embryology," presented recently at the Second Growth Symposium in England, has concerned himself with the necessary conditions for immediate embryological progress, to conclude that what we need is to concentrate our attention on a few key data in order to derive the key hypotheses we require to proceed. There is a fallacy here for embryology. The greatest progressive minds of embryology have not searched *for* hypotheses; they have looked *at* embryos. How they have looked, and how they are looking now, is the burden of the section to follow.

REFERENCES

AGASSIZ, L. 1857 Essay on classification; in Contributions to the Natural History of the United States of America, Vol. I, pp. 1–232. Little, Brown and Company, Boston.

ARISTOTLE 1943 Generation of Animals. With an English translation by A. L. Peck. Harvard University Press, Cambridge, Massachusetts.

———— 1945 Parts of Animals. With an English translation by A. L. Peck and a foreword by F. H. A. Marshall. Movement of Animals. Progression of Animals. With an English translation by E. S. Forster. Harvard University Press, Cambridge, Massachusetts.

BAER, K. E. VON 1828, 1837 Ueber Entwickelungsgeschichte der Thiere. Beobachtung und Reflexion. Gebrüder Bornträger, Königsberg.

———— 1853 Fragments relating to philosophical zoology. Selected from the works of K. E. von Baer; In Scientific Memoirs, Selected from the Transactions of Foreign Academies of Science, and from Foreign Journals: Natural History, edited by A. Henfrey and T. H. Huxley, pp. 176–238. Taylor and Francis, London.

———— 1864 Reden gehalten in wissenschaftlichen Versammlungen und kleinere Aufsätze vermischten Inhalts, Part I: Reden. H. Schmitzdorff, St. Petersburg.

BALFOUR, F. M. 1880, 1881 A Treatise on Comparative Embryology. Two vols. Macmillan and Co., London.

BALSS, H. 1936 Die Zeugungslehre und Embryologie in der Antike. Quellen u. Studien zur Geschichte der Naturw. u. der Med., 5:193–274.

BEER, G. R. DE 1951 Embryos and Ancestors. Clarendon Press, Oxford, England.

BERGMANN, C. AND LEUCKART, R. 1855 Anatomisch-physiologische Uebersicht des Thierreichs. Vergleichende Anatomie und Physiologie. Ein Lehrbuch für den Unterricht und zum Selbststudium. New ed. J. B. Müller, Stuttgart.

BROOKS, W. K. 1902 The intellectual conditions for the science of embryology. Science, N.S., 15:444–454, 481–492.

BUNGE, G. 1902 Textbook of Physiological and Pathological Chemistry. 2d English ed. translated from the 4th German ed. by F. A. Starling and edited by E. H. Starling. P. Blakiston's Son & Co., Philadelphia.

BURNET, J. 1930 Early Greek Philosophy. 4th ed. A. & C. Black, Ltd., London.

COLE, F. J. 1930 Early Theories of Sexual Differentiation. Clarendon Press, Oxford, England.

———— 1944 Dr. William Croone on generation; in Studies and Essays in the History of Science and Learning Offered in Homage to George Sarton on the Occasion of his Sixtieth Birthday 31 August 1944, edited by M. F. Ashley Montagu, pp. 113–135. Henry Schuman, New York.

DARWIN, C. 1902 The Origin of Species by Means of Natural Selection or the Preservation of Favored Races in the Struggle for Life. With additions and corrections from 6th and last English edition. Two vols. in one. D. Appleton and Company, New York.

DIDEROT, D. 1875 Entretien entre D'Alembert et Diderot. Rêve de D'Alembert. Suite de l'entretien; in Oeuvres complètes de Diderot, edited by J. Assézat, Vol. II, pp. 101–191. Garnier, Paris.

ECKERMANN, J. P. 1905 Gespräche mit Goethe in den letzten Jahren seines Lebens, edited by A. Bartels. Two vols. Eugen Diederichs, Jena.

FABRICIUS, H. 1942 The Embryological Treatises of Hieronymus

Fabricius of Aquapendente. The Formation of the Egg and of the Chick (De formatione ovi et pulli). The Formed Fetus (De formato foetu). A facsimile edition, with an introduction, a translation, and a commentary by H. B. Adelmann. Cornell University Press, Ithaca, New York.

GOETHE, J. W. VON 1944 Gedanken und Aufsätze; in Goethes Werke, edited by E. Merian-Genast, Vol. XII. Birkhäuser, Basel.

HAECKEL, E. 1891 Anthropogenie oder Entwickelungsgeschichte des Menschen. Keimes- und Stammes-Geschichte. 4th rev. and enl. ed. Wilhelm Engelmann, Leipzig.

—— [1900] The Riddle of the Universe at the Close of the Nineteenth Century. Translated by J. McCabe. Harper & Brothers, New York.

HARVEY, W. 1653 Anatomical Exercitations, Concerning the Generation of Living Creatures: To Which Are Added Particular Discourses, of Births, and of Conceptions, &c. Octavian Pulleyn, London.

—— 1931 Exercitatio anatomica de motu cordis et sanguinis in animalibus. An English translation with annotations by C. D. Leake. Charles C Thomas, Springfield, Illinois.

HIS, W. 1874 Unsere Körperform und das physiologische Problem ihrer Entstehung. Briefe an einen befreundeten Naturforscher. F. C. W. Vogel, Leipzig.

HUXLEY, T. H. 1849 On the anatomy and the affinities of the family of the Medusae. Philos. Trans. Roy. Soc. London, *139*:413–434.

—— 1853a On the morphology of the Cephalous Mollusca, as illustrated by the anatomy of certain Heteropoda and Pteropoda collected during the voyage of H. M. S. "Rattlesnake" in 1846–50. Philos. Trans. Roy. Soc. London, *143*:29–65.

—— 1853b The cell-theory (Review). British & Foreign Medico-Chirurgical Review, *12*:285–314.

JUNG, C. G. 1927 Psychology of the Unconscious. A Study of the Transformations and Symbolisms of the Libido. A Contribution to the History of the Evolution of Thought. Authorized translation, with introduction, by B. M. Hinkle. Dodd, Mead and Company, New York.

KLEINENBERG, N. 1886 Die Entstehung des Annelids aus der Larve von Lopadorhyncus. Nebst Bemerkungen über die Entwicklung anderer Polychaeten. Wilhelm Engelmann, Leipzig.

KOWALEWSKI, A. 1867 Die Entwickelungsgeschichte des *Amphioxus lanceolatus*. Mém. de l'Acad. de St. Pétersbourg, 7th series, *11*,

No. 4, pp. 1–17 (page numbers recorded from offprint; original journal not available).

MAÎTRE-JAN, A. 1722 Observations sur la formation du poulet, où les divers changemens qui arrivent à l'oeuf à mesure qu'il est couvé, sont exactement expliqués & représentés en figures. d'Houry, Paris.

MALPIGHI, M. 1685 Dissertatio epistolica de formatione pulli in ovo Regiae Societati Londoni ad scientiam naturalem promovendam institutae, dictata; in Bibliotheca anatomica sive recens in anatomia inventorum thesaurus completissimus . . . edited by D. LeClerc and I. I. Mangetus, pp. 575–594. Chovet, Geneva.

MECKEL, J. F. 1821–1833 System der vergleichenden Anatomie. 6 pts. in 7 vols. Renger, Halle.

MEYER, A. W. 1935 Some historical aspects of the recapitulation idea. Quart. Rev. Biol., 10:379–396.

—— 1939 The Rise of Embryology. Stanford University Press, Stanford, California.

NEEDHAM, J. 1934 A History of Embryology. Cambridge University Press, Cambridge, England.

OPPENHEIMER, J. M. 1936 Historical introduction to the study of teleostean development. Osiris, 2:124–148.

—— 1940 The non-specificity of the germ-layers. Quart. Rev. Biol., 15:1–27. Reprinted in this volume, pp. 256–294.

PARPART, A. K. (editor) 1949 The Chemistry and Physiology of Growth. Princeton University Press, Princeton, New Jersey.

PLATO [1944] The Timaeus and the Critias or Atlanticus. The Thomas Taylor translation. Pantheon books [New York].

RÁDL, E. 1930 The History of Biological Theories. Translated and adapted from the German by E. J. Hatfield. Oxford University Press, Oxford, England.

ROUX, W. 1895a Der züchtende Kampf der Theile oder die "Theilauslese" im Organismus. Zugleich eine Theorie der "functionellen Anpassung." Ein Beitrag zur Vervollständigung der Lehre von der mechanischen Entstehung des sogenannten "Zweckmässigen"; in Gesammelte Abhandlungen über Entwickelungsmechanik der Organismen, Vol. I, pp. 135–422. Wilhelm Engelmann, Leipzig.

—— 1895b Die Entwicklungsmechanik der Organismen, eine anatomische Wissenschaft der Zukunft; in Gesammelte Abhandlungen über Entwickelungsmechanik der Organismen, Vol. II, pp. 24–54. Wilhelm Engelmann, Leipzig.

—— 1895c Einleitung. Roux' Arch. Entw.-mech., 1:1–42.

———— 1895d   Ueber den "Cytotropismus" der Furchungszellen des Grasfrosches (*Rana fusca*). Roux' Arch. Entw.-mech., *1*:43–68, 161–202.

SCHRECKER, P.   1938   Malebranche et le préformisme biologique. Revue internat. de philos., *1*:77–97.

SHUMWAY, W.   1932   The recapitulation theory. Quart. Rev. Biol., *7*:93–99.

SINGER, C.   1922   Greek Biology & Greek Medicine. Clarendon Press, Oxford, England.

———— [1941]   A Short History of Science to the Nineteenth Century. Clarendon Press, Oxford, England.

———— 1944   A word on the philosophical background of Vesalius; in Studies and Essays in the History of Science and Learning Offered in Homage to George Sarton on the Occasion of His Sixtieth Birthday 31 August 1944, edited by M. F. Ashley Montagu, pp. 75–84. Henry Schuman, New York.

SPEMANN, H.   1903   Entwickelungsphysiologische Studien am Triton-Ei. III. Roux' Arch. Entw.-mech., *16*:551-631.

———— [1943]   Forschung und Leben. Edited by F. W. Spemann. J. Engelhorns Nachf. Adolf Spemann, Stuttgart.

TEMKIN, O.   1950   German concepts of ontogeny and history around 1800. Bull. Hist. Med., *24*:227–246.

THOMPSON, D'A. W.   1940   Science and the Classics. Oxford University Press, Oxford, England.

WHEELER, W. M.   1898   Caspar Friedrich Wolff and the *Theoria generationis*. Biol. Lect. Marine Biol. Lab. Woods Holl, 1898, pp. 265–284.

WHITEHEAD, A. N.   1925   Science and the Modern World. The Macmillan Company, New York.

WHITMAN, C. O.   1894a   Evolution and epigenesis. Biol. Lect. Marine Biol. Lab. Woods Holl, 1894, pp. 205–224.

———— 1894b   Bonnet's theory of evolution. Biol. Lect. Marine Biol. Lab. Woods Holl, 1894, pp. 225–240.

WOLFF, C. F.   1774   Theoria generationis. New ed., enl. & corr. Hendel, Halle.

WOODGER, J. H.   1948   Observations on the present state of embryology; in Growth in Relation to Differentiation and Morphogenesis, Symposia of the Society for Experimental Biology, No. 2, pp. 351–365. Academic Press, New York.

Analysis of Development:
Methods and Techniques*

INTRODUCTION: SOME GENERAL
CONSIDERATIONS

GREAT advances, in scientific history, have almost always depended more on intellectual than on technological innovations. No new technique has alone either answered any problem of primary importance or has itself set one. In biological history, specifically, so far as technique is concerned, the work of Harvey and of Darwin and of Mendel could have been performed far earlier than it was: their advances were on the intellectual side, rather than technical in any sense. Harvey's greatest contribution was perhaps the application of the principle of measurement to biological material, and his ability to perform his experiment was an inevitable outcome of his quantitative considerations. There was a certain greater ease for him, who was bred in the halls of Padua a generation after Galileo, than for his predecessors to think quantitatively. But there is no *a priori* reason why such thinking might not have emanated from some Greek mind near Archimedes who in considering specific gravity in physical terms was thinking as quantitatively as Harvey who had only to collect and count a few cups of blood. Darwin was led to the formulation of his

* Reprinted from *Analysis of Development*, edited by Benjamin H. Willier, Paul A. Weiss and Viktor Hamburger, W. B. Saunders Company, Philadelphia, Pa., 1955, pp. 25–38.

doctrine by the consideration of Malthus' economic principles and Lyell's geological ones: but might not a clue to the genetic relationship of man and the ape have come from a comparison of their faces? Indeed had it not already done so in Buffon's concept of the ape as a "degraded" man? And what did Mendel do but separate his generations, keep careful records, count accurately and think clearly? The material of these men was the organism pure and simple; the instruments with which they attacked it were primarily their ideas. To quote Woodger, who emphasizes the same point:

Neither Dalton nor Mendel were afraid to put forward their hypotheses because of the absence of physical apparatus like that provided by X-ray photography. Their hypotheses were devised to explain the generalizations of their day — chemical generalizations about combining proportions in Dalton's case, and generalizations about ratios of kinds of offspring of known parentage in Mendel's case. The apparatus which subsequently provided confirmation of these hypotheses might never have been invented (at least in the case of Dalton) if the hypotheses themselves had not first been invented ('48, p. 360).

In embryology, too, as we have seen, the concept developed before the technique to verify or refute it. It was changes in thinking, not the mechanical tool, that permitted Wolff and von Baer to see more than Malpighi, in seeing less. Thinking in terms of concrete units such as Dalton's atoms, Mendel's unit characters in heredity and Pasteur's germs preceded the discovery and observation of discrete particles in the form of chromosomes and cytoplasmic inclusions by the use of improved achromatic lenses in the masterly cytological studies at the turn into the present century that were to become so important for embryology. Boveri ('07) established the fact of qualitative difference of the chromosomes by an intellectual *tour de force* in his analysis of dispermic echinoderm eggs before the technical methods of genetics were available. Spemann reached his primary premises out of thoughtful consideration of methodologically simple constriction experiments; he was later only to test and confirm, by the application of the technically more involved transplantation methods of Born and Harrison, what he had already suspected.

Indeed, one of the more curious phenomena of embryological history is the great lag in the application of more general biological techniques to the particular problems of embryology. Vesalius' *De Fabrica* was published over 75 years before the treatise of Fabricius on the developing chick. Strong magnifying lenses were used fruitfully for a half century on other biological material before Malpighi used the compound microscope to examine the blastoderm of the chick. Alchemy and pharmacology had puzzled over the uses of specific salts, at least since the ninth century, for the adult organism; the modern statement of the fundamental chemical problems of embryology awaited the nineteenth century. If the embryo waited centuries for even such simple quantitative approach as had been devoted to the adult by Sanctorius Sanctorius, it had to wait millennia, from the time surgeons first used their scalpels on biological material to cut off an offending member, for the hot needle of Roux and the discerning eye of Chun (1880) who observed comparable effects of the stormy Mediterranean seas. John Hunter had attempted modern methods of grafting in the adult organism over a century before transplantation techniques were applied to embryological material. There is surely no simple reason to account for these long delays in embryological evolution. But certainly they may be related to the fact that no method or technique developed for other sciences, even within the biological realm, has been adequate to enable the embryologist to come to grips with his fundamental and most inescapable problem, the nature of embryonic organization.

The important progress, then, in the history of embryology, has been in the gradual changes in the cast of thought and clarification, as it seems from our point of view, in the setting of the question to be answered by the embryo. How the question is expressed, at any one moment in history, is of course conditioned by the technical procedures available at the time, as well as by the influence of more general currents of thought; and the problem of the embryologist becomes the problem of asking a question, with whatever means are at his disposal, that the embryo can answer in a manner intelligible to the investigator.

What are the means of investigation available to the embryologist today? How have they developed? To what degree do they permit adequate reply to the problems they purport to attack? What are their limitations and how far can these be overcome? In what measure do they inhibit, as did the late nineteenth century concentration on genealogical research, or in what way do they encourage, as did the happy exploitation of the transplantation method by Spemann and Harrison, the posing of new and searching problems? What does the experience of the past and the present inform us at all usefully as to how the future might best be explored in terms of new techniques and of new problems? These are questions which the embryologist must answer if he is to review his work in proper perspective with relation to larger fields, and only by so doing can he hope to facilitate his approach to the problems next facing him.

OBSERVATION VS. INTERFERENCE AS AN APPROACH TO EMBRYOLOGICAL PROBLEMS

Modern embryology, since Roux, has tended strongly both in its pedagogical and investigational aspects to contrast the descriptive, or morphological, or observational, approach, with the so-called experimental, an only apparent distinction whose illusion of dichotomy leads to an important paradox to be taken up below. But since the observational method, at least in a crude form, has always been available to the investigator, a few of the difficulties inherent in the interpretation of what seem to be the simplest observations may be pointed out at the beginning of this discussion. Since even the results of experiments must be observed in some fashion, and this is only part of the paradox, these difficulties of interpretation are of significance in a much wider sense and therefore will be discussed also in relation to the broader issues.

In the first place, observation of the embryo can rarely, if ever, remain observation pure and simple. This seems a truism; yet there are certain inferences to be drawn from it which are not so completely obvious as it might seem.

Perhaps the greatest interference with constructive and advancing observation derives from the preconceptions already present in the mind of the observer, and there is no need further to labor the point that modern investigators, like the great minds of the past, like Wolff, like Roux, tend to see in terms of what they are looking for.

It is the what-he-is-looking-for that is so strongly conditioned by the mechanical tools at the disposal of the embryologist, which both expand and limit what is visible to him. In the early days of the microscope the embryologist saw organs, tissues, layers, perhaps cells. With the improvement of the techniques of microtomy and staining and with the perfection of achromatic lenses he could examine parts of the nucleus and what now seem the grosser cytoplasmic inclusions. The technique of modern optics and microscopy enable him to push his frontiers far beyond the old limits, and new instruments will continue to help him in this respect. Many other techniques, biophysical, biochemical, immunological, and so forth, allow the identification and description, if not the actual visualization, of components of the embryonic cell at the molecular and even the submolecular level.

Roux was frankly skeptical of the possibility of reducing embryological problems to the molecular level:

177

Auch wenn wir von den letzten Ursachen ganz absehen, so ist es doch fraglich, ob wir das von Carl Ernst v. Baer gesteckte Ziel: "Die bildenden Kräfte des thierischen Körpers auf die allgemeinen Kräfte oder Lebensrichtungen des Weltganzen zurückzuführen," je erreichen werden, vorausgesetzt, dass die zu Grunde liegende Auffassung überhaupt vollkommen richtig ist (1889, cited from Ges. Abh. 2:28–29).

He preferred to approach them by investigating, by means of interference with the embryo, what he called the *Causalnexus* of events. Causality is more suspect to the modern scientist, and becomes mere statistical probability, but following Roux, nevertheless, the tendency is fortunately to describe not simple structure but events, and specifically a sequence of events in time. If Roux believed this sequence capable of being subject to causal analysis, he realized also that the results of any such analysis could become significant only in a frame of reference defined by the normal developing embryo, and must have taken for granted that the "control" for an experimentally treated embryo must he an undisturbed one.

If a primary obligation of the embryologist, before he can evaluate an experimental result, is the knowing of the normal condition of the embryo, the fundamental paradox arises that he cannot perhaps adequately know the normal without the benefit of the experiment, whose whole *raison d'être* can surely be only that it elucidates the normal; yet he cannot interpret his experimental result without comparison with the normal control. Leaving aside, however, for the moment this dilemma, the task of the embryologist concerned with "normal" development becomes the task of describing the sequence of events in time as accurately as possible in terms of what he can see with the tools available to him, and to describe the components which are acting and their manner of action in as precise physical and chemical terms as his instruments and techniques will allow, as objectively as is possible in the light of the general biological and broader philosophical tenets of his times.

A first difficulty arises in that it is virtually impossible to observe an embryo under external conditions that do not interfere with it. Fixation, staining and other chemical treatment disturb the "normal" condition of the embryonic cell and alter it. Suffice it to say about the living embryo, without entering into the obvious detail, that the laboratory is not its normal environment. Indeed, is it always possible to define, let alone reproduce, a "normal" environment?

What is the "normal" environment of a developing Bonellia or Crepidula, whose sexual differentiation may be modified by it, in terms of distance from another Bonellia or Crepidula (Herbst, '36, '37; Baltzer, '37; Coe, '48)? What is the "normal" salinity for the development of Artemia whose form depends on the salt concentration of its environment (Abonyi, '15)? To come to the vertebrate, which we are in the habit of considering more conventional and stable embryological material, *Fundulus heteroclitus* embryos raised at constant temperatures reach specific morphological stages after different periods of time when raised at varying salinities (Merriman, unpublished). The adults live and breed both in brackish water and sea water in nature, and the temperatures of the seas and the estuaries are inconstant. What then is the "normal" environment of the developing Fundulus? What are the criteria for determining objectively which set of conditions is "optimum" for the embryo developing in the laboratory, and what biological significance these have for the organism developing in nature?

Comparable problems arise for the chemical embryologist who tries to describe the constituent systems of the embryonic cell in biochemical terms. Unpublished data of Dumm have suggested that the cholinesterase level of Fundulus embryos at particular morphological stages varies according to the temperature at which the embryos have been raised; and Boell (unpublished) also has data suggesting that the course of enzyme development in the amphibian can be altered by varying the temperatures at which the embryos are reared.

Weiss ('49) has introduced in another connection a useful concept of "molecular ecology" which may well serve to remind the embryologist of what he already knows but sometimes forgets, namely, that the embryo has an internal as well as an external environment that may well bear more strict definition than it has always hitherto received.

For the embryologist who considers himself primarily concerned with descriptive and morphological questions, the problems arising from these examples, and the countless others that could have been enumerated, may seem of little moment. He can evade them by ignoring them, or more profitably, he can meet them by specifying as strictly as possible the conditions under which he is making his observations. For the investigator, however, who is looking for "normal" controls for experimental material, the situation becomes more critical.

It becomes especially so for the interpretation of certain isolation experiments which will be discussed in more detail below, and it presents very particular problems in the case of some transplantation experiments. The rate of growth of an eye or a limb grafted heteroplastically onto an amphibian host varies according to whether or not the host is maximally or less than maximally fed (Twitty and Schwind, '31); how often does an Amblystoma in nature enjoy a condition of maximum repletion? The growth of an Amblystoma embryo varies according to the organisms constituting the diet it is fed; who can define the "normal" diet of Amblystoma in nature? Members of the same species of Amblystoma reared under similar laboratory conditions develop at different rates of growth when collected in Pennsylvania and New Jersey on the one hand, in Illinois on the other (DuShane and Hutchinson, '44); which is the more "normal" larva, that collected in the East or that which is spawned in the Midwest? This is a more than philosophical problem when experimentalists in Princeton, for instance, are comparing their results with those of investigators working at the University of

Chicago in an attempt to work out basic mechanisms of development. And while it is particularly accentuated by the results of the heteroplastic experiments, it touches the heart of each investigation involving the growth of the whole or parts of the developing amphibian.

In the case of more complicated experiments it raises even more complex issues. Haploid tissues developing from the hybrid androgenetic merogons of Hadorn ('34, '37) and Baltzer ('40), for instance, die in the embryos which they constitute but survive in tissue culture or after transplantation to normal diploid hosts of one of the experimental species. Is a favorable tissue culture medium or the tissues of a diploid host to be defined as more "normal" or "abnormal" for these cells than the haploid parent embryo from which they were derived? Under which conditions are the operations of the gene in development more "normal"? In other cases, what seems "optimum" according to the subjective judgment of an investigator concerned with a particular experiment may lack biological significance to the organism. Of what biological significance is it to Lytechinus that its egg can be so treated in the laboratory that it is more readily activated by sperm of a foreign species than by that of its own (Tennent, '25)? Tennent ('10) has found that in reciprocal crosses of Hipponoë × Toxopneustes the larvae were of the Hipponoë type when raised in sea water of higher pH, of the Toxopneustes type when reared in sea water of lower pH, and has suggested that seasonal variations in hybrid echinoderm larvae obtained in other laboratories might be accounted for by seasonal variations in the alkalinity of the seas; who is to say whether autumn or spring is more "normal" for echinoderm hybrids? Under which conditions, and this is the crux of the matter, does the action of the gene, which according to its end-effect varies in the different situations, more closely simulate its norm?

This is not the appropriate place to take up the developmental action of genes, which will be considered in a separate section below; but it is necessary to emphasize here the advantages to the embryologist of working with genetically known and genetically specified material when he is able to do so. Embryos vary. Many of the factors which induce them to vary are difficult to control, as we have seen. The genetic factors are perhaps uncontrollable too when specimens are collected in nature. But when the genetic factors are known, they can be controlled, and thereby great strides into unknown territory can be accomplished (cf. Gluecksohn-Schoenheimer, '49), and, as important, the results can be specified in the best biological sense of the word.

Consideration, in fact, of all the limitations to interpretation discussed above, and of many others like them, leads to the same inescapable necessity for specification of the conditions under which an investigation proceeds. It may often accrue to the advantage of the investigation, rather than otherwise, that observations and experiments carried out in different situations lead to different outcomes as well as different interpretations. Only when investigators specify as closely as possible the conditions against which particular outcomes eventuate will there become available new data and new ideas through which correlations and significances which currently still elude us may eventually be discerned.

Granted that the conditions, intrinsic and extrinsic to the embryo, under which observations are made are specified as accurately as possible, the question arises as to their ideal manner of description once they have been obtained. For embryology, the problem of semantics which faces all scientists arises in a particularly desperate form, perhaps at least partly because embryology, never having formulated its own problems nor having developed its own techniques, has adopted descriptive words from the lingo of other sciences. Spemann, it may be remembered, concluded his great monograph with a confession that he borrowed words to describe embryonic phenomena which point not to physical but to psychical analogies, to emphasize his conviction that

these processes of development, like all vital processes, are comparable, in the way they are connected, to nothing we know in such a degree as to those vital processes of which we have the most intimate knowledge, viz., the psychical ones. It was to express my opinion that, even laying aside all philosophical conclusions, merely for the interest of exact research, we ought not to miss the chance given to us by our position between the two worlds ('38, p. 372).

Investigators more neutral with respect to this issue use the words induction, determination, regulation, organization, and so forth, borrowed, as Spemann would say, from the psychic sphere, partly out of wonderment at the unexplained powers of regulation of the embryo, but largely for lack of more clear-cut or appropriate ones. The problem, however, is not so much of word as of concept; and only when the embryologist can more completely emancipate himself from the domination of other sciences and their techniques, and formulate his problems in his own terms, will he be motivated to create and define such terms with requisite precision.

Roux seems to have been the first, and the last, to worry over this problem, sufficiently, at least, to be driven to a specific attempt to solve it. He drew up his *Terminologie der Entwick- lungsmechanik*, a discursive text with only the remotest re- semblance to our own unfortunate glossaries, with the express aim "das causal-analytische Denken [zu] fördern und auch das vollkommene Verständnis der Autoren untereinander [zu] erleichtern" ('12, p. ix). His recognition of the difficulties inherent in adapting for *Entwicklungsmechanik* terms bor- rowed from other sciences is perhaps nowhere made clearer than by the fact that he found it necessary to include in the *Terminologie* two separate definitions in sequence for *Tropis- mus*, one for zoological material composed by himself, the other for botanical, contributed by Küster, one of the botan- ical collaborators who assisted in the preparation of the book.

No modern attempt to emulate the *Terminologie* has ever been made; no one since Roux has had either the courage or the conceit to try, and modern embryology is still confronted with the old problem of using borrowed terms. Perhaps, however, it is an advantage to the embryologist to be forced to utilize, as a temporizing device, the terminology of physics and chemistry, since in doing so he must also use their methods and resources.

It is indisputably by the application of these resources that the greatest advances are being made at the present time. The results of current investigations of structure and ultrastructure by phase-contrast microscopy and cinemicrography and by electron microscopy; of molecular arrays by polarization optics; of chemical constitution and activity by histochemical and immunological techniques, by microspectrography and microspectrophotometry; of the localization, constitution and kinetics of enzymes and enzyme systems and of other metabolic systems, by microrespirometry, by "biochemical dissection" by antimetabolites and other specific poisons, by modern nutrition studies and by the use of both radioactive and stable isotopes as tracers; of genetic effects of ionizing radiations — all these will be discussed in ensuing chapters of this book.

Continuation and elaboration of such physical and chemical descriptions of the embryo, of its cells and of their components, are a *conditio sine qua non* for further embryological progress. Such description, however, dynamic though it may seem, is essentially structural rather than functional, analytical rather than synthetic, and this new morphology, like the old, is not able to penetrate to the core of the problem of organization. A physical-chemical model of the embryo may ultimately be adequate to represent some phase of what embryonic organization has produced, but as yet there is no assurance that it can reproduce the process by which organization has functioned. Structure, in embryonic material, is not yet adequate to "explain" process.

This may be bound up with the fact that the embryo has the disadvantage, from the point of view of the investigator, of developing in time. The methods appropriated by embryology from other disciplines, which have a different concern for the time factor, have been invented to describe material at a given moment, not to analyze transition from one moment to the next. Insight into the problems of organization demands new approaches to the physiology of development as such, while as yet we confine our efforts to the descriptive physiology of embryos, which is something different. However, it is possible that the clue to new methods for analyzing organization may well come from a deeper comprehension of structure than we now enjoy; and in any case, any knowledge of process we ever may hope to obtain is certain to become more meaningful in the light of as intimate an understanding as possible of ultimate structure.

One evident superiority of the results of the new morphology over those of the old is that they allow quantitative expression. There is no question but that embryological descriptions must be as quantitatively exact as is appropriate for the material and techniques in question, and there is no greater need to justify the benefits of this for embryology than for any other science. There are, however, certain sources of error in interpretation which may be pointed out which are inherent in some attempts to analyze the significance of certain aspects of growth and differentiation by presenting descriptions of them in quantitative form.

It is well to remember that mathematical abstraction is a particular kind of abstraction which is in itself highly specialized. Any progressive science deals in abstraction as well as in measurement, but it requires always to question the appropriateness of whatever abstraction it utilizes to the particular material with which it deals. There is no more fascinating collection of biological facts than those by which Sir D'Arcy Thompson referred growth and form to certain mathematical relationships, but surely Sir D'Arcy's analogies are provocative rather than explanatory, and he himself hardly claimed more for them.

A curve, for instance, which describes the "growth" of a colony of bacteria is useful in that it designates periods of change at particular moments, and these may be periods with which the investigator may wish to concern himself; but the "growth" of a colony of micro-organisms is something different from that of a multicellular organism, and the growth of one organism may be controlled by different factors than that of another. Weiss' warning of a few years ago is still relevant and will continue to remain so:

> A purely formal treatment of growth, as is often attempted through the interpretation of growth curves, is only a valuable guide to and supplement of, but never a substitute for, a precise analysis of the different forms in which growth manifests itself.
>
> There can be no research on growth as such. We can only study growing objects. And different growing objects follow different methods. . . . To know growth we must therefore break down each one of its manifestations into its constituent elementary processes and then study these and describe them in objective terms. This is a long way to go, but there is no short cut ('49, p. 182).

Weiss' admonition holds equally true for other aspects of development: differentiation, determination, or whatever. Exact quantitative description of embryological data is another *conditio sine qua non* for future embryological progress, but only if the embryologist keeps in mind which of his problems quantification cannot solve, as well as those which it can elucidate.

The success of quantitative methods in creating the new morphology has tended to encourage attempts to adapt quantitative methods to the results of the older; and this condition, together with the fact that the journals currently encourage the publication of data in graphic and tabular form, leads to a growing tendency to make material appear quantitative which

186

may not necessarily be so in its own right. An example is the current procedure of using morphological stage numbers from stage series to represent ordinates or abscissae of graphs. This may be useful provided the author works with a footnote, in his thinking if not on his page, calling for caution in interpretation, but it is a question to what extent this reservation is kept in mind. The presence, in the curve of such a graph, of maxima or minima, and whether a line rises or falls is surely significant; not in the same way the slope of the line nor the character of the curve in other respects. A straight line in such a graph is not what it purports to be; "morphological age," as Needham ('42) calls it, is not equivalent to time, which can be quantified. *Stage 5* of an embryo is not something that equals *the sum of stage 2 plus stage 3,* which, unless specifically qualified, is what the conventional graphic representation implies.

There are innumerable cases, too, where presentation of quantitative data is inadequate and perhaps irrelevant to answer the basic question presented by the material to be analyzed. What is the meaning, for instance, of the "quantitative" results described in percentages of positive differentiation in grafts? Luther ('36), for instance, has concluded that there is a gradient of physiological activity (*Aktivitätszustand*) around the rim of the trout blastoderm on the basis of the fact that differentiation occurs in a decreasing percentage of grafts as the material for grafting is removed from progressively greater distances from the midline of the embryonic shield. If a particular factor, or group of factors, or a certain quantity of such factors necessary for differentiation, characterizes the cells near the embryonic shield should not every graft from that area differentiate if the experiment is adequately performed? What is the meaning, in terms of the functions of the grafted cells, of the fact that only 84% of the grafts removed from a particular region have differentiated? May not the significance of these results be that the grafts have been removed in different

ways from zones of transition, or that they have been implanted under differing experimental conditions? In other
words, may not the quantitative variations in such results
indicate variation in the technique of experimental procedure
as well as variation in the activity of the tissue? Too many
factors, which need no enumeration here, are varied in even
such a simple experiment as the implantation of a graft on
the yolk sac, which though in some ways is simple in others is
drastic and crude; and the experimental procedure, which is
manual and therefore difficult to subject to critical control, is
probably differently performed each time.

It can be of the greatest advantage to the investigator to
acknowledge that quantitative variation in his results reflects
his own uncertainties as well as the accomplishment of his
embryonic material, if he wishes to improve his experimental
approach both from the technical and the intellectual aspect.
The value of statistical treatment and its advantages in connection with the endeavor to attain the maximum precision in
analysis are particularly great in the case of embryological
material where so bewilderingly many variations are inherent
in the material and where so many sources of error confuse
the methods of analysis. But statistical results must not be
interpreted as final to such a degree that they mask the weaknesses of the technical procedure where these actually affect
the interpretation of results. Embryology has not yet sufficiently matured towards the perfection of its methods that
quantification can be its only desideratum, and it may well
be that the necessity to improve upon these methods represents
the most urgent challenge immediately confronting us.

TECHNIQUES OF INTERFERENCE
WITH THE EMBRYO

It was Wilhelm Roux who first had the insight to appreciate
the inadequacy of the descriptive method, no matter how pre-

cise the terms in which its results are couched, to demonstrate what he called the *Causalnexus* of events, and to formulate a program designed to analyze that causal relationship within sequences of events which had already been so clearly expressed on an inferential basis by His (see quotation on p. 159). It was the simplicity of Roux' first statement of his problem that enabled him to try to answer his question with an apparently simple experiment:

Fast alle aber führten im Weiterfolgen zu einer und derselben grossen Vorfrage, *zu einer Alternative, von welcher aus die causale Auffassung fast aller Bildungsvorgänge in zwei wesentlich verschiedene Bahnen gelenkt wird.* Dies ist die Frage: *Ist die Entwicklung des ganzen befruchteten Eies resp. einzelner Theile desselben "Selbstdifferenzierung" dieser Gebilde resp. Theile oder das Produkt von "Wechselwirkungen mit ihrer Umgebung?"* Eventuell, *welches ist der Antheil jeder dieser beiden Differenzirungsarten in jeder Entwicklungsphase des ganzen Eies und seiner einzelnen Theile?*

In der Beantwortung dieser Frage liegt meiner Einsicht nach der Schlüssel zur causalen Erkenntnis der embryonalen Entwicklung (1885; cited from Ges. Abh. 2:14).

The question with which he was concerned happened to involve the relationship of the part to the whole, and happened to revive in a new form the old controversy between preformationists and epigeneticists; but this was not its main significance. His great contribution from the methodological point of view was that he saw his problem in terms of a single alternative and in terms of clearcut relationships; relationships so expressed that he could alter them in what was to him a simple experiment. An embryo or an embryonic part depends for its capacity to differentiate on a mutual interaction with its surroundings, or it does not; remove it from its surroundings, and its reply should be unequivocal.

The significance, however, of the behavior of a part removed from its surroundings is lost except in comparison with its behavior in those surroundings, as Roux already knew. In most cases, except where natural pigments are present, the observation of the egg as a whole sheds all too little light on the separate activities of its individual parts, and Roux himself attempted to circumvent this difficulty by inventing a crude marking experiment and by pricking his eggs to produce extra-ovates which might serve as markers. This experiment is open to the obvious criticism that it may alter the status of the part whose normal behavior it purports to elucidate, and it was to obviate this that the technique of local vital staining was developed. It has reached its highest perfection as developed for application to the amphibian egg by Vogt ('25), where its success depends on the fact that inclusions of the egg adsorb the stain from the carrier more rapidly than it diffuses into the solution, and a mark of the utmost sharpness of outline is therefore achieved and maintained.

The data obtained by the local vital staining method are indispensable for the interpretation of experiments in which the activities of particular parts are to be studied by other means, and the dyes currently used (Nile blue sulfate, neutral red and Bismarck brown) are sufficiently nontoxic that the data derived from their use are thoroughly valid. There are conditions, however, under which the method has strong limitations. In some cases the dyes may be transformed to leukobases within the cells. In the case of embryos whose cells lack inclusions with special affinity for the dyes, for instance young stages of chick and teleost, the stains are far more diffuse and ephemeral than in the amphibian, and the results of their use may prove unreliable when checked against results obtained by other methods. The newer method of following morphogenetic movements by the application to the cells of carbon particles (Spratt, '46) has, for instance, produced results for the chick which are incompatible with those previously derived for the same form by vital staining (Pasteels, '37). The use of carbon particles holds great promise for the future, but the introduction of macroscopic particles within the cells raises certain dangers for the interpretation of what are supposed to be unhampered movements; and when the particles are applied to the outer surface of the cell there may always remain some doubt as to whether they may have shifted in position.

So far as the localization and retention of a marker is concerned, the least reproachable method of distinguishing one group of cells from another remains the observation of forms in which natural pigments occur. It may be remembered in this connection that the method of heteroplastic grafting was at its earliest inception used to trace the migration of elements distinguished by natural pigment (Harrison, '03; see Harrison, '35, for later uses of heteroplastic grafting). Grafting, however, as an operative method, introduces new sources of error not inherent in the methods of marking cells in an unoperated embryo. Unfortunately there is still no equivalent of a Geiger counter to report on the migrations of cells in the embryo. The data, however, which have been accumulated by the present techniques as applied by cautious investigators are adequate to serve as a frame of reference against which studies of the parts may be judged.

Since killing a cell is probably the easiest thing that an embryologist can do, it was perhaps inevitable that the study of the behavior of parts of an embryo should have first been examined by defect methods, and it is appropriate next to mention some of the ways in which defects have been produced. Experiments involving the removal or the supposed inactivation of cells or their parts have been carried out by mechanical, chemical, thermal and electrical methods and by combinations of them, and by the use of various sorts of radiations.

A primary and insidious source of error common to all these methods is that in applying them the investigator may alter more factors than he knows. The classical experiment of Roux (1888) was designed by killing a blastomere to eliminate its influence on its neighbor; the fact that its corpse exerted mechanical influence of moment could be appreciated only after McClendon ('10) completely removed a blastomere to demonstrate a different accomplishment by the remaining cell than had been achieved in Roux' experiment. Comparable sources of error may lie hidden in many if not all of the defect experiments subsequently performed.

In dealing with the deletion or inactivation of components of cells, the perils of interpretation may be as great. Boveri ('18) long ago recognized as an inevitable source of error in experiments designed to exclude nuclear influence that nuclear residues might remain undetected in the cytoplasm, which in any case has necessarily been produced under the influence of the nucleus. The centrifuge is a tool which can translocate substances from a particular part whose behavior is to be studied in their absence, but who knows what effects it may have had on the invisible components of the zone?

Nor are the mechanical methods the only ones open to suspicion. It is unthinkable that in anything kinetically as complex as the simplest protoplasm, alteration of its equilibria by chemical or thermal changes could be limited in its effects to a single system alone. Temperature changes probably affect all its constituent systems in some measure, and indeed the laws of thermodynamics are hardly such as to permit such effects to remain local. Methods involving the use of radiations and electricity, in spite of the advantage that the amounts of energy applied may be measured, cannot be construed in most cases as affecting single localizable or identifiable systems within the cell. Exception, however, may be made in the cases where radiations or other agents affect the known gene; the most reliable defect method, perhaps the ideal, is that which excludes identified genes (Poulson, '40, '45). Manipulation of the gene, by man or nature, is probably the most satisfactorily controlled experimental method available to the embryologist to date, and it will become the more useful the more exhaustively the intermediate steps between the primary action of the gene and the end-effects of its activity, as expressed in differentiation, become known.

Despite the reservations enumerated, however, excellent contributions to embryology have been made by the use of all of the defect methods. These methods were the first to demonstrate the high degree of regulability of which the embryo is capable, and thus have led directly to the primary embryological problem of ultimate organization, and the data which they have provided will be indispensable for the final solution of it.

A fact to be kept in mind in this connection is the impossibility of consideration of the defect experiment as separate from the isolation or explantation experiment, which is its corollary as well as its complement. In the ideal situation the embryologist wishes to consider both experiments. In one, the investigator studies what remains after something has been taken away; in the other, he studies the behavior of what he has removed. In this sense, the study of a single blastomere isolated from a two-celled egg may be regarded either as a defect experiment or as an isolation experiment. Roux, as a preformationist, considered it as an isolation experiment. He knew that in the egg one blastomere forms half an embryo, and interpreted the blastomere in his experiment as duplicating its normal action. He concluded that its processes of development were identical in normal and experimental material, and the experiment seemed to him essentially a way to confirm what he had postulated the behavior of the normal part to be.

The questions that are put to the isolated part are now framed by more open minds, but they still deal in the main with the degree to which a cell is dependent for its differentiation on factors impinging upon it from its surroundings. To what degree does a part begin or continue differentiation when isolated from its usual cellular surroundings? Does it differentiate the same structures it was destined to form in the normal embryo? If not, what is the direction of its differentiation and what factors determine this direction? Attempts to isolate these factors involve not only the negative phase of the experiment and determining what factors usually present are lacking when the part is isolated, but also the more positive one of demonstrating the new or different ones to which it is subjected. This was a side of the problem on which Roux did not concentrate, though it is clear that he recognized its importance; and it is this aspect of it which raises some of the most immediate issues facing the present interpreters of isolation or explantation experiments.

Ideally the investigator may express a wish to culture his isolate in a neutral or indifferent medium (cf. Needham, '42, p. 175) which will permit it to continue its own development in its own way. This is essentially what Harrison ('07) did when he isolated the neuroblast in clotted lymph, a medium which did not inhibit the production of the axon yet which excluded the presence of the cells which had been thought by some to manufacture it. If the behavior of a cell is to be studied in the absence of influence from surrounding cells, it is essential that the medium to which it is removed cannot itself alter the chain of reactions to be studied. To what degree can this ideal be achieved?

First and foremost, the emancipation of a cell from influences emanating from its neighbors may now be recognized as more difficult to achieve than formerly was anticipated, in view of Holtfreter's ('44) recent demonstration that some of the cells constituting the very cultures being studied may attain a sublethal state of cytolysis, as a result of reaction to the medium, which may exert hitherto unsuspected effects on other cells nearby in the cultures.

Even in cases, however, where such effects may be discounted in the interpretation of results, many other difficulties arise in attempts to prepare a suitable medium. Cells can never be independent of mechanical factors in their environment, and indeed are notoriously susceptible to their influence, as was so clearly demonstrated by Harrison ('14). In a liquid environment they take quite different shape than when they have access to a solid substrate, and the physical framework of the matrix in which they develop is of paramount importance in determining their form (cf. Weiss, '49). Sometimes hidden mechanical influences quite prejudice the interpretation of investigations designed to analyze the effects of quite different factors; for an example, the reader is referred to Weiss' ('50) critique of Marsh and Beams' ('46) experiments where developing nerve cells were subjected in vitro to apparent modification by the passage of electrical currents. Indeed the demonstration of the degree to which cells are susceptible to influences of external mechanical factors has been one of the most fruitful contributions of the isolation method.

From the point of view of nutritive and chemical effects of the milieu on isolates, the analysis is more highly complex. If a part is isolated in inorganic media of easily reproducible composition, many components of the normal environment are lacking which may be essential to foster the processes of normal differentiation; and even such simple factors as a change in pH (though in view of the widely divergent systems in the cell which this might affect its simplicity is only apparent) can alter the accomplishment of cells in such media (Holtfreter, '45). If the isolate is explanted to parts of another organism, as in implants to the eye cavity, the anterior chamber of the eye, the chorioallantois, or to the various sites employed for the window techniques, or even to culture fluids containing embryonic extract, plasma or other body fluids, it is impossible in our present state of knowledge to ascertain what components are present. While to some the ultimate aim may seem the perfection of synthetic media — and the embryologists proper lag far behind the tissue culture experts and the microbiologists in their progress towards this goal — it is a little soon to divine what all the ingredients of such media might be, since embryologists have hardly yet exhausted the knowledge of all the biochemical requirements of their material.

A fundamental problem arises as to the criteria by which a neutral or indifferent medium could be recognized as such, granted the validity of the assumption that it exists and granted that it would be capable of preparation. Just as there are various conditions under which cells removed from an embryo behave differently than in the normal embryo, so there are various sets of conditions under which cells removed from the embryo might carry out the same performance as in the embryo; the most striking manifestations of embryonic organization are those regulatory phenomena whereby processes resembling the normal are carried out under a great variety of abnormal conditions.

Devillers ('50), for instance, has found the trout blastoderm incapable of differentiation in triple-strength Holtfreter's solution but able to differentiate in modified White's solution. It is unthinkable that this is the single solution capable of supporting differentiation in this form. Devillers' result demonstrates the fact that triple-strength Holtfreter's solution is unsatisfactory for his particular experiment, but provides no essential information about the blastoderm; the fact that modified White's solution is more favorable furnishes little information about differentiation as such, but signifies primarily that the medium used permits certain embryonic processes to occur. The absence of differentiation of cultures in solutions of particular composition does not necessarily demonstrate that the cells are characterized by the presence or absence of particular potencies, but rather may indicate that the media lack certain factors required as stimuli for the realization of normal potencies, or even that they include agents which may actively inhibit such realization.

Whether or not the cells will differentiate, furthermore, is not the only test of the suitability of the medium; the direction of differentiation and what the factors are which determine it are as important considerations. Using the prospective nervous system of the young urodele gastrula as an example, when isolated in salt solution it will under some conditions form only simple epidermis, under others nervous tissue (Holtfreter, '45). Implanted in vivo, where it is subjected to a wider variety of influences, it is capable of differentiating widely divergent structures (Holtfreter, '29; Bautzmann, '29; Kusche, '29) quite other than those it would have formed in the normal embryo, hence Bautzmann's term *bedeutungsfremde Selbstdifferenzierung*. The occurrence of these and other examples of *bedeutungsfremde Selbstdifferenzierung* signifies that the cells have sufficient plasticity to differentiate in other than their normal direction as a result of change in the conditions with reference to which they are differentiating, but is not adequate to define the changes which have produced an alteration in the direction of differentiation.

It has been postulated that one way, theoretically, to come closer to a definition of conditions essential to differentiation might be the testing of differentiation capacity in the widest possible variety of media. But if the reactions and directions of differentiation should be studied under as many experimental conditions as possible, how is the information to be referred to the cells in action in the normal embryo? Observations would be available as to media satisfactory to elicit all ranges of differentiation; but would not the ascertained data remain knowledge of reactions in an external medium rather than of processes internal to the embryo itself? The comparison of different results in various solutions fails to permit reference of the experimental results to the processes which might have been carried out by the cells *in situ*. What is the way to prove in the isolation experiment whether the cells which have differentiated particular structures are the same which would have done so in the embryo or whether they have used the same method to reach their end?

If, however, the processes studied experimentally cannot be referred without caution back to the normal embryo, it is clear that the processes examined experimentally require rigid definition as to the conditions under which they occur. No medium can be neutral or indifferent with respect to early differentiation; if it were actually either of these, isolates could continue no development at all; a medium can be neutral or indifferent only to a cell that is dead. The failure to come to grips with the problem of relationship between embryo and medium grows partly out of the tendency to emphasize the degree to which cells "self-differentiate." The concept of self-differentiation implies a contradiction in terms; no cell can "self"-differentiate, *bedeutungsfremd* or *bedeutungsgemäss*, insofar as no cell can be separated from its environment.

Roux expressed the problem more cogently when he opposed dependent and independent differentiation, a classification which demands enumeration of the *factors with reference to which* differentiation might be defined as either of these. One of the strong needs of the moment is more specific definition of the conditions with reference to which both normal and abnormal differentiation occur; only this will permit evaluation of the meaning of changes in the differentiating systems proper, since only in this way can embryologists be certain when they are dealing with these systems themselves and not something extraneous to them.

While attempts to invent the medium ideal to support specific types of differentiation may suffer in that the results of the studies lack referability to the normal embryo, the attempts must still be continued, though as a means to an end. Only when knowledge is available concerning the reactions of the cells to the media in which they develop can other experiments be interpreted which are conducted in other ways to answer the more searching questions which remain at the backs of our minds; but the fact must not be lost sight of that these more fundamental questions remain to be asked by other experimental methods.

The remaining one of these methods to be discussed is the transplantation method, which allows the framing of different questions than those methods already discussed, or which perhaps rather allows comparable questions to be asked in a slightly different way.

Strictly speaking, the implantation of cells to such cellular environments as the chorioallantois, the eye chamber and the other sites used for studies in vivo might be considered either as transplantation or as explantation experiments; and perhaps some of the best uses to which the transplantation method has been put have been those in which it has been employed as an isolation method, as in the case of Harrison's ('03) early experiments on the lateral line.

When cells are isolated in culture in some synthetic medium, the direction of their differentiation presumably may be influenced by the reaction of cells to factors in the medium; if they are transplanted to a new cellular environment, it will be conditioned in relationship to factors emanating from neighboring cells, and therefore by mutual interactions between cells of graft and cells of host.

When cells are transplanted to a cellular environment they are transferred, as in many explantation experiments, to a milieu in which many factors are still unknown, and to this extent the transplantation method shares the limitations of many of the isolation methods. In addition, furthermore, it has many of its own incident to the complexity of variables introduced by using a living organism as host; the results in grafting experiments vary according to the species used, according to the size, age and growth rate of the graft and host, according to the site of implantation and so forth. However, in spite of these, indeed perhaps because of them, the method has advantages peculiar to itself, in that it permits, and in fact leads to, the demonstration of interactions at cellular rather than subcellular levels. It thus encourages some analysis, at least, of that *Wechselwirkung* between cell and environment postulated by Roux (cf. quotation on p. 189), and the exploitation of the method by Spemann and Harrison has demonstrated the reality of the progressive quality of differentiation which Roux and His before them had postulated.

The significance, after all, of what a cell can do in isolation can reach its full value only in the light of what the cell does in combination with other cells, and recombination therefore by means of grafting is obligatory to clarify interpretation of the results of the isolation and deletion experiments. Without physical and chemical description of the cells and their components, and without the knowledge of the separate activity of the cells as ascertained by vital staining and defect and isolation experiments, the results of the transplantation experiments themselves might have little meaning. But it is the results of the transplantation experiments which impute final validity to these others, by presenting as a frame of reference not some chance combination of inert substances but the organized living embryo itself.

It is when the embryologist attempts to refer the phenomena which the transplantation experiments demonstrate as occurring at the cellular level to phenomena with which he is familiar at the subcellular level that he meets his greatest difficulty. But though this problem may seem to present itself more acutely at a time when biochemistry is forging the most rapid advances, it is not in any way a new one, nor was it new when Roux found himself confronted with his passage between the Scylla of the overphysical and the Charybdis of the overmetaphysical interpretation of his results (cf. quotation on p. 167). Nor is it any new solution to claim that between these two levels a biological plane exists, and to recognize that here, where problems of organization are concerned, all biology works to its least satisfaction. Embryology, as a matter of fact, occupies a more favorable position in this respect than many other fields of biology, because it is so fortunate in having had a Spemann and a Harrison whose special genius lay in their ability to probe more deeply than investigators in other areas into the forbidden territories. Their method, as a synthetic one rather than an analytic, as a method dealing with mutual interactions in terms of cell and cell, rather than simpler reaction of cell to some less organized entity, has the unique merit to come as close to the biological plane of investigation as has yet been approached.

For the knowledge to proceed still further into the investigation of these intercellular phenomena and finally into those obscurer supracellular ones which express themselves as organization, embryology must bide its time, but while awaiting the new insight it is clear what its investigators may do. They may continue to elaborate their physical and chemical descriptions as precisely as possible, though recognizing the limitations of these with respect to the fundamental problem of organization. They may specify, as strictly as possible, the conditions under which work is carried out, in the hope of arriving at possible correlations that may eventually provide new clues. And last, but not least, they will do well to remain as closely preoccupied as possible with the living embryo itself. Spemann, it may be remembered, had the habit of considering the embryo as a *Gesprächspartner* who must be allowed to answer in his own language; as a subject, in this sense, rather than a mere object of investigation (cf. Goerttler, '50). The attitude may seem excessively anthropomorphic, but serves to keep freshly in mind that the embryo, if given the initiative, may have some wise instruction to offer. How intelligibly the embryo can answer the questions directed towards it depends on the questions asked; these must of course be reduced to simple terms, but they must be terms which the embryo can comprehend. Roux accomplished this, in setting up his first simple alternative; Harrison did so when he isolated the neuroblast, and indeed in many of his subsequent experiments.

The most formidable task of the embryologist is the intellectual one of restating the problems, not the technical one of physical manipulation. The embryo makes its replies at a supracellular level, and inspiration as how best to address it at this level can come only from the embryo alive, from *Beobachtung und Reflexion* freely expended upon it, in the future as in all the great advances in the past.

REFERENCES

ABONYI, A. 1915 Experimentelle Daten zum Erkennen der Artemia-Gattung. Zeit. wiss. Zool., *114*:95–168.

BALTZER, F. 1937 Analyse des Goldschmidtschen Zeitgesetzes der Intersexualität auf Grund eines Vergleiches der Entwicklung der Bonellia- und Lymantria-Intersexe. Zeitlich gestaffelte Wirkung der Geschlechtsfaktoren (Zeitgesetz) oder Faktorengleichzeitigkeit (Gen-Gleichgewicht). Roux' Arch. Entw.-mech., *136*:1–43.

——— 1940 Ueber erbliche letale Entwicklung und Austauschbarkeit artverschiedener Kerne bei Bastarden. Naturwiss., *28*:177–187.

BAUTZMANN, H. 1929 Ueber bedeutungsfremde Selbstdifferenzierung aus Teilstücken des Amphibienkeimes. Naturwiss., *17*:818–827.

BOVERI, T. 1907 Zellen-Studien. VI. Die Entwicklung dispermer Seeigel-Eier. Ein Beitrag zur Befruchtungslehre und zur Theorie des Kerns. Jena. Zeit. Wiss., *43*:1–292.

——— 1918 Zwei Fehlerquellen bei Merogonieversuchen und die Entwicklungsfähigkeit merogonischer und partiell-merogonischer Seeigelbastarde. Roux' Arch. Entw.-mech., *44*:417–471.

CHUN, C. 1880 Die Ctenophoren des Golfes von Neapel; in Fauna und Flora des Golfes von Neapel. Monographie I. W. Engelmann, Leipzig.

COE, W. R. 1948 Variations in the expression of sexuality in the normally protandric gastropod *Crepidula plana* Say. J. Exp. Zool., *108*:155–169.

DEVILLERS, C. 1949 Explantations en milieu synthétique de blastodermes de Truite (*Salmo irideus*). Journ. Cyto-embryol. belgonéerland., *1949*: 67–73.

DuSHANE, G. P., AND HUTCHINSON, C. 1944 Differences in size and developmental rate between eastern and midwestern embryos of *Ambystoma maculatum*. Ecol., *25*:414–423.

GLUECKSOHN-SCHOENHEIMER, S. 1949 Causal analysis of mouse development by the study of mutational effects. Growth Suppl., *12*:163–176.

GOERTTLER, K. 1950 Entwicklungsgeschichte des Menschen. Ein Grundriss. Springer-Verlag, Berlin.

HADORN, E. 1934 Ueber die Entwicklungsleistungen bastardmerogonischer Gewebe von *Triton palmatus* (♀) × *Triton cristatus* ♂ im Ganzkeim und als Explantat in vitro. Roux' Arch. Entw.-mech., *131*:238–284.

——— 1937 Die Entwicklungsphysiologische Auswirkung der disharmonischen Kern-Plasmakombination beim Bastardmerogon *Triton palmatus* (♀) × *Triton cristatus* ♂. Roux' Arch. Entw.-mech., *136*:400–489.

HARRISON, R. G. 1903 Experimentelle Untersuchungen über die Entwicklung der Sinnesorgane der Seitenlinie bei den Amphibien. Arch. mikr. Anat., *63*:35–149.

——— 1907 Observations on the living developing nerve fiber. Anat. Rec., *1*:116–118.

——— 1914 The reaction of embryonic cells to solid structures. J. Exp. Zool., *17*:521–544.

——— 1935 Heteroplastic grafting in embryology. Harvey Lectures for 1933–1934, pp. 116–157.

HERBST, C. 1936 Untersuchungen zur Bestimmung des Geschlechtes. VI. Mitteilung. Neue Gedanken zur Geschlechtsbestimmung bei Tieren. Roux' Arch. Entw.-mech., *135*:178–201.

——— 1937 Untersuchungen zur Bestimmung des Geschlechts. VII. Mitteilung. Ueber die Bedeutung des SO_4-ions für die Weiterentwicklung und geschlechtliche Differenzierung der Bonellia-Larven und über den Einfluss des erhöhten Ca-Gehaltes im SO_4-armen Medium auf diese Prozesse. Roux' Arch. Entw.-mech., *136*:147–168.

HOLTFRETER, J. 1929 Ueber die Aufzucht isolierter Teile des Amphibienkeimes. I. Methode einer Gewebezüchtung in vivo. Roux' Arch. Entw.-mech., *117*:421–510.

——— 1944 Neural differentiation of ectoderm through exposure to saline solution. J. Exp. Zool., *95*:307–343.

——— 1945 Neuralization and epidermization of gastrula ectoderm. J. Exp. Zool., *98*:161–209.

HUTCHINSON, C., AND HEWITT, D. 1935 A study of larval growth in *Amblystoma punctatum* and *Amblystoma tigrinum*. J. Exp. Zool., *71*:465–481.

KUSCHE, W. 1929 Interplantation umschriebener Zellbezirke aus der Blastula und der Gastrula von Amphibien. I. Versuche an Urodelen. Roux' Arch. Entw.-mech., *120:*192–271.

LUTHER, W. 1936 Potenzprüfungen an isolierten Teilstücken der Forellenkeimscheibe. Roux' Arch. Entw.-mech., *135:*359–383.

MARSH, G., AND BEAMS, H. W. 1946 In vitro control of growing chick nerve fibers by applied electric currents. J. Cell. Comp. Physiol., *27:*139–157.

MCCLENDON, J. F. 1910 The development of isolated blastomeres of the frog's egg. Am. J. Anat., *10:*425–430.

NEEDHAM, J. 1942 Biochemistry and Morphogenesis. Cambridge University Press, Cambridge, England.

PASTEELS, J. 1937 Etudes sur la gastrulation des vertébrés méroblastiques. III. Oiseaux. IV. Conclusions générales. Arch. de Biol., *48:*381–488.

POULSON, D. F. 1940 The effects of certain X-chromosome deficiencies on the embryonic development of *Drosophila melanogaster.* J. Exp. Zool., *83:*271–325.

——— 1945 Chromosomal control of embryogenesis in Drosophila. Am. Nat., *79:*340–363.

ROUX, W. 1885 "Einleitung" zu den "Beiträgen zur Entwickelungsmechanik des Embryo." Ges. Abh., *2:*1–23.

——— 1888 Beiträge zur Entwickelungsmechanik des Embryo. V. Ueber die künstliche Hervorbringung "halber" Embryonen durch Zerstörung einer der beiden ersten Furchungszellen, sowie über die Nachentwicklung (Postgeneration) der fehlenden Körperhälfte. Ges. Abh., *2:*419–521.

——— 1889 Die Entwicklungsmechanik der Organismen, eine anatomische Wissenschaft der Zukunft. Ges. Abh., *2:*24–54.

——— *et al.* 1912 Terminologie der Entwicklungsmechanik der Tiere und Pflanzen. Wilhelm Engelmann, Leipzig.

SPEMANN, H. 1938 Embryonic Development and Induction. Yale University Press, New Haven, Connecticut.

SPRATT, N. T. 1946 Formation of the primitive streak in the explanted chick blastoderm marked with carbon particles. J. Exp. Zool., *103:*259–304.

TENNENT, D. H. 1910 The dominance of maternal or of paternal characters in echinoderm hybrids. Roux' Arch. Entw.-mech., *29:*1–14.

——— 1925 Investigations on specificity of fertilization. Carnegie Inst. Wash. Yrbk., *24:*240–242.

TWITTY, V. C., AND SCHWIND, J. L. 1931 The growth of eyes and limbs transplanted heteroplastically between two species of Amblystoma. J. Exp. Zool., *59:*61–86.

VOGT, W. 1925 Gestaltungsanalyse am Amphibienkeim mit örtlicher Vitalfärbung. Vorwort über Wege und Ziele. I. Methodik und Wirkungsweise der örtlichen Vitalfärbung mit Agar als Farbträger. Roux' Arch. Entw.-mech., *106:*542–610.

WEISS, P. 1949 Differential growth; in The Chemistry and Physiology of Growth, edited by A. K. Parpart, pp. 135–186. Princeton University Press, Princeton, New Jersey.

—— 1950 The deplantation of fragments of nervous system in amphibians. I. Central reorganization and the formation of nerves. J. Exp. Zool., *113:*397–461.

WOODGER, J. H. 1948 Observations on the present state of embryology; in Growth in Relation to Differentiation and Morphogenesis, Symposia of the Society for Experimental Biology, No. 2, pp. 351–365. Academic Press, New York.

Embryology and Evolution:
Nineteenth Century Hopes
and Twentieth Century Realities *

INTRODUCTION

EVOLUTION and development have had much to do with each other for over two centuries: and the history of the very words by which we name them attests to their long interinvolvement. The word *evolution:* — EVOLUTIO — was in general use from the middle of the 18th century to describe one aspect of what we consider development, namely, what we now call preformation. As to the other side of the coin, during the 19th century, before what we call evolution had received its habitual appellation, it was called the Development Hypothesis in English; and as Ernst Mayr (1959) has recently reminded us, *Entwicklungsgeschichte* was used in German to describe both the development of the individual and that of the race.[1]

* This article was written at Osborn Zoological Laboratory, Yale University, during the tenure of a National Science Foundation Senior Postdoctoral Fellowship, and is based on a lecture given as part of a symposium on evolution and embryology sponsored by the Division of Developmental Biology, American Society of Zoologists, at the autumn 1959 meeting of the American Institute of Biological Sciences. Reprinted from *Quarterly Review of Biology*, Vol. XXXIV, 1959, pp. 271–277.

[1] Herbert Spencer is usually given credit for introducing the word *Evolution* in its present sense, and it is often emphasized that Darwin himself did not use it in the *Origin of Species*. Actually, the last word in the *Origin of Species* is "evolved," used in exactly our present sense.

The 19th century in fact saw *Geschichte* — history — come into its own: and all these concepts, which involve the assumption of *change,* had some profound common philosophical basis (Temkin, 1950). We have the feeling now that change is accelerating in human affairs; perhaps the rush made itself felt already during the last century.

It is in a way a tribute to the power of Haeckel's ideas that the words "evolution and embryology," chained together in a phrase, still, after the middle of the 20th century, bring the recapitulation theory to mind first of all. I shall not, however, concentrate on the recapitulation doctrine alone. Too much has already been said about it. Kohlbrugge (1911), as I have recently reminded a different group of readers (Oppenheimer, 1959), in 1911 published a list of 72 authors — and at that the list is incomplete — who between the years 1797 and 1866 expressed concepts akin to Haeckel's recapitulation doctrine, and any one who wishes a catalogue of these ideas can turn to Kohlbrugge's essay. For a modern discussion of the recapitulation doctrine, the third edition of *Embryos and Ancestors* by De Beer (1958) is now available. This author brings together evidence from many sides to demonstrate that Garstang's (1922) phrase *ontogeny causes phylogeny* is a much more appropriate slogan than Haeckel's *phylogeny causes ontogeny.* De Beer's study does not, however, take full cognizance of the contributions of modern developmental genetics towards the support or the modification of the old recapitulation theory, and it is to be hoped that soon a new synthesis which goes beyond De Beer's will incorporate this relevant new material.

Being unwilling myself to focus my remarks on the recapitulation doctrine *per se,* I wish to try to evaluate in another way the influence of the Darwinian evolutionary concepts on embryological thinking. A scientist can proceed to his work only if he has in his mind certain assumptions, which, if he is a thoughtful scientist, he recognizes as assumptions, not as axioms nor demonstrated principles. What I propose to attempt is an examination of the assumptions made by the embryologist, or other investigator of what we call development, before the publication of the *Origin of Species,* and after, in the hope that a comparison will reveal how deeply or how superficially the concept of evolution has affected the body of working assumptions of the embryologist, and thus shed light on the question raised in my title, namely, whether the hopes of the 19th century investigators for a synthesis on the common ground shared by evolution and embryology have been fulfilled by the work of nearly a century. "Development," wrote Haeckel, "is now the magic word by means of which we shall solve the riddles by which we are surrounded" (quoted from Rádl, 1930, pp. 126–127). Has his prophecy been fulfilled? And if so, how much of the credit for its fulfillment belongs to Haeckel?

ASSUMPTIONS OF THE EMBRYOLOGIST

Let us start out by trying to become clear as to what we mean by assumptions. Assumptions are not hypotheses that the investigator tries to test in his laboratory. In science, one man's findings do not become an assumption for the next man, they are merely something whose validity may be tested. Assumptions are something taken so much for granted that their validity is rarely questioned, and it does not often occur to the scientist to verify them. Perhaps the mark of the really great scientist is that he takes less for granted than others and goes back beyond the assumptions for his starting point. Von Baer's so-called Laws, which embryologists still live by today, were not assumptions for him, they were derived from his evidence; his assumptions lay deeper, actually, nurtured by the fantasies of nature philosophy.[2]

2 The validity of von Baer's laws, as conceived by himself, has recently been denied by an important philosopher of biology (Lovejoy, 1959) but the laboratory embryologist must disagree with the latter.

But that is too far back in the 19th century. Here, there are two kinds of assumptions with which we must concern ourselves, assumptions about embryology itself, as well as those about embryos, and the nature of the first set affects that of the other group.

Assumptions about Embryology as a Science

First, for embryology. We assume, I believe, that embryology is both interesting and important. But it was hardly always so. Haeckel himself had something to say about this. "The embryology of organisms occupies in the present," he wrote in 1875, "a position very different from that in the first half of our century. This science, although the youngest of its sister sciences, has in a very short time soared to a height which is not merely prominent but actually dominating. Still a rather isolated specialty of a few naturalists a few decades ago, embryology has with unprecedented progress become a universal science, and has stimulated an intellectual movement that has sent forth its waves to the farthest reaches of human knowledge" (translated from Haeckel, 1875, p. 1).

It can easily be documented that Haeckel was correct in that embryology developed its importance during the middle of the 19th century. It is also probably safe to say that Haeckel's emphasis on embryology in relation to evolution was an important factor in influencing this development. What is not so certain is that the recapitulation doctrine itself played the dominating role in this influence. Many investigators, and developmentally oriented ones at that, attest to the stimulus they received from Haeckel's writings, Spemann and Goldschmidt among them. Goldschmidt, for instance, wrote of his first exposure to the ideas of Haeckel: "I found Haeckel's history of creation one day and read it with burning eyes and soul. It seemed that all problems of heaven and earth were solved simply and convincingly; there was an answer to every question which troubled the young mind. Evolution was the key to everything and could replace all the beliefs and creeds which one was discarding" (Goldschmidt, 1956, p. 35). In other words, what inflamed Goldschmidt was Haeckel's whole synthesis of everything from inorganic matter to organism, from carbon to the soul of man — his concept of the unity of nature, his whole *Weltanschauung,* not the mere fragment of it which he termed the biogenetic law.

Spemann's statement supports the same interpretation. He wrote of reading *Die Seele des Kindes,* by Wilhelm Preyer, and continued: "That came from the realm of Ernst Haeckel, who led into biology so many young men of my generation and of the previous one. There too I met for the first time the concept of biology as an all-embracing science of life, with teachings stirring it to its last depths" (Spemann, 1943, p. 116).

Goldschmidt's comment, in particular, brings us to our next assumption about embryology, as fundamental as the first. This is that developmental phenomena are investigable. They are to be analyzed, at least in some degree, not only admired. This too, like our first assumption, was not commonly held by all before the time of Darwin.

For instance, see what the *Encyclopedia Britannica* said of generation in its 1842 (7th edition) article on Physiology:

"The immediate agency by which one living being is rendered capable of giving rise to another similar to itself is enveloped in the most profound and most hopeless obscurity. No means within the compass of our understanding, no combination of the powers of matter which we can possibly conceive, no process of which the utmost stretch of human imagination can give us the most remote idea, has ever made the least approach towards the solution of this most inexplicable of all enigmas, the production, nay, the apparent creation, of a living plant or animal by powers inherent in the organization of a similar being. We must content ourselves, in studying this inscrutable mystery, to observe and generalize the phenomena, in silent astonishment at the marvelous manifestation of design and of power exhibited in this department of the wonderful works of the Almighty" (anonymous article "Generation," *Encycl. Brit.*, 1842, 7th ed., vol., 17, p. 684).

To what degree was it the influence of Haeckel that led to the alternative assumption, that the problems of development are soluble? Goldschmidt has already answered the question for us. Haeckel believed that the riddles of the universe were in fact solved during the 19th century, and his so-called explanations were so simple, so dogmatic that he easily swept his readers into the conviction that all was explained or explicable. This new conviction that development was capable of being understood — on whatever basis — may have been more important for the progress of embryology than that the basis on which Haeckel explained it was recapitulation. To this degree, the sequel to evolution was responsible for a new outlook in developmental science.

But in how far was evolution alone responsible for it? Allen Thomson, who wrote the article on Generation in Todd's *Cyclopedia of Anatomy and Physiology* (1836–39), answers for us: "It is a common remark that generation is at once the most obscure and the most wonderful of the processes occurring in organized bodies. Hence, perhaps, it has happened that, while there are few subjects of physiological inquiry upon which so many authors have written, there is none upon which so many have freely indulged their fancies in framing unwarranted hypotheses and absurd speculations. This is an error which belongs to the early stage of investigation in most branches of natural knowledge, and which in the instance before us may be traced very directly to the comparative want of correct information which for a long time prevailed regarding the phenomena of the generative processes. . . . When extended observation shall have rendered more familiar to the physiologist the different steps of the intricate processes by which an egg is formed, and the young animal is developed from it, although he may not cease to admire the changes in which these processes consist, the feeling of wonder will be in a great measure lost to him. . . . The man of science regards the ultimate causes of all vital processes as equally inexplicable, and, aware of the bounds set to his knowledge of life, limits his inquiries concerning its various processes to the investigation of their phenomena" (Thomson, 1836–39, p. 426).

In other words, many years before the publication of the *Origin of Species* and of Haeckel's commentaries on it, it was clear that sober laboratory scientists, independent of the great generalizers, were initiating laboratory investigations that might soon have sufficed to send tottering the assumption that developmental phenomena are beyond investigation.

One more assumption we make about embryology as a science: I believe that even now we many of us find it difficult not to assume that embryology is a morphological science. Haeckel himself made this same reproach to his predecessors and contemporaries, and coined a number of words for the physiological aspects of development that he hoped would be investigated. But even in our own days, when chemical embryology has won its ascendency over anatomical study, the goal of the chemical and biochemical investigation is often expressed as the explanation of structure. That is, the structure seems to be the main thing, to be accounted for by something else.

Of course form is the most essential attribute of the developing organism. But it is a dynamic form, in which the molecules and molecular systems constituting and developing structure are as important *as* the structure, and perhaps to be explained *by* structure as much as explanatory *of* it. Is not this the essence of that elusive property, embryonic organization?

Our inabilities to free ourselves from some of our unconscious bondage to over-static concepts of morphological structure we inherit from the early days of the welding of embryology and evolution. Haeckel was a morphologist, he was a structural biologist, and we still suffer from the fact that though he talked about physiogeny he drew his evidence from structural form. Haeckel would not admit that what His was thinking was physiology, by the way. He said of it that explaining ontogeny in its own terms was like Munchhausen pulling himself out of the swamp by his own pigtail (Haeckel, 1875, p. 20). Thus the facts that Haeckel drew too sharp a distinction between form and function instead of viewing them as part and parcel of one another, and that he therefore led his followers to study recapitulation through a formal study of structure, may have been as important in dictating the assumptions of modern embryology as that he returned to a specific theory of recapitulation that had already been expressed and taken issue with before his time.

Form was important for the nature philosophers who preceded Haeckel; it was Goethe, after all, who coined the word morphology (Goethe, 1807, p. 115). But if my interpretation is correct, it was Haeckel who made static structure rather than dynamic form the stock-in-trade of the developmental biologist, and this may be construed as having been a great disservice to developmental biology.

Assumptions about Embryos

Now let us turn to some assumptions that are less related to how we study, more to what we think; less of *-ology*, more of *-ogeny*.

The first thing we assume about embryogeny is that development occurs, that is, that the embryo is generated by the egg. "The life of an animal may be said to start from the egg which has just been fertilized," is the way De Beer (1955, p. 1) puts it. Agassiz and Gould (1848, p. 103) said that it is an "old adage" of zoology that all animals are produced by eggs. In fact, we do more than assume it, we consider it a demonstrated principle that eggs make multicellular organisms, that organisms are not being spontaneously generated on our earth at this time. This was not yet a general assumption at the time that the *Origin of Species* was published. In 1859, Pasteur had not yet completed his experiments. It should require no emphasis here that Pasteur's thought was far from being influenced by concepts of natural selection, recapitulation, or even evolution more generally.

Actually it is only a very recent flare of interest in evolution which is restoring respectability to concern with spontaneous generation, and by many spontaneous generation is considered as compatible with, even necessarily related to, concepts of evolution and development. What is responsible for this new enthusiasm? Partly our recognition of continuity between inorganic and organic, which is very old, far older than formal evolutionary doctrine. Since we accept that the organic evolved from the inorganic (and Oparin, 1957, gives due credit to Haeckel for his naive notions on this subject), evolution is somehow involved. But is this the kind of evolution which is directly related to recapitulation? Some of the evidence may be interpreted *in terms of* recapitulation, but that is something different. It seems to me most unlikely that the recapitulation doctrine carried to its ultimate extreme could alone have led to the modern attempts to explain the origin of life. The lines of thought that led to the development of modern biochemistry originated from points far distant from those with which we are concerned.

We also assume, having assumed development, that development is epigenetic, and since the days of von Baer we are convinced that something new comes from something old. Shortly after the Darwinian period an assumption of causality crept into our concepts of epigenesis (though to be sure it had been creeping in and out of them for centuries). His (1874) stated specifically that one step in development is the cause of the next, or at least its necessary condition. He was laughed down by Haeckel who marshalled all the evidence from recapitulation to ridicule him. The formulation of our principal working assumption of today was thus not only not favorably influenced by, but was most vigorously opposed by, the proponents of evolutionary embryology.

Now again, we are not so sure that the concept of epigenesis is as simple as it once seemed; we must worry about molecular precursors in differentiation; about whether or not enzymes are induced, and if so, how; about DNA as a hereditary determiner. The real problem of causality, in so far as the 20th century still admits the concept of causality, is related to the materials with which genetics deals. But again, the lines that led to the development of genetic concepts came from Mendel, not Darwin, and were not in their origins influenced by concepts of evolution except in the remotest sense. Mendel was not concerned with phylogeny, nor even with embryos.

I suspect that many will question my interpretations of what our assumptions are in embryology, in fact I question some of them myself, they are still very tentative. But I believe it is safe to say that if anything is assumed by developmental biologists, it is that the cell is not only the structural and functional unit of the organism, but its developmental unit as well. The aggregationists and disaggregationists are I believe not questioning whether or not the cell has a role in development, they are attempting to elucidate what its role is. Now, the cell theory was being developed at the same time that Darwin was working out the arguments later to be incorporated in the *Origin of Species;* the development of the concept of the cell as a unit of the organism was on the whole simultaneous with the development of the concept of natural selection. But these concepts developed quite independently of one another at the outset. Before the second half of the 19th century, developmental biologists not only did not consider the cell the unit of development, they were not thinking in terms of units at all. The assumption of units was a 19th century addition to the concept of development; Wolff's and von Baer's layers were agents of development without having the unitary value that was later to be ascribed to the cell.

Both the cell theory and the evolution theory were synthesizing and unifying doctrines for biology, and to this degree they were useful to each other. But which most gave support and which most received it has, I believe, never been fully evaluated. Darwin never mentioned cells in the *Origin of Species* (though Haeckel was to make the most of them). And Virchow, who put the important finishing touches on cell theory, was critical of some aspects of Darwinian theory, and became a famous anti-Haeckelian, though not, to be sure, on developmental grounds alone.

Now, for a final word about our developing assumption that the molecule is the developmental agent within the cell, which begins to dominate the minds of contemporary developmental biologists. We look to the molecule, many of us, to account for the structure of the cell. Surely this concept has received its latest stimulus for growth from biochemistry, not from evolution theory, and the same remarks are relevant here as were made above concerning the related assumptions on spontaneous generation and the origin of life. General concepts that the materials of which living and nonliving entities are composed obey similar laws reach far back into antiquity and have been expressed off and on for millennia. It was hardly Haeckel's commentary on them that brought about the development of modern biochemistry; the French medical physiologists who were Haeckel's contemporaries and others who were similarly unconcerned with evolution may have had much more to do with it.

CONCLUSIONS

How, then, do we answer our question as to whether development has solved the riddles by which we are surrounded, with evolution as the clue? This was the 19th century hope, what is the 20th century reality? The outstanding contribution of 20th century embryology remains, to my mind, the analysis,

216

incomplete though it still is, of the relationships between embryonic parts at a cellular or supracellular level. It is something new that developmental biology no longer confines
itself to the materials which the 19th century thought proper
to embryology, and is expanding its domain to include considerations of pathological, immunological, serological, biochemical — the biophysical ones have unfortunately been neglected — cytological, and genetic phenomena, as well as those
which we might call physiological in our sense, not Haeckel's.
In drawing together data collected by these various techniques
of investigation, it is becoming central in our core of biological
thinking, of which Haeckel would have approved. But in so
changing, it has raised new problems rather than solving the
old ones.

Consider, for instance, the problem of growth and differentiation of proteins. If organisms are to grow and differentiate,
proteins must grow and differentiate. Their development has
been related to the properties of ribonucleic acids. The properties of ribonucleic acids have been postulated as related to
the properties of deoxyribonucleic acids. Establishment of the
structure, function, and organization of deoxyribonucleic
acids thus becomes a developmental problem. The properties
of DNA have their developmental effects, as do the properties
of RNA, and those of proteins, and of formed cell inclusions,
small and large, nuclear and cytoplasmic, as do indeed the
properties of the cell itself. By calling attention to the fact
that these various entities participate in development, the
study of development should theoretically elucidate them.
Practically, it is barely beginning to do so.

Those who are more directly occupied than I with molecules may disagree, but I believe that their great day as developmental biologists is ahead of them, not yet in the present
or past. The nucleic acids so important to present-day concepts are so far better understood on a genetic than on a
strictly developmental basis, unless all of the phenomena of

genetics are to be comprehended in developmental biology, and to make this exaggerated claim might be as foolhardy as it was to omit developmental phenomena from the study of genetics, as was so long the practice.

To this extent, development is not the magic word that either Haeckel considered it or that some modern biologists might wish it to be. At the risk of being as rash as Haeckel, I should like to say, however, that it has the capacity and promise still of becoming it. And when some great developmental biologist rises above our present concern with the concomitants of development, and learns to frame an answerable question as to the manner in which the developing organism as a whole progressively in time *organizes* its constituent developmental and concomitant processes, there will prove to have been some magic in having emphasized development after all.

To return to the question of Haeckel's responsibility for our emphasis on development: we admit that his enthusiasm for embryology was a factor in developing the popularity of the subject as a discipline. But I for one believe that the important contribution of Haeckel in this respect was primarily his desire and pursuit of the whole, not his emphasis on recapitulation. And I personally believe that many of our most important working assumptions of today developed independently of classical evolution doctrine, in so far as anything could be independent of it after its promulgation. [Embryologists cannot forget that Roux's first major contribution (Roux, 1881) was based on an analogy between the interaction of embryonic parts and the struggle for existence of organisms in nature.]

I have pointed out elsewhere (Oppenheimer, 1956) the difficulties of agreeing upon a body of principles of embryology in the present state of our science. Perhaps developmental biologists are working too hard at attempting to express principles. When the principles are valid, they speak for themselves: the principle of progressive differentiation, for instance, has asserted itself so convincingly it requires no developmental biologist nor historian to speak for it. Perhaps we should leave the striving for formulation of principles momentarily aside, and instead examine our assumptions more often, not only for the light they may shed on or have shed on them by history, but for the sake of the scientist at work, who can interpret his findings with maximum validity only when he knows how much of his thinking about them is based on hope that his assumptions are justified, and how much on what, in his own temporal frame of reference, seems to be reality.

LIST OF LITERATURE

AGASSIZ, L., AND A. A. GOULD. 1848. *Principles of Zoology.* 216 pp. Gould, Kendall, & Lincoln, Boston.

ANONYMOUS. 1842. Physiology. *Encycl. Brit.* (7th ed.), 17: 577–733.

DE BEER, G. 1958. *Embryos and Ancestors* (3rd ed.). 197 pp. Clarendon Press, Oxford.

GARSTANG, W. 1922. The theory of recapitulation. A critical restatement of the biogenetic law. *J. Linn. Soc. Lond. (Zool.),* 35: 81–101.

GOETHE, J. W. VON. 1807. Bildung und Umbildung organischen Naturen. In *Goethes Morphologische Schriften* (W. Troll, ed.), pp. 111–123. Eugen Diederichsverlag, Jena [1932].

GOLDSCHMIDT, R. B. 1956. *Portraits from Memory. Recollections of a Zoologist.* 181 pp. University of Washington Press, Seattle.

HAECKEL, E. H. 1875. *Ziele und Wege der heutigen Entwickelungsgeschichte.* 99 pp. Hermann Dufft, Jena.

HIS, W. 1874. *Unsere Körperform und das physiologische Problem ihrer Entstehung.* 224 pp. F. C. W. Vogel, Leipzig.

KOHLBRUGGE, J. H. F. 1911. Das biogenetische Grundgesetz. Eine historische Studie. *Zool. Anz.,* 38: 447–453.

LOVEJOY, A. O. 1959. Recent criticism of the Darwinian theory of recapitulation: its grounds and its initiator. In *Forerunners of Darwin, 1745–1859* (B. Glass, O. Temkin and W. L. Straus, Jr., eds.), pp. 438–458. Johns Hopkins Press, Baltimore.

MAYR, E. 1959. Agassiz, Darwin, and evolution. *Harvard Libr. Bull.,* 13: 165–194.

OPARIN, A. I.   1957.   *The Origin of Life on the Earth* (3rd ed.). 495 pp. Academic Press, New York.

OPPENHEIMER, J. M.   1956.   Sorts and conditions of development. A review of *Vorlesungen über Entwicklungsphysiologie,* by A. Kühn. *Quart. Rev. Biol.,* 31: 31–34.

——.   1959.   An embryological enigma in the *Origin of Species.* In *Forerunners of Darwin, 1745–1859* (B. Glass, O. Temkin and W. L. Straus, Jr., eds.), pp. 292–322. Johns Hopkins Press, Baltimore. Reprinted in this volume, pp. 221–255.

RÁDL, E.   1930.   *The History of Biological Theories.* 408 pp. Oxford University Press, London.

ROUX, W.   1881.   *Der Kampf der Theile im Organismus.* 244 pp. Wilhelm Engelmann, Leipzig.

SPEMANN, H.   1943.   *Forschung und Leben* (F. W. Spemann, ed.). 344 pp. J. Engelhorns Nachf. Adolf Spemann, Stuttgart.

TEMKIN, O.   1950.   German concepts of ontogeny and history around 1800. *Bull. Hist. Med.,* 24:227–246.

THOMSON, A.   1836–39.   Generation. In *The Cyclopaedia of Anatomy and Physiology* (R. B. Todd, ed.), II, pp. 424–480. Longman, Brown, Green, Longmans, & Roberts, London.

An Embryological Enigma
in the *Origin of Species** *

I

CHARLES DARWIN was far from an embryologist. He devoted only one part of one short chapter of the *Origin of Species* to embryological considerations. Yet he spoke in it of the leading facts in embryology as "second in importance to none in natural history,"[1] and although his embryological remarks were brief, they were expressed in a tone that indicates that they came straight from his heart.

"Hardly any point gave me so much satisfaction when I was at work on the 'Origin,' " he wrote in his "Autobiography," "as the explanation of the wide difference in many classes between the embryo and the adult animal, and of the close resemblance of the embryos within the same class. No notice of this point was taken, as far as I remember, in the early reviews of the 'Origin,' and I recollect expressing my surprise on this head in a letter to Asa Gray."[2] Darwin's memory on this occasion, in contrast to some others, was correct: "Embryology

---

* Reprinted from *Forerunners of Darwin 1745–1859*, edited by Bentley Glass, Owsei Temkin, and William L. Straus, Jr., The Johns Hopkins Press, Baltimore, Md., 1959, pp. 292–322.

[1] Charles Darwin, *On the Origin of Species by Means of Natural Selection*, . . . A Reprint of the First Edition, . . . Watts & Co., London, 1950, p. 382. The first edition was originally published by John Murray, London, 1859.

[2] Darwin, "Autobiography," in *The Life and Letters of Charles Darwin, including an Autobiographical Chapter*, ed. by Francis Darwin, D. Appleton and Company, New York, 1888, I, 72.

is to me," ran his letter of September 10 [1860] to Gray, "by far the strongest single class of facts in favour of change of forms, and not one, I think, of my reviewers has alluded to this."[3] He had made a similar comment the previous year to J. D. Hooker: "Embryology is my pet bit in my book, and, confound my friends, not one has noticed this to me";[4] and in 1857, two years before he had begun the final construction of the book, he wrote to Gray that "embryology leads me to an enormous and frightful range."[5]

Although it was only after the publication of the *Origin of Species,* and not before, that embryology's claim to relationship with evolution reached full voice, nonetheless the fact remains that there existed in pre-Darwinian writings many statements of embryological concepts akin to those expressed by Darwin. Embryology itself, furthermore, was undergoing in the years shortly prior to the completion of the *Origin of Species* the most drastic transformation ever to occur in its own history, as it developed away from *Naturphilosophie* in the direction of what is often called modern epigenetic theory. It should therefore prove rewarding to investigate what influence his acquaintance with the old or the new embryology might have exerted on the genesis of Darwin's ideas.

The reader of this essay will be spared detailed enumeration of all the eighteenth and early nineteenth century statements of the so-called laws, and their variations, relating embryos to ancestors. These are discussed in a number of accessible works; Kohlbrugge,[6] in particular, has presented a list of seventy-two authors, beginning with Goethe and Autenrieth in 1797 and concluding with Haeckel in 1866, who anticipated or expressed concepts of parallelism or of recapitulation, and it is superfluous either to abbreviate or to amplify his catalog here.

3 Darwin, *Life and Letters,* II, 131.
4 Darwin, *Life and Letters,* II, 39.
5 Darwin, *Life and Letters,* I, 478.
6 J. H. F. Kohlbrugge, "Das biogenetische Grundgesetz. Eine historische Studie," *Zoologischer Anzeiger,* XXXVIII (1911), 447-453.

We may leave it also to others to attempt to establish priorities for these ideas. Such speculations are idle, and since it is hardly either feasible or desirable to examine here the thought of more than six dozen of Darwin's embryologically-minded precursors, we might instead best proceed by searching into the works of the most distinguished and influential of the early nineteenth century embryologists, Karl Ernst von Baer, for facts and concepts in which Darwin might have been interested.

It is appropriate for a number of reasons to center the discussion on von Baer. His great embryological treatise[7] was published two or three decades before the *Origin of Species,* and Darwin might be expected to have known it. It was a climactic study, the culmination of all embryology that had gone before and the point of departure of all that was to follow; this was the book which transformed the embryology of *Naturphilosophie* to that of the laboratory of today. And von Baer's mind was of equal intellectual power with Darwin's, a judgment in which even Huxley, one of Darwin's most ardent admirers, concurred. "Von Bär was another man of the same stamp"[8] as Darwin, wrote Huxley, shortly after Darwin's death.

Von Baer himself, although he expressed himself as strongly opposed to Darwin in later years,[9] knew that he was somehow

7 Karl Ernst von Baer, *Über Entwickelungsgeschichte der Thiere. Beobachtung und Reflexion,* Gebrüder Bornträger, Königsberg, I. Theil, 1828; II. Theil, 1837. The second part was incomplete at publication, and its conclusion was published posthumously: II. Theil, Schlussheft, ed. by L. Stieda, Wilh. Koch, Königsberg, 1888.

8 Leonard Huxley, *Life and Letters of Thomas Henry Huxley,* D. Appleton and Company, New York, 1901, II, 42.

9 "Über Darwins Lehre," in Karl Ernst von Baer, *Reden gehalten in wissenschaftlichen Versammlungen und kleinere Aufsätze vermischten Inhalts.* Zweiter Theil. Studien aus dem Gebiete der Naturwissenschaften. H. Schmitzdorf (Karl Röttger), St. Petersburg, 1876, pp. 235-480. A much shorter version had been published in 1873: "Zum Streit über den Darwinismus," *Augsburger allgemeine Zeitung,* No. 130, pp. 1986-88. For an excellent critique of von Baer's views on evolution see S. J. Holmes, "K. E. von Baer's Perplexities over Evolution," *Isis,* XXXVII (1947), 7-14. Holmes also discusses Darwin's knowledge and interpretations

involved as one of his precursors. Now, von Baer had not only a uniquely great mind, but also a uniquely great personality; and like many another uniquely great personality, von Baer's was extraordinarily complicated. More of this on another occasion; the fact is mentioned here as an introduction to the statement that at different times he painted his earlier thoughts in different lights. "Know thyself," he began his first lecture on anthropology, ". . . I know of no inquiry which is worthier of free and thinking man than the exploration of himself,"[10] yet he was himself highly inconsistent in his various portrayals of the development of his thinking, and this is plainly evident in what he said about his relationships to Darwinian evolution.

He wrote to Huxley in the year 1860 about the similarity of some of his own ideas to those of Darwin, and in his letter he specified particularly that only in the area of geographical distribution did his thought overlap that of Darwin. Huxley reported this to Darwin in a letter which merits full quotation:

August 6th, 1860

My dear Darwin, — I have to announce a new and great ally for you. . . .

Von Bär writes to me thus: — "Et outre cela, je trouve que vous écrivez des rédactions. Vous avez écrit sur l'ouvrage de M. Darwin une critique dont je n'ai trouvé que des débris dans un journal allemand. J'ai oublié le nom terrible du journal anglais dans lequel se trouve votre récension. En tout cas aussi je ne peux pas trouver le journal ici. Comme je m'intéresse beaucoup pour les idées de M. Darwin, sur lesquelles j'ai parlé publiquement et sur lesquelles je ferai peut-être imprimer quelque chose — vous m'obligeriez infiniment si vous pourriez me faire parvenir ce que vous avez écrit sur ces idées.

"J'ai énoncé les mêmes idées sur la transformation des types ou origine d'espèces que M. Darwin. Mais c'est seulement sur la géogra-

---

of embryology in "Recapitulation and its supposed causes," *Quart. Rev. Biol.*, XIX (1944), 319-331.

10 "Erkenne Dich selbst! . . . In der That weiss ich keine Untersuchung, welche des freien und denkenden Menschen würdiger wäre, als die Erforschung seiner selbst." Cited from Ludwig Stieda, *Karl Ernst von Baer, Eine biographische Skizze*, 2nd ed., Friedrich Vieweg und Sohn, Braunschweig, 1886, p. 202.

phie zoologique que je m'appuie. Vous trouverez, dans le dernier chapitre du traité 'Ueber Papuas und Alfuren,' que j'en parle très décidément sans savoir que M. Darwin s'occupait de cet objet."

The treatise to which von Bär refers he gave me when over here, but I have not been able to lay hands on it since this letter reached me two days ago. When I find it I will let you know what there is in it.[11]

The "something" which von Baer wrote to Huxley of having in mind to put into print about Darwin certainly was to include the long essay "Über Darwins Lehre" published in 1876. In this he confessed his belief that he had "supplied some material for [the] foundation [of Darwin's doctrine], even though time and Darwin himself have erected on the fundament a structure to which I feel myself alien,"[12] and acknowledged that others of his ideas besides those concerned with geographical distribution anticipated those of Darwin. Before proceeding to his analysis of the doctrine, he took up his "own small scientific efforts, to explain in what relationship they stand to the transmutation doctrine,"[13] first, his embryo-

11 Darwin, *Life and Letters*, II, 122-123. Von Baer's French letter to Huxley might be translated as follows: "And besides, I find that you are still writing reviews. You have written on Mr. Darwin's work a criticism of which I have found only fragments in a German journal. I have forgotten the terrible name of the English journal in which your review appeared. Also in any case I cannot find the journal here. As I am much interested in the ideas of Mr. Darwin, on which I have spoken publicly and on which I shall perhaps have something put into print, you would oblige me infinitely if you would be able to have forwarded to me what you have written about these ideas. I have expressed the same ideas on the transformation of types or origin of species as Mr. Darwin. But it is only on zoological geography that I rely. You will find, in the last chapter of the treatise "Über Papuas und Alfuren" that I speak of it very positively without knowing that Mr. Darwin was concerning himself with the subject." The treatise to which von Baer refers is "Über Papuas und Alfuren. Ein Commentar zu den beiden ersten Abschnitten der Abhandlung *Crania Selecta*, . . ." *Mém. de l'Acad. Imp. des Sci. de St. Pétersbourg*, VI. Sér. Sci. Nat., VIII (1859), 269-346.

12 "In der That glaube ich für die Begründung derselben einigen Stoff geliefert zu haben, wenn auch die Zeit und Darwin selbst auf das Fundament ein Gebäude aufgeführt haben, dem ich mich fremd fühle," von Baer, *Reden*, II, 240.

13 "Ich will jetzt ganz einfach meine eigenen kleinen wissenschaftlichen Bestrebungen durchgehen, um darzulegen, in welchem Verhältniss sie zu der Transmutationslehre stehen," von Baer, *Reden*, II, 241.

logical studies, next, an essay entitled "Das allgemeinste Gesetz der Natur in aller Entwickelung," and finally the treatise "Über Papuas und Alfuren" mentioned in the letter to Huxley.

The "Papuas und Alfuren" may be considered first here. In this anthropological study von Baer expressed, to put it in Darwin's words, "his conviction, chiefly grounded on the laws of geographical distribution, that forms now perfectly distinct have descended from a single parent-form."[14] This essay was read to the Academy at St. Petersburg, according to Stieda,[15] on April 1, 1859. A notation accompanying the title in the volume in which it appears stated that the paper was read on April 8th, and a note elsewhere in the volume specified that this was published in September 1859, the month that the corrected proofs of the *Origin of Species* were returned to their publisher. Von Baer himself emphasized how few readers the treatise enjoyed.[16] And in fact, when Darwin finally got around to adding a reference to it to the historical sketch in the fourth edition of the *Origin of Species* (1866), he referred not to the original article but to "Rudolph Wagner, '*Zoologisch-Anthropologische Untersuchungen*,' 1861."[17] Thus it exerted no influence on the pattern of Darwin's ideas on geographical distribution, which had already begun their development by the time Darwin left the *Beagle* in 1837.

It is equally clear that Darwin was without influence on von Baer with respect to theories of geographical distribution. It will be remembered that when Huxley wrote to Darwin about von Baer in the letter reproduced at the beginning of this essay, he stated that von Baer when in London had given him a copy of the article in question. Von Baer was in London

14 Darwin, *Origin of Species*, . . . 4th ed., John Murray, London, 1866, pp. xx-xxi. The statement was found also in the 5th and in the 6th editions.

15 Stieda, *Karl Ernst von Baer*, p. 163.

16 Von Baer, *Reden*, II, 247.

17 Darwin, *Origin of Species*, 4th ed., p. xx. The reference remained the same in the subsequent editions.

during the late summer or early autumn of 1859.[18] He devoted only one short final chapter of his autobiography to his life after 1834, and there he gave no details of the visit to London beyond making the remark that the journey, which included also visits to Copenhagen, Stockholm, and Paris, was devoted primarily to anthropological interests.[19] In the essay "Über Darwins Lehre" he was, however, more specific:

> I must expressly point out that this treatise was not written under the influence of Darwinian theory. I already had it with me when I visited England in 1859 and I gave it to Messrs. Owen and Huxley along with another communication on distinctive skulls of different peoples from the St. Petersburg collections. On this occasion I first learned that Charles Darwin was occupied with a complete demonstration of the transmutation doctrine. The book itself had however not yet appeared. I became acquainted with it after my return to St. Petersburg after the end of the year.[20]

According to his biographer Stieda,[21] von Baer delivered a lecture to the Geographical Society in St. Petersburg on October 10, 1859, and thus he must have returned there well before November 24th, the publication date of the *Origin of Species*.

In the second contribution in which, in the essay of 1876, von Baer considered himself a forerunner of Darwin, "Das allgemeinste Gesetz der Natur in aller Entwickelung,"[22] he

---

18 Stieda, *Karl Ernst von Baer*, p. 163.

19 Von Baer, *Nachrichten über Leben und Schriften des Herrn Geheimraths Dr. Karl Ernst von Baer*, mitgetheilt von ihm selbst, . . . 2d ed., Friedrich Vieweg und Sohn, Braunschweig, 1886, p. 436.

20 "Ausdrücklich muss ich bemerken, dass diese Abhandlung nicht unter dem Einflusse der Darwinschen Theorie geschrieben ist. Ich hatte sie schon mit, als ich im Jahre 1859 England besuchte, und theilte sie mit einer anderen Abhandlung über ausgezeichnete Schädel verschiedener Völker aus der St. Petersburger Sammlung den Herren Owen und Huxley mit. Bei dieser Gelegenheit erfuhr ich erst, dass Charles Darwin mit einer vollständigen Demonstration der Transmutationslehre beschäftigt sei. Das Buch selbst war aber noch nicht erschienen. Ich lernte es nach meiner Rückkehr nach St. Petersburg nach dem Schlusse des Jahres kennen," von Baer, *Reden*, II, 248.

21 Stieda, *Karl Ernst von Baer*, p. 164.

22 Von Baer, "Das allgemeinste Gesetz der Natur in aller Entwickelung," in

considered among other things what would now be called the phylogeny of various animal groups. He went so far in this communication, originally a lecture delivered in Königsberg in January 1833 or 1834, as to conceive the possibility — he did not state it as a fact — that what are now separate species of a single genus, or at most those of a closely related genus, might have resulted from the development and propagation of a common type. "Yet I especially point out," he wrote in the essay published in 1876, "that I found no probability that all animals have developed through transformation."[23]

In the words of the original essay itself:

> If under these circumstances it is easier to suppose that one form of antelope, or of sheep, or of goat, was created for the old world, and was transformed here into the now separate and permanent-appearing forms, than it is to suppose that many antelope, sheep and goats were created for the old world and none at all for the new world, where in contrast other genera resolve themselves into other species, — if it is even permitted to imagine that antelope, sheep and goats, that are related in so many ways, may have developed from a common original form, — yet I can on the other hand find no probability that all animals have developed from one another through transformation.[24]

It is unlikely in the extreme that Darwin knew this essay, which was originally published in 1834 in what must have

---

Reden, . . . Erster Theil, H. Schmitzdorf (Karl Röttger), St. Petersburg, 1864, pp. 35-74.

23 "Doch bemerke ich ausdrücklich, dass ich keine Wahrscheinlichkeit gefunden habe, die dafür spräche, dass alle Thiere sich durch Umbildung entwickelt hätten," von Baer, Reden, II, 245.

24 "Wenn es unter diesen Verhältnissen näher liegt, anzunehmen, dass Eine Form von Antilopen, vom Schaaf, von der Ziege für die alte Welt geschaffen wurde und hier in die jetzt getrennt und bleibend erscheinenden Formen umgewandelt wurde, als anzunehmen, viele Antilopen, Schaafe und Ziegen wurden für die alte Welt geschaffen und gar keine für die neue, wo dagegen andere Geschlechter sich in andere Arten auflösten, wenn es sogar erlaubt scheinen möchte, sich zu denken, dass Antilope, Schaaf und Ziege, die so vielfach verwandt sind, sich aus einer gemeinschaftlichen Urform entwickelt haben, so kann ich dagegen keine Wahrscheinlichkeit finden, dass alle Thiere sich durch Umbildung aus einander entwickelt hätten," von Baer, Reden, I, 55-56.

been to Darwin an obscure journal;[25] in any case, it was not referred to by Darwin either in his correspondence or note-books as so far published, or in the historical introduction which formed part of the last four editions of the *Origin of Species*.

The principal work, however, in which von Baer might have contributed to the basis of evolutionary doctrine was his monograph *Über Entwickelungsgeschichte der Thiere*. Von Baer wrote with extreme lucidity concerning the relevance of this embryological study to Darwinian theory:

I believe that it was through my investigations of the manner of development of animals and the general speculations connected with them — however much these have been obscured through recent work of this kind — that I furnished some material for the currently prevailing opinions concerning the development of organic forms. Only I cannot subscribe to all the applications of this material. Although in the work which bears the title "Ueber die Entwickelungsgeschichte der Thiere," I have demonstrated the transformations of animal organisms during individual development, I believe I did not speak in support of a descendence theory in the sense of the more recent one. On the contrary, in the Fifth Scholion of the first volume I have emphatically expressed myself as opposed to the then dominant theory of transmutation.[26]

---

25 *"Vorträge aus dem Gebiete der Naturwissenschaften und der Oekonomie*, gehalten vor einem Kreise gebildeter Zuhörer in der physikalisch-ökonomischen Gesellschaft zu Königsberg. Erstes Bändchen mit Vorträgen von . . . herausgegeben von dem Prof. K. E. v. Baer. Königsberg 1834, bei Unger." This reference is given by von Baer in the introduction to the essay as published in *Reden*, I, 37.

26 "Ich glaube allerdings durch meine Untersuchungen über die Entwickelungsweise der Thiere und die daran geknüpften allgemeinen Betrachtungen, so sehr sie auch durch die neuesten Arbeiten dieser Art verdunkelt sind, einigen Stoff zu den jetzt vorherrschenden Ansichten über die Ausbildung der organischen Formen geliefert zu haben. Allein ich kann nicht mit allen Verwendungen dieses Materials mich einverstanden erklären. In dem Werke, welches den Titel führt: "Ueber die Entwickelungschichte der Thiere," habe ich allerdings die Umwandlungen der thierischen Organismen in der Entwickelung der Individuen nachgewiesen, allein einer Descendenztheorie, in dem Sinne der Neueren, glaube ich nicht das Wort geredet zu haben. Vielmehr habe ich mich im fünften Scholion des ersten Bandes gegen eine damals herrschende Ansicht von Transmutation nachdrücklich ausgesprochen," von Baer, *Reden*, II, 241.

In fact the Fifth Scholion was an eloquent disputation against "the prevalent notion, that the embryo of higher animals passes through the permanent forms of the lower animals."[27] Only in a footnote to it did von Baer deign to speak explicitly of the allied concept, with which he disagreed, "that all forms are immediately developed out of one,"[28] and the whole argument served to refute on an embryological basis the theory that embryological sequences mirror the transformations of one animal type to another:

The embryo of the vertebrate animal is from the very first a vertebrate animal, and at no time agrees with an invertebrate animal. A permanent animal form, however, which exhibits the vertebrate type, and yet possesses so slight a histological and morphological differentiation as the embryos of the Vertebrata, is unknown. *Therefore, the embryos of the Vertebrata pass in the course of their development through no (known) permanent forms of animals whatsoever.*[29]

"My opposition to the view of recapitulation" [to call it by its later name], wrote von Baer in the 1876 essay, "received fairly general recognition. Johannes Müller, who in the first

27 "Die herrschende Vorstellung, dass der Embryo höherer Thiere die bleibenden Formen der niederen Thiere durchlaufe," von Baer, *Entwickelungsgeschichte,* I, 199. The English translation in my text is not by myself, but, for reasons to be apparent below, one made by T. H. Huxley, which is to be found in "Article VII. Fragments relating to Philosophical Zoology. Selected from the Works of K. E. von Baer," in *Scientific Memoirs, selected from the Transactions of Foreign Academies of Science, and from Foreign Journals. Natural History,* ed. by Arthur Henfrey and T. H. Huxley, Taylor and Francis, London, 1853, p. 186.

28 "Es war natürlich, ja nothwendig, dass man nun versuchte, die *einfachste* Form dieser Modificationen durchzuführen, die der unmittelbaren Entwickelung aller Formen aus einer," von Baer, *Entwickelungsgeschichte,* I, 201 fn. Translation in text by Huxley, *Scientific Memoirs,* ed. by Henfrey and Huxley, p. 189.

29 *"Der Embryo des Wirbelthiers ist schon anfangs ein Wirbelthier,* und hat zu keiner Zeit Uebereinstimmung mit einem wirbellosen Thiere. Eine bleibende Thierform aber, welche den Typus der Wirbelthiere hätte, und eine so geringe histologische und morphologische Sonderung, wie die Embryonen der Wirbelthiere, ist nicht bekannt. *Mithin durchlaufen die Embryonen der Wirbelthiere in ihrer Entwickelung gar keine (bekannten) bleibenden Thierformen,"* von Baer, *Entwickelungsgeschichte,* I, 220. Translation in text by Huxley, *Scientific Memoirs,* ed. by Henfrey and Huxley, p. 210. Huxley's italics, reproduced in the current text, conform to those of von Baer in the original work.

edition of his physiology had adopted the doctrine of Meckel and Oken, deleted it from the second edition. In general nothing was heard of it for a long while. Only most recently it is cropping up again here and there, yet without serious foundation."[30]

It is inexplicable that in von Baer's letter to Huxley about his partial agreement with Darwin he mentioned only the "Papuas und Alfuren," and neither the embryological treatise nor the essay on "Das allgemeinste Gesetz." It is also puzzling that in neither the letter of 1860 nor the essay of 1876 did he mention his extensive communication "Beiträge zur Kenntniss der niedern Thiere," in which already in 1826 he had refuted the law of parallelism: "It has been concluded by a bold generalization from a few analogies, that the higher animals run in the course of their development through the lower animal grades, and sometimes tacitly and sometimes expressly they have been supposed to take their way through all forms. We hold this to be not only untrue, but also impossible."[31]

In the main substance of the essay "Über Darwins Lehre" von Baer expressed strong opposition to Darwin's general concept of the processes responsible for evolution. As a teleologist, he regretted its ethical implications. On a strictly biological basis, he was at odds with what is perhaps its most central feature, namely, the assumption that the forces which acted in

[30] "Mein Widerspruch gegen die Ansicht vom Durchlaufen niederer Thiere hat auch ziemlich allgemeine Anerkennung gefunden. Johannes Müller, der in der ersten Auflage seiner Physiologie die Lehre von Meckel und Oken angenommen hatte, strich sie in der zweiten Auflage. Ueberhaupt war lange nichts von ihr zu hören. Allein in der neusten Zeit taucht sie hie und da doch wieder auf, jedoch ohne ernstliche Begründung," von Baer, *Reden*, II, 243.

[31] "Man hat . . . mit kühner Verallgemeinerung aus wenigen Analogien geschlossen, die höhern Thiere durchliefen in ihrer Ausbildung die niedern Thierstufen, und bald ausdrücklich, bald stillschweigend, sie den Weg durch alle Formen gehen lassen. Das halten wir nicht nur für unwahr, sondern auch für unmöglich," von Baer, "Beiträge zur Kenntniss der niedern Thiere," *Verh. d. kaiserl. Leopold.-Carolin. Akad. d. Naturforscher*, XIII (1827), IIte Abth., p. 760. Translation in text by Huxley, *Scientific Memoirs*, ed. by Henfrey and Huxley, p. 184.

the past were similar to those operating in the present. Von Baer believed, in contrast, that "we have to admit that in a far distant earlier time, a much stronger formative force must have prevailed on earth than we know now, whether this operated through the transformation of already existing forms or through the creation of completely new series of forms."[32] When Georg Seidlitz, a strong Darwinist in Dorpat, where von Baer was then living in retirement, published in 1876 a detailed and polemic treatise[33] attempting to prove that von Baer was more of a Darwinist than he knew, that he misunderstood Darwin, and thus that his divergencies from him were of less significance than he believed, von Baer was highly indignant. First he wished not to read the book at all, but finally did so; then he wanted to answer it "because it was too vexatious for him."[34] But only the introduction had been dictated by the time he died.

II

No matter what von Baer considered his own position vis-à-vis Darwin, it is evident that their thought converged in a number of areas. If Darwin was not cognizant very promptly of the works of von Baer which touched upon zoological affinities and geographical distribution, he seems to have become acquainted, fairly soon in the period during which he was developing his concepts on the *Origin of Species,* with von Baer's embryological ideas. He stated that he opened his first note-

32 "Wir müssen also . . . zugestehen, . . . dass in einer weit entlegenen Vorzeit eine viel gewaltigere Bildungskraft auf der Erde geherrscht habe, als wir jetzt erkennen, möge diese nun durch Umbildung der bereits bestehenden Formen oder durch Erzeugung ganz neuer Reihen von Formen gewirkt haben," von Baer, "Das allgemeinste Gesetz der Natur in der Entwickelung," *Reden,* I, 57. This passage was repeated word for word in "Über Darwins Lehre," *Reden,* II, 245.

33 Georg Karl Maria von Seidlitz, *Beiträge zur Descendenz-Theorie.* Engelmann, Leipzig, 1876.

34 "Weil es ihm doch zu arg sei." In quotation marks in Stieda, *Karl Ernst von Baer,* p. 192.

book "for facts in relation to the Origin of Species" in July 1837;[35] and according to Charles Singer, in Darwin's notebooks for 1842 and 1844 he "devotes much space to embryological discussion relying on von Baer."[36]

The early editions of the *Origin of Species* failed, however, to acknowledge explicitly any influence von Baer's ideas may have played on the formation of Darwin's. It was only in the third and subsequent editions that von Baer's name was found at all. In the third edition, a reference to what Darwin called von Baer's standards of advance in organization was first introduced into the chapter on natural selection.[37] In the section of the chapter on geological succession entitled "On the State of Development of Ancient compared with Living Forms," a specific quotation from von Baer was added in the same edition: "To attempt to compare in the scale of highness members of distinct types seems hopeless; who will decide whether a cuttle-fish be higher than a bee — that insect which the great Von Baer believed to be 'in fact more highly organized than a fish, although upon another type'? "[38] The most extensive allusion to the work of von Baer in this edition made use of a quotation from von Baer's embryological treatise, in connection with what Darwin designated the law of embryonic resemblance. Darwin's section on embryology began, in the third edition, as follows:

It has already been casually remarked that certain organs in the individual, which when mature become widely different and serve for

35 Darwin, *Life and Letters*, I, 56.

36 Charles Singer, *A History of Biology*, revised ed., Henry Schuman, New York, 1950, p. 473.

37 Darwin, *Origin of Species*, 3d edition, John Murray, London, 1861, p. 133. This reference is also included in the later editions.

38 Darwin, *Origin of Species*, 3d ed., p. 365. This statement of Darwin's remains virtually unchanged, except for minor variations in punctuation and wording, in the later editions. The quotation from von Baer was not made by Darwin but is almost identical with that published by Huxley (*Scientific Memoirs*, ed. by Henfrey and Huxley, p. 196). "Ich glaube daher, dass in der That die Biene höher organisirt ist, als der Fisch, obgleich nach einem andern Typus," von Baer, *Entwickelungsgeschichte*, I, 208.

different purposes, are in the embryo exactly alike. The embryos, also, of distinct animals within the same class are often strikingly similar: a better proof of this cannot be given, than a statement made by Von Baer, namely, that "the embryos of mammalia, of birds, lizards, and snakes, probably also of chelonia are in their earliest states exceeding like one another, both as a whole and in the mode of development of their parts; so much so, in fact, that we can often distinguish the embryos only by their size. In my possession are two little embryos in spirit, whose names I have omitted to attach, and at present I am quite unable to say to what class they belong. They may be lizards or small birds, or very young mammalia, so complete is the similarity in the mode of formation of the head and trunk in these animals. The extremities, however, are still absent in these embryos. But even if they had existed in the earliest stage of their development we should learn nothing, for the feet of lizards and mammals, the wings and feet of birds, no less than the hands and feet of man, all arise from the same fundamental form."[39]

The first two of these allusions to von Baer's work had no counterparts in the first and second (1859 and 1860) editions. And as for the third reference, von Baer's ideas on embryological resemblance were attributed in the two earlier editions not to their rightful author but to Louis Agassiz, as will be familiar to all who know these versions:

[39] Darwin, *Origin of Species*, 3d ed., pp. 470-471. The passage remains principally the same, except for minor changes in wording and punctuation, in the later editions. While this paragraph begins the section on embryology in the 3rd edition, two paragraphs precede it in the 6th and one in the 4th and 5th editions. The quotation from von Baer was not original with Darwin but is identical with that published by Huxley, *Scientific Memoirs*, ed. by Henfrey and Huxley, p. 210. "Die Embryonen der Säugethiere, Vögel, Eidechsen und Schlangen, wahrscheinlich auch der Schildkröten, sind in frühern Zuständen einander ungemein ähnlich im Ganzen, so wie in der Entwickelung der einzelnen Theile, so ähnlich, dass man oft die Embryonen nur nach der Grösse unterscheiden kann. Ich besitze zwei kleine Embryonen in Weingeist, für die ich versaümt habe die Namen zu notiren, und ich bin jetzt durchaus nicht im Stande, die Klasse zu bestimmen, der sie angehören. Es können Eidechsen, kleine Vögel, oder ganz junge Säugethiere seyn. So überstimmend ist Kopf- und Rumpfbildung in diesen Thieren. Die Extremitäten fehlen aber jenen Embryonen noch. Wären sie auch da, auf der ersten Stufe der Ausbildung begriffen, so würden sie doch nichts lehren, da die Füsse der Eidechsen und Säugethiere, die Flügel und Füsse der Vögel, so wie die Hände und Füsse der Menschen sich aus derselben Grundform entwickeln," von Baer, *Entwickelungseschichte*, I, 221.

The embryos, also, of distinct animals within the same class are often strikingly similar: a better proof of this cannot be given than a circumstance mentioned by Agassiz, namely, that having forgotten to ticket the embryo of some vertebrate animal, he cannot now tell whether it be that of a mammal, bird, or reptile.[40]

Singer[41] has stated that in his notes Darwin has correctly ascribed the passage to von Baer, and if this is the case, the error as to authority in the *Origin of Species* can only be explained by a lapse of memory. Huxley considered "a great memory" to be one of Darwin's outstanding characteristics; he emphasized this to Romanes when he wrote to him about the latter's obituary notice of Darwin.[42] But Darwin was more critical of himself, and said in his "Autobiography": "My memory is extensive, yet hazy: it suffices to make me cautious by vaguely telling me that I have observed or read something opposed to the conclusion which I am drawing, or on the other hand in favour of it; and after a time I can generally recollect where to search for my authority."[43] We can only conclude that when Darwin paraphrased the passage for the first edition he failed to exert his usual caution in searching for his authority.

No one could have been more meticulous with respect to the labelling of specimens than Darwin, as he made clear in offering to potential field collectors

a few pieces of advice, some of which I observed with much advantage, but others, to my cost, neglected. Let the collector's motto be, "Trust nothing to the memory," for the memory becomes a fickle guardian when one interesting object is succeeded by another still more interesting. . . . Put a number on every specimen, and every fragment of a specimen; and during the very same minute let it be entered in the catalogue, so that if hereafter its locality be doubted, the collector may say in good truth, "Every specimen of mine was ticketed on the spot."

40 Darwin, *Origin of Species*, 1st ed., 1950 reprint, pp. 372-373. Second ed., John Murray, London, 1860, pp. 438-439.
41 Singer, *A History of Biology*, p. 468 fn.
42 Huxley, *Life and Letters*, ii, 42.
43 Darwin, *Life and Letters*, i, 82.

Anything which is folded up in paper, or put into a separate box, ought to have a number on the outside (with the exception perhaps of geological specimens) but more *especially* a duplicate number on the inside attached to the specimen itself. A series of small numbers should be printed from 0 to 5000; a stop must be added to those numbers which can be read upside down (as 699. or 86.). It is likewise convenient to have the different thousands printed on differently coloured paper, so that when unpacking, a single glance tells the approximate number.[44]

That a labeller so conscientious as Darwin could forget whether it was von Baer or Agassiz who had committed the zoologist's unpardonable sin suggests that his memory must have had a compelling reason indeed for the fickleness of its own guardianship. Von Baer, as a matter of actual fact, did not in so many words speak of his defection in terms of a lost label designated as such, he merely said that he had forgotten to make a note of the embryos' names (see his original statement quoted in footnote 39, p. 234, above).

It would be interesting to know what finally moved Darwin to correct his mistake. The error was presumably not noticed in the early reviews; we have said that Darwin remarked that these made no mention of his embryological discussion. Less than two months elapsed between the publication of the first edition (November 24, 1859) and that of the second (January 7, 1860), and while Darwin managed to make some changes during the short interval — he stated in his "Autobiography" that "during the last two months of 1859 [he] was fully occupied in preparing a second edition"[45] — the second edition differed little from the first. It "is only a reprint," he wrote to Asa Gray on December 21 [1859], "yet I have made a *few* important corrections."[46] Most of the changes that were made were inserted at Lyell's suggestion: "It is perfectly true,"

44 Charles Darwin, *Charles Darwin and the Voyage of the Beagle*, ed. by Nora Barlow, Philosophical Library, New York, 1946, pp. 152-153.
45 Darwin, *Life and Letters*, I, 73.
46 Darwin, *Life and Letters*, II, 40.

Darwin wrote to Lyell on January 10 [1860], "that I owe nearly all the corrections to you, and several verbal ones to you and others."[47] Who were the others?

The third edition was published on April 30, 1861, and Darwin wrote Huxley that he must begin work on it November 22, 1860.[48] He may of course have learned of his mistake earlier in 1860. On November 23, 1859, the day before the publication of the first edition, Huxley wrote to Darwin to present his compliments after reading a prepublication copy:

I finished your book yesterday, a lucky examination having furnished me with a few hours of continuous leisure.

Since I read Von Bär's essays, nine years ago, no work on Natural History Science I have met with has made so great an impression upon me, and I do most heartily thank you for the great store of new views you have given me. Nothing, I think, can be better than the tone of the book; it impresses those who know about the subject.[49]

Huxley went on to enumerate the chapters with which he was in total or partial agreement, and of Chapter XIII, which in the first edition covered classification, morphology, embryology, and rudimentary organs, he said that it contained "much that is most admirable, but on one or two points I enter a *caveat* until I can see further into all sides of the question."[49]

Huxley's mention of von Baer at this time was apparently not sufficient to prick Darwin's memory, otherwise Darwin would presumably have made his correction to the second, not the third, edition. When he replied to Huxley's letter two days later, Darwin said in a postscript, "Hereafter I shall be particularly curious to hear what you think of my explanation of Embryological similarity."[50] On Saint Valentine's Day [1860], Darwin commented to Hooker that Huxley "has never alluded to my explanation of classification, morphology, em-

47 Darwin, *Life and Letters*, II, 59.
48 Darwin, *Life and Letters*, II, 144.
49 Huxley, *Life and Letters*, I, 188.
50 Darwin, *Life and Letters*, II, 28.

bryology, etc.,"[51] which hardly suggests that Huxley had then yet replied to Darwin's plea of the previous November for embryological criticism. We know that several months later, in August, 1860, Huxley was writing to Darwin about von Baer's notions of geographical distribution and transformation of types (see page 224, this article); was it this, close to the time of preparation of the third edition, which first incorporated the correction, that stimulated Darwin to look again into the writings of von Baer or into his notes concerning them?

The fact that he mentioned von Baer to Darwin in several letters is not the only reason to connect Huxley with the correction of the error. When Darwin finally made the amendment in the third edition, substituting the name of von Baer for that of Agassiz, and quoting rather than paraphrasing the anecdote of the absent label, he did not himself translate von Baer's statement in his own words, but used a translation by Huxley that had been published in 1853. The simultaneous insertion of all three text references to von Baer into a single edition, with the two direct quotations both borrowed (without acknowledgment, by the way) from Huxley's translation, makes it appear possible that Darwin, once aware of his mistake, returned to reread von Baer not in the original but in Huxley's translation, and that, having finally checked the passage on embryonic resemblance, he also found elsewhere in the translation ideas which he could use to bolster up his argument in other spots.

As a matter of fact, Darwin never in the *Origin of Species* referred to the works of von Baer in the original. Huxley, we have shown, drew Darwin's attention to "Papuas und Alfuren" in August, 1860, shortly before Darwin began the work for the third edition. This was the edition to which the historical sketch was first added, but reference was made to "Papuas und Alfuren" in the sketch for the first time only in the fol-

---

[51] Charles Darwin, *More Letters of Charles Darwin*, ed. by Francis Darwin and A. C. Seward, D. Appleton and Company, New York, 1903, I, 140.

lowing (fourth) edition, and even here it was not the original essay that was cited, but Rudolph Wagner's reference to it (see above, p. 226 this article). Perhaps Huxley never found his own copy, which he admitted was misplaced when he originally wrote Darwin of von Baer's having given it to him. But is it meaningful that Huxley promised Darwin that, if he found it, he would tell him what was in it, and not that he would lend it to him?

It is no secret that Darwin was something less than fluent in German. One annotation suggesting his concern with this fact dates as far back as 1836, where an entry in a shopping list prepared aboard the *Beagle* read "German books — Spelling Dict."[52] He was frankly struggling with the language, and protesting about its difficulty, eight years later: he wrote to Hooker in 1844, "I am now reading a wonderful book for facts on variation — Bronn, 'Geschichte der Natur.' It is stiff German: it forestalls me, sometimes I think delightfully, and sometimes cruelly."[53] Similar grumblings about the difficulties of the language were scattered throughout his letters for the rest of his life. Even in 1881, almost exactly a year before he died, when he wrote to Romanes of having received a copy of Roux's *Kampf der Theile,* he complained: "It is full of reasoning, and this in German is very difficult to me, so that I have only skimmed through each page; here and there reading with a little more care."[54] The important sections of von Baer's *Entwickelungsgeschichte* had been full of reasoning, too! Darwin's son Francis portrayed his father's perplexities over the language more vividly than he perhaps recognized when he wrote the chapter of "Reminiscences" included in the *Life and Letters:*

Much of his scientific reading was in German, and this was a great labour to him; in reading a book after him, I was often struck at see-

52 *Charles Darwin and the Voyage of the Beagle*, p. 252.
53 Darwin, *Life and Letters*, I, 390.
54 Darwin, *Life and Letters*, II, 419.

ing, from the pencil-marks made each day where he left off, how little he could read at a time. He used to call German the "Verdammte," pronounced as if in English. . . . He himself learnt German simply by hammering away with a dictionary; he would say that his only way was to read a sentence a great many times over, and at last the meaning occurred to him. . . .

In spite of his want of grammar, he managed to get on wonderfully with German, and the sentences that he failed to make out were generally really difficult ones. He never attempted to speak German correctly, but pronounced the words as though they were English.[55]

What a model Englishman Darwin was! Yet he was not alone among English biologists in his deficiencies in the use of the German language. In 1853, when Huxley published his translations of excerpts from von Baer's Fifth Scholion and from the concluding section of his "Beiträge zur Kenntniss der niedern Thiere," he claimed that it "seemed a pity that works which embody the deepest and soundest philosophy of zoology, and indeed of biology generally, which has yet been given to the world, should be longer unknown in this country," and he added in a footnote the remark that "Dr. Carpenter (Principles of General Physiology), is, so far as we know, the only English physiologist who has publicly drawn attention to Von Bär's philosophical writings."[56] Huxley himself first read von Baer's essays in 1850, as he wrote to Darwin in 1859 (see p. 237, this article). Hence if Darwin was in fact, as Singer stated, writing notes about von Baer by 1842 and 1844, he was one of his early devotees in Great Britian.

The "Dr. Carpenter" to whom Huxley referred was William B. Carpenter, a friend both of Darwin and of Huxley; he was sufficiently intimate with Huxley to have attended his wedding. His *Principles of General and Comparative Physiology* passed through three editions before 1853, when Huxley referred to it; they were dated respectively 1839, 1841, and 1851. One more edition, entitled simply *Principles of Com-*

55 Darwin, *Life and Letters,* I, 103-104.
56 Huxley, *Scientific Memoirs,* ed. by Henfrey and Huxley, p. 176 and 176 fn.

parative Physiology (1854),[57] was published before the *Origin of Species*. Huxley late in 1851 specifically mentioned reading the "last edition,"[58] presumably the third. Darwin wrote to Carpenter in 1859 of "the admiration which he had long felt and expressed" for the "Comparative Physiology";[59] was this merely an elliptical way of writing, or did he mean thus to designate that he was referring particularly to the fourth edition, the only one to be entitled simply *Comparative Physiology*? In any case, two months later he wrote to Carpenter in particular approbation of the latter's embryological knowledge,[60] so we may assume him to have been acquainted with Carpenter's references to von Baer.

Carpenter himself, while he referred to the ideas of von Baer even in the first two editions, apparently read von Baer's works in their original form only some time after the publication of the second edition of his *Principles* in 1841. At least, when writing in the fourth edition about von Baer's principle of development from the general to the special as related to "those resemblances which are sometimes discernible, between the transitory forms exhibited by the embryos of higher beings, and the permanent conditions of the lower," he added in a footnote:

It is owing to the ignorance of Von Baer's writings which has generally prevailed in this country, that the credit has been recently assigned to others, of having first enunciated the true view of this subject. The Author may refer to the second edition of the present work, published in 1841, as having contained the doctrine stated above, which he was also accustomed to teach in his Physiological Lectures; and although

57 William B. Carpenter, *Principles of General and Comparative Physiology*, . . . John Churchill, London, 1839; 2d ed., John Churchill, London, 1841; 3d ed., John Churchill, London, 1851; 4th ed., published under the title *Principles of Comparative Physiology*, John Churchill, London, 1854. The third edition was available to me only in the American edition, *Principles of Physiology, General and Comparative*, 3d ed., Blanchard and Lea, Philadelphia, 1851.

58 Huxley, *Life and Letters*, I, 100.

59 Darwin, *Life and Letters*, II, 18.

60 Darwin, *Life and Letters*, II, 57.

his own acquaintance with Von Baer's works at that time extended but little beyond the references made to them by Dr. Martin Barry, yet these were sufficient to enable him to comprehend and apply the great developmental law which Von Baer had so clearly enunciated.[61]

Carpenter was correct in judging that he had comprehended von Baer's concepts by 1841. Even in his first edition he presented them with clarity:

There is a greater variety of dissimilar parts in the higher organisms than in the lower; and hence the former may be said to be *heterogeneous,* whilst the latter are more *homogeneous,* approaching in some degree the characters of inorganic masses. This law is, therefore, thus concisely expressed by Von Bär, who first announced it in its present form. *"A heterogeneous or special structure arises out of one more homogeneous or general, and this by a gradual change...."*

Allusion was just now made to the correspondence which is discernible between the transitory forms exhibited by the embryos of the higher beings, and the permanent conditions of the lower. When this was first observed, it was stated as a general law, that all the higher animals in the progress of their development pass through a series of forms analogous to those encountered in ascending the animal scale. But this is not correct; for the *entire animal* never does exhibit such resemblances.[62]

In the second edition, which according to the author's preface enjoyed the advantage of Barry's revision of the chapter on animal reproduction, the concepts of von Baer were further elucidated by the addition of a passage beginning: "It is to be remembered that every Animal must pass through *some* change, in the progress from its embryonic to its adult condition; and the correspondence is much closer between the embryonic Fish and the foetal Bird or Mammal, than between

[61] Carpenter, *Principles of Comparative Physiology,* 4th ed., pp. 96, 98 fn.

[62] Carpenter, *Principles of General and Comparative Physiology,* 1st ed., pp. 170, 171. The quotation attributed to von Baer is taken not from the original works of von Baer, but, with one word omitted, from Martin Barry, "On the Unity of Structure in the Animal Kingdom," *Edinburgh New Philosophical Journal,* XXII (1836-37), 141, 345.

these and the adult Fish."[63] In the third and fourth editions all these ideas were elaborated in very considerable detail.

Clearly Carpenter was profoundly influenced by von Baer. His whole treatment of comparative physiology was based on a developmental analysis for which von Baer's generalizations provided the principal unifying concept. It is permitted to wonder, then, why he waited for so long a time to read what von Baer had really written; and it is inevitable to conclude that he too, like Darwin, was at least in his early years poorly versed in the German language. This is partially borne out by the fact that, out of the forty-three works which he enumerated in the preface to the first edition as having relied upon or consulted in the preparation of the volume, seven were by German authors, and all seven of these were cited in either English or French translation.

But what of Barry, who seems first to have introduced von Baer's concepts to Carpenter? Huxley may have been accurate to the letter when he named Carpenter the "only English physiologist" to have publicly called attention to the philosophical works of von Baer before 1853; but Martin Barry, a Scottish physician, before then had not only read these in German but had discussed them publicly and extensively in the English language.

In 1837, the very year that the principal portion of von Baer's second embryological volume appeared in print, Barry published in the *Edinburgh New Philosophical Journal* a pair of essays "On the Unity of Structure in the Animal Kingdom";[64] some brief excerpts from the second of these may suffice to demonstrate that if Barry did not literally translate von Baer's words, as Huxley was to do sixteen years later, he

[63] Carpenter, *Principles of General and Comparative Physiology*, 2d ed., p. 196.
[64] Martin Barry, "On the Unity of Structure in the Animal Kingdom," *Edinburgh New Philosophical Journal*, XXII (1836-37), 116-141; "Further Observations on the Unity of Structure in the Animal Kingdom, and on Congenital Anomalies, including 'Hermaphrodites'; with some Remarks on Embryology, as facilitating Animal Nomenclature, Classification, and the Study of Comparative Anatomy," *ibid.*, 345-364.

at least gave a reliable presentation of some aspects of his theories in English:

A heterogeneous or special structure arises only out of one more homogeneous or general, and this by a *gradual* change. . . . The manner of the change, is probably the same throughout the animal kingdom, however much . . . the *direction* (or *type*) and *degree* of development may differ, and thus produce variety in structure. . . .

It is not unusual, however, to hear of the "higher" animals *repeating* or *passing through* in their development, the structure of the "lower": and though this is said in reference, of course, to no more than single organs, it is a mode of speaking calculated to mislead.

Such expressions might not be improper, did there exist in the animal kingdom a scale of structure differing in *degree* alone. But there is no such scale. We must "distinguish between the degree of elaboration and the type of structure . . . ."

No structure peculiarly *characterizing* any one set of animals in the perfect state, makes its appearance even in the embryonal life of any other. . . .

Besides which, as Von Bär has truly said, were it a law of nature, that individual development should *consist* in passing through permanent but less elaborate forms, there is not a feature in embryonal life, nor a part then present, that we should not expect to find, somewhere at least, in the animal kingdom. Yet in what direction are we to look for an animal carrying about its food, as the embryo the yolk, or a pendant portion of intestine, like the vesicula umbilicalis? . . .

The same author has well remarked, that inasmuch as embryonal relations produce forms that are present in no grown animal . . . it is also impossible that any embryo can repeat the state of many groups of animals. All embryos are surrounded with fluid; and consequently incapable of immediately respiring air. The real character of insects, therefore, — a lively relation to the air, — can never be repeated in an embryo. For the same reason, the embryo of mammals can never resemble perfect birds.[65]

The periodical in which Barry published his interpretations of von Baer's concepts was not obscure; the volume in which they appeared included also papers by Berzelius, Trevir-

---

[65] Barry, "Further Observations on the Unity of Structure," pp. 345-346, 347, 348-349.

anus, Rathke, Ehrenberg, and Milne Edwards, among others. Neither was Barry an unknown figure in his own day. At the time he published the essays he had already been President of the Royal Medical Society in Edinburgh. He published in 1837, 1838, and 1839 a series of distinguished communications on mammalian embryology in the *Philosophical Transactions of the Royal Society*,[66] for two of which he received the Royal Medal in 1839. Surely Darwin knew of these latter articles. In speaking of his preparation for writing the *Origin of Species* he said in his "Autobiography" that "when I see the list of books of all kinds which I read and abstracted, including whole series of Journals and Transactions, I am surprised at my industry";[67] certainly the transactions he covered included the publications of the Royal Society, in which he always showed such a vital interest. Furthermore, Darwin's own article on Glen Roy,[68] his only paper in the *Philosophical Transactions*, appeared in the same volume as the final article in Barry's series; and in the Glen Roy paper Darwin referred a number of times to a geological communication in the *Edinburgh New Philosophical Journal* of the previous year (1838).

Besides, there was another reason for Darwin, and Huxley too, to have known the work of Barry. In the first two editions of the *Principles of General and Comparative Physiology* Carpenter made, on the same page on which he referred to von Baer's law of the development from the homogeneous to the heterogeneous, a brief footnote reference to the *Edinburgh Philosophical Journal* for July 1837; in the third edition, on the page immediately preceding his statement of this law, he referred not only to the periodical but also to Barry by name.

---

[66] Martin Barry, "Researches in Embryology," First Series, *Philos. Transacs.*, CXXVIII (1838), 301-341; Second Series, *ibid.*, CXXIX (1839), 307-380; Third Series, "A Contribution to the Physiology of Cells," *ibid.*, CXXX (1840), 529-593.

[67] Darwin, *Life and Letters*, I, 68.

[68] Charles Darwin, "Observations on the Parallel Roads of Glen Roy, and of other parts of Lochaber in Scotland, with an attempt to prove that they are of marine origin," *Philos. Transacs.*, CXXIX (1839), 39-81.

In a footnote in the fourth edition, on the same page as the beginning of the paragraph in which von Baer's principle is applied as an explanation of the resemblances of embryos to lower forms, he not only gave the author's name and the journal reference, but also spelled out the title of the essays.[69]

Hence it is puzzling that Huxley in 1853 implied that Carpenter was the sole individual to have published von Baer's ideas in English. But it is even more extraordinary that in 1894 he could still admit, when referring to his own "translation of 'Fragments relating to Philosophical Zoology, selected from the Works of K. E. von Baer,' ... published in 'Scientific Memoirs' for February and May 1853," that he still believed that "up to that time . . . Von Baer's ideas were hardly known outside Germany."[70]

Great honor has accrued to Huxley for his part in convincing English biologists of the importance of German science. His son as his biographer, among others, has emphasized the significance of his role in so doing: "One characteristic of his early papers should not pass unnoticed," wrote Leonard Huxley. "This was his familiarity with the best that had been written on his subjects abroad as well as in England. Thoroughness in this respect was rendered easier by the fact that he read French and German with almost as much facility as his mother tongue," and then he quoted an article by P. Chalmers Mitchell that had been published in *Natural Science* in 1895: " 'It is true of course that scientific men read French and German before the time of Huxley; but the deliberate consultation of all the authorities available has been maintained in historical succession since Huxley's earliest papers, and was absent in the papers of his early contemporaries.' "[71]

[69] Carpenter, *Principles of General and Comparative Physiology*, 1st ed., p. 170 fn; 2d ed., p. 195 fn; 3d ed., p. 575 fn; 4th ed., p. 580 fn.

[70] T. H. Huxley, "Owen's Position in Anatomical Science," in Richard Owen, *The Life of Richard Owen*, John Murray, London, 1894, II, 299 fn.

[71] Huxley, *Life and Letters*, I, 160.

It was not absent from the papers of Barry; not only the essays in the *Edinburgh New Philosophical Journal* but also the articles in the *Philosophical Transactions* provided abundant references to the appropriate French and German works. In 1841 Huxley as a boy of sixteen noted in his Journal

> Projects begun —
> 1. German ⎫ to be learnt.
> 2. Italian ⎭
> 3. To read Müller's *Physiology*.[72]

Four years earlier Barry had already published the following passage (which may be of interest to those who remember Darwin's wonderful analogy of the great Tree of Life found at the end of his chapter on natural selection):

Naturalists have begun, just where they should have ended. They have attended to details, but neglected general principles. Instead of analyzing, their process has been one of synthesis. Their attention has been directed to the grouping of the *twigs*, — as if thus they were to find their natural connections, without even looking for assistance towards the branches, or the trunk that gave them forth. . . .

But what other course *could* naturalists have taken? Truly none: their "circumstance" allowed no other. It is only now that a way is beginning to be opened, by which it may by and by be possible to proceed in an opposite direction; viz. from trunk to branches and to twigs.

This, if ever accomplished, must be by the means of the *History of Development* or *Embryology*, both human and comparative; a science almost new, and regarding which, there prevails in this country the profoundest ignorance and indifference. The French are in advance of us; but it is to *German* enterprise, industry, and perseverance, that we are indebted for almost every fact known to us on this subject; at least of those brought to light in recent times. It is to be hoped, however, that ere long this science will begin to obtain, even among ourselves, some degree of the attention which its importance claims.[73]

Huxley later, through his vast popularity, may have succeeded in accelerating a movement towards the recognition of Ger-

[72] Huxley, *Life and Letters*, I, 11.
[73] Barry, "Further Observations on the Unity of Structure," pp. 362-363.

man contributions that without his spurring might have proceeded more slowly. But surely Barry merits some credit from history for his early, exhaustive, and influential treatment in British periodicals of the work of the most important of the German investigators in his field.

III

If the ideas of von Baer were becoming known to British investigators in general and to Darwin in particular during the late thirties and early forties, it remains to evaluate to what degree Darwin's thought was affected by what he learned of them. Fortunately we are able to investigate the early growth of Darwin's embryological thinking by examining two preliminary sketches which he drew up in 1842 and 1844,[74] many years prior to the framing of the *Origin of Species* in its final form.

Darwin himself laid great emphasis on the importance for the later success of the *Origin of Species* of having written these sketches. "In June 1842," he wrote in his "Autobiography," "I first allowed myself the satisfaction of writing a very brief abstract of my theory in pencil in 35 pages; and this was enlarged during the summer of 1844 into one of 230 pages. . . . The success of the 'Origin' may, I think, be attributed in large part to my having long before written two condensed sketches, and to my having finally abstracted a much larger manuscript, which was itself an abstract."[75] Now if, as Singer said, Darwin's notebooks for 1842 and 1844 discussed von Baer's embryological ideas, to what degree was this fact reflected in the sketches written in these very years?

Without doubt some of von Baer's principal ideas concern-

[74] Charles Darwin, *The Foundations of the Origin of Species. Two Essays Written in 1842 and 1844*, ed. by Francis Darwin, University Press, Cambridge (England), 1909.

[75] Darwin, *Life and Letters*, I, 68, 70.

ing embryonic resemblances were echoed in them. The rather brief embryological passage in the essay of 1842 included the following statement:

This general unity of type in great groups of organisms (including of course these morphological cases) displays itself in a most striking manner in the stages through which the foetus passes. In early stage, the wing of bat, hoof, hand, paddle are not to be distinguished. At a still earlier <stage> there is no difference between fish, bird, &c. &c. and mammal. It is not that they cannot be distinguished, but the arteries <illegible>. It is not true that one passes through the form of a lower group, though no doubt fish more nearly related to foetal state.[76]

The essay of 1844 expanded the embryological section to eight pages, from which the following excerpts may be relevant:

The unity of type in the great classes is shown in another and very striking manner, namely, in the stages through which the embryo passes in coming to maturity. Thus, for instance, at one period of the embryo, the wings of the bat, the hand, hoof or foot of the quadruped, and the fin of the porpoise do not differ, but consist of a simple undivided bone. At a still earlier period the embryo of the fish, bird, reptile and mammal all strikingly resemble each other . . . . From the part of the embryo of a mammal, at one period, resembling a fish more than its parent form; from the larvae of all orders of insects more resembling the simpler articulate animals than their parent insects; and from such other cases as the embryo of the jelly-fish resembling a polype much nearer than the perfect jelly-fish; it has often been asserted that the higher animal in each class passes through the state of a lower animal; for instance, that the mammal amongst the vertebrata passes through the state of a fish: but Müller denies this, and affirms that the young mammal is at no time a fish, as does Owen assert that the embryonic jelly-fish is at no time a polype.[77]

It is noteworthy that, although according to Singer Darwin was thinking about the ideas of von Baer in 1842 and 1844, he did not designate him by name in these sketches. The ref-

[76] Darwin, *Foundations of the Origin of Species*, p. 42. Words in angular brackets supplied by Francis Darwin.
[77] Darwin, *Foundations of the Origin of Species*, pp. 218, 219.

erence to Müller in the 1844 essay is of interest in that his *Elements of Physiology*[78] had been recently translated into English; in fact, this was one of the books by German authors, referred to above, which Carpenter referred to in English translation.

The tenor of these passages indicates that Darwin incorporated at least one of von Baer's concepts into his own thinking many years before the completion of the *Origin of Species*. He grasped that mutual resemblances of embryos could be explained by unity and community of descent, and to this degree he utilized the contribution of von Baer as a bulwark for his own beliefs. Unfortunately, however, in his adoption of the ideas of von Baer he concluded from them very different generalizations than had von Baer himself. This was already demonstrated in the essay of 1844. Here the chapter including the embryological discussion terminated with a paragraph entitled "Order in time in which the great classes have first appeared," and this drew, at least tentatively, inferences incompatible with the beliefs of von Baer:

It follows strictly from the above reasoning only that the embryos of (for instance) existing vertebrata resemble more closely the embryo of the parent-stock of this great class than do full-grown existing vertebrata resemble their full-grown parent-stock. But it may be argued with much probability that in the earliest and simplest condition of things the parent and embryo must have resembled each other, and that the passage of any animal through embryonic states in its growth is entirely due to subsequent variations affecting *only* the more mature periods of life. If so, the embryos of the existing vertebrata will shadow forth the full-grown structure of some of those forms of this great class which existed at the earlier period of the earth's history: and accordingly, animals with a fish-like structure ought to have preceded birds and mammals; and of fish, that higher organized division with the

[78] Johannes Müller, *Elements of physiology,* translated . . . with notes by W. Baly. 2 vols., London, 1837-42. Reference from *British Museum Catalogue,* which does not name the publisher. Carpenter in the preface to the 1839 edition of his *Principles* made his acknowledgment to "Müller's Elements of Physiology, translated by Dr. Baly, London, 1838."

vertebrae extending into one division of the tail ought to have preceded the equal-tailed, because the embryos of the latter have an unequal tail. . . . This order of precedence in time in some of these cases is believed to hold good; but I think our evidence is so exceedingly incomplete regarding the number and kinds of organisms which have existed during all, especially the earlier, periods of the earth's history, that I should put no stress on this accordance, even if it held truer than it probably does in our present state of knowledge.[79]

If, in his essay of 1844, Darwin was inconsistent in that he adopted some of von Baer's ideas, and deviated from others of them, he showed no improvement in this respect when he completed his argument fifteen years later. He did state specifically in the *Origin of Species* that "certain organs in the individual, which when mature become widely different and serve for different purposes, are in the embryo exactly alike. The embryos, also, of distinct animals within the same class are often strikingly similar,"[80] and here is where he told the story of the missing label. But at this time too he said further what von Baer could never have accepted:

As the embryonic state of each species and group of species partially shows us the structure of their less modified ancient progenitors, we can clearly see why ancient and extinct forms of life should resemble the embryos of their descendants — our existing species. Agassiz believes this to be a law of nature; but I am bound to confess that I only hope to see the law hereafter proved true.[81]

In other words, in the *Origin of Species* as in the preliminary draft he went beyond von Baer's conclusions regarding embryonic resemblances to draw the inferences which Haeckel was later to exploit. He explained embryonic resemblances on the basis of community of descent, with great profit to his own argument; but he wished to believe what von Baer had so vehemently denied, namely, that embryos could mirror the

79 Darwin, *Foundations of the Origin of Species*, p. 230.
80 Darwin, *Origin of Species*, 1st ed., 1950 reprint, pp. 372-373.
81 Darwin, *Origin of Species*, 1st ed., 1950 reprint, p. 381.

history of the race by being similar to adult, though extinct, forms.

It was indubitably from Agassiz that Darwin derived his support for his claims of parallel development in fossils and embryos. He was obligated to Agassiz for the example of the heterocercal and homocercal tails of fishes which he used in the paragraph of the 1844 essay dealing with the order of time in which the great classes appeared. Agassiz had written in the first volume of his great work on fossil fishes (1833-1843):

Nothing will dispute that the form of the caudal fin is of high importance for zoological and geological considerations, since it demonstrates that the same thought, the same plan, which presides today over the formation of the embryo has also manifested itself in the successive development of the numerous creations which have formerly populated the earth.[82]

Within five years of Darwin's drafting of his 1844 essay, Agassiz made his unequivocal statement concerning the more general bearing of embryology on classification:

[The] natural series again correspond with the order of succession of animals in former geological ages; so that it is equally true to say that the oldest animals of any class correspond to their lower types in the present day, as to institute a comparison with the embryonic changes, and to say that the most ancient animals correspond with the earlier stages of growth of the types which live in the present period.[83]

Is it not possible that Darwin's unconscious may have tricked him into naming Agassiz rather than von Baer in connection with embryonic resemblances in the first edition because in reality he favored Agassiz' conclusions over those

[82] "Nul ne contestera que la forme de la caudale (sic) ne soit d'une haute importance pour les considérations zoologiques et paléontologiques, puisqu'elle démontre que la même pensée, le même plan, qui préside aujourd'hui à la formation de l'embryon, s'est aussi manifesté dans le développement successif des nombreuses créations qui ont jadis peuplé la terre," Louis Agassiz, *Recherches sur les Poissons Fossiles*, Petitpierre, Neuchâtel, 1833-1843, I, 102.

[83] Louis Agassiz, *Twelve Lectures on Comparative Embryology,* . . . Henry Flanders & Co., Boston, 1849, p. 26.

of von Baer? Darwin, like other scientists, prided himself on his open mind. "I have steadily endeavoured to keep my mind free," he wrote in his "Autobiography," "so as to give up any hypothesis, however much beloved (and I cannot resist forming one on every subject), as soon as facts are shown to be opposed to it."[84] But like other scientists, he could unconsciously succumb to his own prejudices.

"I am rather sorry you do not think more of Agassiz' embryological stages," he wrote to Huxley in 1854, "for though I saw how excessively weak the evidence was, I was led to hope in its truth."[85] Two months later he thanked Huxley for an abstract of the lecture in which the latter had demolished Agassiz' argument with respect to homocercal and heterocercal tails, and also the generalizations drawn from it: "Thank you for your abstract of your lecture at the Royal Institution, which interested me much, and rather grieved me, for I had hoped things might have been in a slight degree otherwise."[86] Darwin did not repeat the example of the heterocercal and the homocercal tails in the *Origin of Species,* but of the truth of Agassiz' general conclusions he became more rather than less convinced during the course of the years. True, when he spoke of them in the chapter on geological succession in the first edition of the *Origin of Species,* he described them temperately, and even referred to Huxley's misgivings about them:

Agassiz insists that ancient animals resemble to a certain extent the embryos of recent animals of the same class; or that the geological succession of extinct forms is in some degree parallel to the embryological development of recent forms. I must follow Pictet and Huxley in

84 Darwin, *Life and Letters,* I, 83.

85 Darwin, *More Letters,* I, 75.

86 Darwin, *More Letters,* I, 82. An abstract of Huxley's lecture, "On Certain Zoological Arguments commonly adduced in Favour of the Hypothesis of the Progressive Development of Animal Life," was published in *Proc. Royal Inst.,* II (1854-58), 82-85, and in *The Scientific Memoirs of T. H. Huxley,* ed. by Michael Foster and E. Ray Lankester, Macmillan and Co. Limited, London, 1898, I, 300-304.

thinking that the truth of this doctrine is very far from proved. Yet I fully expect to see it hereafter confirmed, at least in regard to subordinate groups. For this doctrine of Agassiz accords well with the theory of natural selection.[87]

But by the time the final edition was completed in 1872, he had withdrawn his reservations, and here the passage reads:

Agassiz and several other highly competent judges insist that ancient animals resemble to a certain extent the embryos of recent animals belonging to the same classes; and that the geological succession of extinct forms is nearly parallel with the embryological development of existing forms. This view accords admirably well with our theory.[88]

Darwin's option in favor of Agassiz had its effects on subsequent embryology. While Haeckel in any event, even without Darwin behind him, might have reverted to Meckel's antiquated concept of parallelism, yet it was Darwin's thesis that fortified his position with respect to the biogenetic law. Thus Darwin, through Haeckel, looked in two ways in the history of embryology. In so far as Haeckelianism had its progressive side, by inspiring so many young men to enter biology and embryology, Darwin made a positive contribution by having encouraged Haeckel's beliefs and by having facilitated their acceptance. But Haeckel had his retrogressive influence in embryology, also. So powerfully dogmatic was his teaching of the outworn law of recapitulation that for years embryos were investigated primarily for what they might reveal of their ancestry; and the development of analytical and physiological embryology had to await the subsidence of his surge of ideas. For this Darwin too must share responsibility.

Although it is fruitless, it is nonetheless fascinating to speculate what direction embryology might have followed had Darwin in the *Origin of Species* placed less emphasis on Agas-

[87] Darwin, *Origin of Species*, 1st ed., 1950 reprint, pp. 286-287.

[88] Darwin, *Origin of Species*, 6th ed., 1902 reprint, D. Appleton and Company, New York, II, 120. The 6th edition was originally published by John Murray, London, 1872.

siz' conclusions and more on von Baer's. And it is tempting to wonder whether he might not have better understood the contributions of von Baer, and have become more convinced of the cogency and significance of his criticisms of the old recapitulation theories, had he read his works in the original more easily, or more frequently, or more comprehendingly. In 1881, the year before he died, he still did not even own von Baer's works.[89]

What Darwin took from von Baer emanated from von Baer's speculations about the whole embryo, or at most about the whole organ. He never so much as mentioned the most important factual contribution of von Baer to embryology, his descriptions of the germ layers, though it was these which provided the phenomenological basis for von Baer's conclusions and for the new embryology to follow. Darwin may have believed, as he said he did, that his embryological considerations were vital to the successful development of his concepts of natural history. But what he accepted from von Baer to further them was drawn from von Baer's reflections more than from his observations. What von Baer described that was new Darwin mainly ignored. The power of von Baer's ideas was sufficiently strong that these could eventually triumph, no matter how they were treated by the more revisionistic apostles of Darwin. And the strength of the *Origin of Species* need not be measured alone by the tenuousness of some of its constituent arguments; in it as in the other creations of nature and of men, the significance of the whole transcends that of its parts.

[89] Darwin, *More Letters*, II, 27.

The Non-Specificity
of the Germ-Layers[*]

Eigentlich beginnt in jeder dieser drei Schichten eine eigene Metamorphose, und jede eilt ihrem Ziele entgegen; allein es ist jede noch nicht selbstständig genug, um allein das darzustellen, wozu sie bestimmt ist; sie bedarf noch der Hülfe ihrer Gefährtinnen, und daher wirken alle drey, obgleich schon zu verschiedenen Zwecken bestimmt, dennoch, bis jede eine bestimmte Höhe erreicht hat, gemeinschaftlich zusammen. . . .

Chr. Pander

INTRODUCTION

PROBABLY the single set of facts that biologists who specialize in other branches of their science than embryology carry away in their store of general information is that describing the histological accomplishments of the germ-layers. The embryologists themselves as pedagogues are probably more dogmatic concerning these facts than concerning any other [the recent edition of the Brachet (1935) textbook is a welcome exception]. The fixed and simple concept as expressed in the germ-layer doctrine is easy to remember and accordingly has been gratefully retained for its usefulness as a rule of thumb.

Time and time again contradictions have found their way into the specialized literature of embryology but they have only rarely penetrated into general consciousness. Since the

* Reprinted from *Quarterly Review of Biology* Vol. XV, 1940, pp. 1–27.

recent work in embryology has had important bearings on the problem, it seems well to review the field once more. The historical approach to the problem has been chosen simply because it is so interesting to trace through the dogged attempt of the human mind to cling to a fixed idea.

EARLY HISTORY

Up to the middle of the eighteenth century, the existence of the process of development was recognized, but its constituent mechanisms were quite unknown. Aristotle, Fabricius, Harvey and many others less illustrious had seen embryos or foetuses and had even watched them develop; they had seen in them the forerunners of adult structures, and had noted the appearance of some of these. How the structures were formed — what their source and what their material — was a question unaskable for many reasons. In the earlier days of embryology, before the Renaissance, unquestioning belief in a rigidly Aristotelian philosophy limited the explanation of all biological processes, development included, to the basis of a concoction of four humours. Even after the Renaissance, when this explanation had been abandoned in anatomy, it sufficed for embryology because no one could detect, with unaided eye, those developmental processes whose very existence defied suspicion until the invention of the microscope.

For some reason embryologists delayed using this instrument until a century after its introduction, and then, ironically enough, the results of its first employment denied the process of development. Malpighi, in perhaps the most famous error of biology, thought that he discovered the principal adult organs present in the unincubated egg. It was in the refutation of this error, that the possibility that there might be such a thing as a germ-layer was called into existence. Caspar Friedrich Wolff (1758; 1812) looked at the unincubated chick blastoderm and found that the organ rudiments were not yet present in it. He further found that later the gut and probably also the nervous system were formed by a process of folding of a layer of the stuff of which the blastoderm is composed.

Wolff, however, simply saw that the adult organs were not necessarily preformed in the unincubated blastoderm, but that some of them were formed later from layers of the blastoderm. It was Pander, however, student of Döllinger, who really elucidated what these layers were.

First Description of the Layers

Christian Pander, in his two papers published in Würzburg in 1817, first described the trilaminar structure of the incubated chick blastoderm. [It was Pander who originally coined the word "blastoderm": "Because the embryo chooses this as its seat and its domicile, contributing much to its configuration out of its own substance, therefore in the future we shall call it *blastoderm*" (1817b, p. 21).] His own description of the three layers (1817a, pp. 5, 11–12) is better translated than paraphrased:

At the twelfth hour the blastoderm consists of two entirely separate layers, an inner one, thicker, granular and opaque, and an outer one, thinner, smooth and transparent. The latter, because of its development and for the sake of greater accuracy of description, we may call the serous layer and the former the mucous layer. . . . There arises between the two layers of the blastoderm a third middle one in which the blood vessels are formed, which we therefore call the vessel-layer; from its origin events of the greatest importance subsequently occur. . . . Actually there begins in each of these three layers a particular metamorphosis, and each one strives to achieve its goal; only each is not yet sufficiently independent by itself to produce that for which it is destined. Each one still needs the help of its companions; and therefore all three, until each has reached a specific level, work mutually together although destined for different ends.

Pander not only recognized the layers once they were formed, but he also realized clearly that one layer was formed at the expense of another. He wrote elsewhere (1817b, pp. 26–27):

What merits most attention is the composition of the blastoderm out of two layers. For before incubation this membrane consists of a single layer, made up of granules which cohere to each other by their own viscosity. As incubation progresses, however, there originates from this another layer, more delicate but firmer in structure, so that at a specific time the blastoderm can be divided by a fairly long macera-tion into two layers.

Elaboration of the Germ-Layer Concept

Pander crystallized the germ-layer concept for the chick embryo. His friend and colleague, Karl Ernst von Baer, also a student of Döllinger's, extended it to encompass all of ver-tebrate development, thereby laying down the fundamental bases for the study of comparative embryology.

Von Baer (1837, Bd. 2, S. 68) recognized the value of Pander's contribution; only in a way he reorganized it per-haps a trifle too assiduously, since he unjustifiably stretched Pander's three layers to four, breaking up the middle layer into two layers — roughly the equivalent of what we know as somatic and splachnic mesoderm:

We can speak of an upper and a lower layer; the former we call the skin layer and the latter the mucous layer. The material that lies be-tween the two clings partly to the upper layer and partly to the lower. In this way there gradually develop two inner layers, an upper and a lower. In the lower of the inner layers the granules become clear and dissolve into vesicles, and finally part of the contents of this layer be-gins to flow. It becomes a vessel-layer. In the upper the granules become darker; this becomes a flesh- or muscle-layer.

It seems hardly necessary to emphasize that von Baer's most significant contribution, so far as the germ-layers are con-cerned, was the recognition of the fact that Pander's discov-ery for the chick was valid for all the rest of vertebrate devel-opment. This has been the basis of embryology from von Baer's time until today.

The question often arises as to what the status of embryology would be without the contribution of von Baer. It might conceivably be little different than it is, because of the insight of another investigator who had the misfortune, from posterity's point of view, to be a contemporary of von Baer. In 1825, several years before the publication of von Baer's treatise, Martin Heinrich Rathke, who had read Pander's paper, applied this author's observations on the germ-layers to the development of an Invertebrate, *Astacus*, describing the splitting of the blastoderm into a serous and mucous layer which fit one inside the other "like the coats of an onion" (quoted in E. S. Russell, 1916, p. 208). As a matter of fact Rathke seems to have applied Pander's figurative vocabulary as well as his concept to the Invertebrates, since he wrote, without anywhere in his paper referring to Pander: "After the blastoderm has divided into two particular layers, each of these layers proceeds by itself towards its final goal" (translated from Rathke, 1825, pp. 1094-5). So much was stated in the preliminary note. The final paper, which was published in 1829, described the layers more explicitly:

One of them clings closely to the yolk and corresponds to the mucous layer of vertebrates, and is subsequently used for the production of the intestine and of a special yolk-sac. The other, on the other hand, is essentially comparable to the serous layer of the vertebrate, insofar as it . . . forms the body wall of the embryo, from which the different appendages as well as the central part of the central nervous system take their origin. A special and separate vessel-layer is never perceptible . . . [there is] more the idea of it than its actual presence (translated from Braem, 1895, S. 495).

These words show clearly that Rathke saw the implication of Pander's discovery as well as did von Baer. He was able to transfer the analogy even to the Invertebrates. His work was less well known than von Baer's, probably principally because his generalizations were more on the embryological and less on the transcendental side. So far as their actual content is concerned, it would have made as solid a groundwork on which to build the science of embryology as the more celebrated *Scholia* of von Baer.

The significance of von Baer's concept was immediately recognized. In one way, however, it seemed almost a culmination rather than a new point of departure, and for many years the concept was accepted with only slight amplification and refinement.

The refining, very nearly completed by Robert Remak between 1850 and 1855, consisted of a double process: first, the interpretation of the germ-layers as composed of cells which were derived from the single cell of the original egg; second, the essentially correct demonstration that each of the germ-layers has a specific histological future. Remak recognized two primary germ-layers: (1) the upper, or sensory layer, subdivided into medullary plate and its derivatives, and the epidermic plate, and (2) the under layer subdivided into (2a) the trophic layer which gives rise to the alimentary canal and its derivatives, and (2b) the motorgerminative layer which furnishes peripheral nerves, muscle, blood vessels, connective tissue, sex glands, etc. Furthermore, this middle motorgerminative layer is separated into dorsal and ventral somite plates by the pleuroperitoneal cavity, which is the precise equivalent of what we know as the coelome. It is obvious that these are the precise facts of the germ-layer concept as we recognize them today, with the exception of the one major error concerning the origin of the peripheral nerves.

Germ-Layers in the Vertebrate Embryo and the Adult Coelenterate

Even before Remak had published his book, one investigator was beginning to realize that the two so-called primary germ-layers formed as fundamental a part in the architecture of the adult coelenterate as in the molding of the vertebrate embryo, and he laid the foundation of what was subsequently to become the whole superstructure of phylogenetic and onto-genetic studies so extravagantly elaborated by the adherents of the evolution concept.

Huxley is credited with this discovery. He wrote, in a matter-of-fact manner, in a short paper "On the Anatomy and Affinities of the Family of the Medusae" (1849, pp. 414, 425):

> I would lay particular stress upon the composition of this (stomach) and other organs of the Medusae out of *two distinct membranes,* as I believe that this is one of the essential peculiarities of their structure, and that a knowledge of the fact is of great importance in investigating their homologies. I will call these two membranes as such, and inde-pendent of any modification into particular organs, 'foundation mem-branes' . . . . A complete identity of structure connects the 'founda-tion membranes' of the Medusae with the corresponding organs in the rest of the series; and it is curious to remark, that throughout the outer and the inner membranes appear to bear the same physiological rela-tion to one another as do the serous and the mucous layer of the germ; the outer becoming developed into the muscular system and giving rise to the organs of offense and defense; the inner, on the other hand, appearing to be more closely subservient to the purposes of nutrition and generation.

In a way, it is almost surprising that this discovery had not been made earlier, in view of the fact that Rathke had so early noted that Invertebrates as well as Vertebrates were bilaminar in early development. Also, Cuvier, as Huxley knew, had re-marked on the bilaminar structure of the Coelenterates. In speaking of the Tubularians, Cuvier wrote (1846, p. 557):

> Here the polyps do not form simple aggregations in which the indi-viduals are distinct: but they are intimately united in such a way that they compose a more or less complicated individual which we call a compound polyp.
>
> Whatever way the compound polyp is composed, the alimentary or digestive cavity of each polyp opens into a common nutritive tube, into which flows, or is secreted, the nutrient fluid produced by the digestive processes of each polyp.
>
> The walls of the nutritive tube are formed by a double membrane, always intimately fused in this part of the compound polyp; the ex-

ternal corresponds to the skin; the internal is a continuation of the digestive portion of the alimentary cavity (of the individual polyps).

The former, in the compound polyp, secretes from its external surface a tube or sheath, thin like parchment, or horny in nature. . . .

As a matter of fact, however, the investigator who came closest to anticipating Huxley's brilliant generalization was none other than von Baer himself. Von Baer (1837, Bd. 2, S. 67) early compared the primary germ-layers with the walls of the Coelenterate, in the following statement:

> Yet originally there are not two distinct or even separable layers, it is rather the two surfaces of the embryo which show this difference, just as polyps show the same contrast between their internal digestive and external surface. In between the two layers there is in our embryo as in the polyp an indifferent mass.

The primary germ-layers of the Coelenterates were given their definitive names shortly after the publication of Huxley's paper. In a paper "On the Anatomy and Physiology of *Cordylophora,*" Allman wrote in 1853 (p. 368): "All the hydroid zoophytes can be proved to consist essentially of two distinct membranes; to the external of these membranes I shall give the name of ectoderm, and to the internal that of endoderm."

In spite of its importance, the implications of Huxley's brilliant observation remained unnoticed for almost twenty years. Haeckel's *Generelle Morphologie,* for instance, published in 1866, makes no mention of the germ-layers. The dearth of progress is perhaps nowhere better shown than by a study of Huxley's own *Introduction to the Classification of Animals,* published in 1869, exactly 20 years after his first statement concerning the Medusae. In this book, the only statements concerning the germ-layers are: (1) that the Hydrozoa are separated into two layers of tissue, the ectoderm and the endoderm, (2) that the Actinozoa are likewise constructed of two membranes, ectoderm and endoderm, (3) that the author can confirm Remak's statement that the brain and spinal cord of Vertebrates are a result of the modification of the serous layer of the germ, and (4) that the serous layer of the germ helps to form the amnion in the chick embryo while the allantois is formed from neither mucous nor serous layer but from the intermediate stratum. In no case here does he mention any relationship between coelenterate ectoderm and endoderm on the one hand and embryonic serous and mucous layers on the other. In other words, although Huxley had appreciated the fundamental relationship between the body-layers of Invertebrates and the embryonic layers of Vertebrates, yet twenty years later he and all other investigators were still waiting to utilize the generalization in any way, even for pedagogic reasons.

Even at this early date, before the word mesoderm had even been coined, and before the obvious generalization had been made, the germ-layer concept became subject to distortion. In 1865 Wilhelm His formulated his "archiblast-parablast" theory. This theory, based on a study of the extremely specialized teleostean development, claimed that the archiblast, composed of the three classical germ-layers, gives rise to all the embryo except the blood vessels and connective tissue which are furnished by the parablast. His's theory bore little lasting effect on the development of embryology, and fortunately was ultimately abandoned even by its author. But it gives perhaps the first example of the way in which the germ-layer theory has been distorted in the course of its development.

Evolutionary Significance of the Germ-Layers

In the same years when Huxley was issuing lectures on comparative anatomy that included the words ectoderm and endoderm only in discussion of the Coelenterates, and when His was worrying about the archiblast and parablast, a Russian investigator was making the observations that were most instrumental — partly because of their own inherent worth and brilliance, partly because of the fortunate time at which they were published — in effecting the bond between embryology and anatomy, and between the study of ontogeny and phylogeny.

Alexander Kowalewski, in the years 1867–71, found that all the invertebrate embryos he studied, and these were of many types, were formed of the same primary layers as the vertebrate embryos, and, furthermore, that in all of them alike the layers arise in the same fashion, the inner layer being produced from the outer by a process of invagination. Kowalewski's words can speak for himself more convincingly than we can speak for him (1867a, p. 3):

The first change in the embryo [*Psolinus,* a holothurian] consists of an insignificant invagination which becomes visible at one pole of the egg, and whereby the whole embryo takes on a somewhat conical form. The invagination progresses gradually farther and after a few hours forms a deep sac. . . . A similar division of the cells of the embryo into two layers, an outer and a central one, I have also observed in many other animals, and especially clearly in the eggs of *Phoronis.*

Nineteen days later, when he presented his paper on "*Amphioxus*" (1867b, pp. 3, 5), the generalization had broadened considerably:

The embryo now consists of two sheets of germ-layers, the outer and the inner; we can therefore compare it with the embryonic anlage of the bird, mammal and turtle-egg, when these still consist of two layers. If we compare figure 15 of Reichert's paper on the development of the guinea-pig with our figures 8 and 9, the similarity between these two forms of development immediately strikes us. . . . The embryo quite agrees, even in the most insignificant details, with the embryo of the corresponding stages of *Phoronis,* of *Limnaeus,* of *Asteracanthion berylinus* Ag., of *Ophiura* and of *Echinus,* according to my own still unpublished observations; and if we leave the cilia out of consideration, our larva agrees also with the corresponding stage of *Sagitta,* of the Ascidians (*As. intestinalis* and *Phalusia mammillata*); if we consider that the segmentation cavity is filled with yolk, it resembles also the larva of *Escholtzia,* of *Cestum* and of *Sepiola.* In all of the embryos mentioned here the formation of the two laminae or layers proceeds in exactly the same way. . . . Thus the first formation of the embryo would be quite in agreement for all these different animals; only in the further changes do we see appear the differences which characterize the individual type.

And in 1869 (p. 29), he wrote in a paper on worms and arthropods:

Now if we compare the development of the worms we have described with that of other animals, the analogy of the germ-layers of the worms with those of the Vertebrates, even in the details, astonishes us. The same two primitive layers which play the leading rôles in the development of the worm appear also in the Vertebrates; as in the one group so in the other the middle layer appears only later. The destinies of the layers and of the organ anlagen are in very great agreement even down to the individual processes.

Rathke's comparison of the embryonic germ-layers of Vertebrates and Invertebrates remained buried. Huxley's recognition of the relationship of the germ-layers in the adult coelenterate and the embryonic vertebrate, so strangely anticipated by von Baer, scarcely received comment for two decades. But the researches of Kowalewski bore immediate fruit. By 1870 the scientific world was flaming with the debate on evolution that was kindled by the publication of Darwin's *Origin of Species*. The publication of Kowalewski's observations on the universality of the germ-layers and on their comparable origin in a multitude of forms made it possible to consider the evolution of the individual and the evolution of the race in the same light. The decade of the 1870's saw embryology adduced as a complete confirmation of the evolution-hypothesis, and the evolution of the race as an explanation *sine qua non* of the course of evolution or development of the individual.

The first significant attempt to relate phylogeny with ontogeny was that of Kleinenberg, who published in 1872 his monograph on the histology and development of *Hydra*, a paper dedicated, by the way, to Ernst Haeckel. In this the author found the Coelenterate the perfect organism to represent the transition form from Coelenterate to vertebrate embryo, and to represent the fundamental type on which all other forms are patterned and from which they are necessarily derived:

The low position of the Coelenterates in the system is perfectly understandable from their developmental history. Their type is determined by their maintenance of the fundamental spatial relationship of the germ-layers, and of their different layers in turn, to each other and to the external world. . . . The resultant great simplicity and uniformity of the whole body structure distinguishes the Coelenterates from all other animal groups: in the latter the definitive body arises through far-reaching histological segregations, but principally through manifold transformations and interminglings of the germ-layers, with the result that these are scarcely recognizable at all in the completed organs, and only in vague outlines in the body as a whole. But if we follow the developmental history of these complicated organizations backwards, we arrive finally, in the Vertebrates and probably in all animal groups, to forms which correspond essentially to those of the Coelenterates. Now since these forms are necessary, but transitory, developmental stages upon which the specific type is built, while on the other hand among the Coelenterates the same forms, maintained unchanged, portray the type, so the conclusion is apparent that not only the developmental processes in all animals are identical up to a certain stage, but that even in individual development the transition of one type into another occurs, since the constant type of the Coelenterate is passed through as a developmental stage by all higher animals. The simple type of the Coelenterate is the common ground form to which all the infinitely rich and manifold configurations of the animal body can be directly or indirectly referred (Kleinenberg, 1872, pp. 87–88).

In 1869 the terms ectoderm and endoderm had not yet been applied to describe the germ-layers of the embryo: in 1872 the terms were being used as they are now by Haeckel in Germany and in 1873 by Lankester in England. The term mesoderm was introduced by Huxley in 1871 (pp. 10–11 of the 1872 edition) in his *Manual of Anatomy,* and it was used by Haeckel (1872) in his monograph *Die Kalkschwämme.* Lankester's paper, published in May 1873, represents, according to its author, "part of a course of lectures commenced in the University Museum, Oxford, during Michaelmas term 1872." Haeckel's *Die Kalkschwämme* appeared in 1872 after Lankester's paper was drawn up but before it was published; whether he adopted Lankester's terminology, or whether Lankester adopted his, or whether both independently used the same terminology, is not apparent. In 1873 Balfour and Lankester both were using the terms epiblast, mesoblast and hypoblast in place of the other terms. The history of terminology may be a futile study, but in the present case it is interesting since the men we have mentioned as changing the use of words simultaneously deflected the course of thought.

Lankester published in 1873 the preliminary and in 1877 the final communication in which he created a classification of animals based on their constitution into layers: All animals are homoblastic, diploblastic or triploblastic; the triploblastic forms are derived from the diploblastic through the Vermes; the planula, or the larva of the Coelenterate, is the parent, phylogenetically speaking, of all diploblastic and triploblastic forms.

Haeckel (1872), in Germany, published simultaneously a similar theory destined to become of greater influence than Lankester's because of Haeckel's genius of expression. Haeckel's concept, in a way, was influenced heavily by the English school, partly because of Haeckel's blind acceptance of the evolution-doctrine and partly because of his deep personal affection for Huxley. The parent of all forms, in Haeckel's theory, is a two-layered sac similar to the bilaminar stage of all embryos described so skillfully by Kowalewski and known to us by Haeckel's term "gastrula." Haeckel wrote in 1872 (Bd. 1, S. 466–467) in the general part of his monograph on the Calcispongiae:

In all of these representatives of the most varied animal groups the gastrula has exactly the same structure. In each case its simple monaxial oval body encloses a simple central cavity (gastral cavity) which opens through a mouth at one pole; in each case the thin wall of the cavity consists of two cell-layers, an inner layer of larger darker cells (endoderm, gastral layer, inner, trophic or vegetative germ-layer) and an outer layer of smaller generally ciliated lighter cells (exoderm, dermal layer, outer, sensory or animal germ-layer). I conclude from this identity of the gastrula in representatives of the most diversified animal groups, from the Sponges to the Vertebrates, according to the fundamental biogenetic law, that the animal phyla have a common descent from a single unknown stock form, gastraea, which is constructed essentially like the gastrula.

According to this theory, the gastrula, Kowalewski's bilaminar sac, produces all embryos; a similar *Urmutter* is therefore the necessary progenitor of all multicellular forms. Finally, the course of evolution of the embryo is step by step explained and *caused* by the evolution of the race to which the developing individual belongs. The development of the gill-slits in a mammalian embryo, to take a familiar instance, would be caused according to Haeckel necessarily and solely by the fact that in the course of evolution the ancestor of the mammal possessed gill-slits. One wonders how the promulgator of such a distorted doctrine of cause and effect could have been championed by the same Huxley who wrote: "Fact I know and Law I know: but what is this Necessity save an empty Shadow of my own mind's throwing?"

Haeckel was probably the transcendentalist par excellence of all biology. Equipped naturally with those rarely combined virtues, an aesthetic appreciation of a high degree and a passion for methodical terminology and organization, he produced in the gastraea theory a scheme of ideas as intricate and symmetrical as the figures of Radiolarians which he loved to portray with his pen. The most perfect example imaginable of fitting the facts to the theory, a beautiful intellectual feat, totally devoid of scientific value, his gastraea theory was the culmination of the early work on the germ-layers. Some of his contemporaries realized that phylogeny could not explain away

269

ontogeny, and His (1874), for instance, vainly suggested and even attempted a study of the mechanical causes of development. But the beautiful unity of Haeckel's scheme was too seductive. Huxley and the English embryologists spent their days apotheosizing its author and looking at embryos only for the purpose of fitting the facts of ontogeny into the ideal of phylogeny.

Kleinenberg (1886, p. 2), who had nominated *Hydra* and the Coelenterates for the throne usurped by Haeckel's "gastraea," gave a succinct and vivid critique of the gastraea theory in his paper on the development of *Lopadorhyncus* which this time bore no dedication:

The good in it (the gastraea theory) belongs to Huxley; what Haeckel has done to it is false, or perverted, or meaningless. It is false to trace all kinds of endoderm-formation back to the invagination of the blastoderm. It is perverted to substitute a problematical gastraea in the place of the coelenterate type. The value of Huxley's idea lay for the greater part in that it brought the early developmental stages of the higher Metazoa into immediate alliance with the completed forms of countless living Coelenterates. These latter are very diverse among themselves and still remain Coelenterates; that greater differences must exist between an adult coral and the larval form of an annelid is understandable, and will hinder no one from seeing the essential similarity of both organizations. In any case it was unnecessary to leave the Present and to descend into the Laurentian night to call forth as lean an animal-spectre as the gastraea. It is, incidentally, obvious that the gastraea is not able by itself to create the slightest hypothetical conception of the unknown origin of the Coelenterates, because the gastraea *is* nothing more than the coelenterate type schematized. Courageous hypotheses — daring conclusions — these almost always are of service to Science. But Schemata injure her if they bring existing knowledge into an empty and warped pattern, and claim thereby to give deeper understanding. Unfortunately the gastraea was not fertile, but it was strongly infectious; it has propagated itself as Neuraea, Nephridaea, etc. and is guilty of all the Original-animals, the Trochosphaera, the Trochophora, the Original-insect, and I know not what besides.

Meaningless is the homologizing of the gut-cavity of the higher

Metazoa with the endoderm-cavity of the gastraea; a hole is a hole anywhere in the world. If once the equivalence of the walls is established,
people will not need to worry their heads about the empty spaces inside.

EARLY OBJECTIONS TO THE GERM-LAYER
DOCTRINE

The first voices were raised against the germ-layer doctrine
during the 1870's. Since those of Kölliker and the Hertwigs
were loudest, and since the precepts of these authors epito-
mized those of their contemporaries, they may best be chosen
as an example of the mode of reasoning of the opponents of
the doctrine.

Kölliker (1879, '84, '89) questioned the validity of the
doctrine principally from the histologist's point of view. While
some of his reasoning now seems quaint, and some has since
been invalidated by modification of the doctrine, some is still
cogent. He claimed that the outer layer gives rise to many
diverse types of cells — to epithelium, nervous cells, neuroglia,
the pigment epithelium in the eye, etc. He added, however,
basing his statement on his own observations and those of
Leydig and Ranvier, that the outer germ-layer could give rise
to smooth musculature in the case of the sweat-glands.

So far as the middle germ-layer is concerned, Kölliker
claimed that this also gave rise to too many diversified types of
cell to have any meaning as a single entity. He emphasized that
chorda is in some cases derived from the mesoderm and in
others from endoderm — a fact without significance to us, who
know that chorda and mesoderm each stem from a different
group of cells, but which was at one time one of the most
disputed facts of the whole doctrine. He adds further that so
far as the hindmost part of the embryo is concerned, in a certain sense even the nervous system is formed from mesoderm,
since the blastema from which all the hindmost structures are
formed is predominantly mesodermal in origin.

So far as the endoderm is concerned, he erroneously claims that in *Amphioxus* it goes so far as to form somites and muscle and connective tissue, and that in many lower forms it produces chorda.

When Kölliker turns to a study of the Coelenterates, he claims, on the basis of his own work and that of other authors, that muscles and germ-cells, and in some cases even nervous tissue, are formed sometimes from ectoderm and sometimes from endoderm. His evidence so far as the germ-cells are concerned is invalidated by the later discovery that these are derived from neither germ-layer but from cells which were probably segregated during early development. However, his conclusions concerning the muscle are still valid. He concluded:

> In consequence of all these considerations the conviction is irresistably striking that the significance of the germ-layers is not histo-physiological but morphological. If we proceed from the fact that originally all the cells of the embryo, as they are produced by cleavage, are equivalent, so we may assert the proposition that all three germ-layers possess the potency and the capacity also for transformation into all tissues, but because of their specific morphological configurations they cannot everywhere manifest this power (1879, S. 389).

While many of the facts on which Kölliker based his claims have been disputed, many of them still hold true, and as a matter of fact his reasoning does not suffer even when the evidence has been invalidated. Many of Kölliker's conclusions were admittedly based on evidence derived from the Hertwigs' studies on the Coelenterates. In 1878 the Hertwigs raised their first questions about the application of the germ-layer theory in a small monograph dealing with the histology of the Medusae. Inquiring, as had Kleinenberg, into the relationships of ectoderm and endoderm to mesoderm, they concluded that what they consider mesoderm in the Medusae is simply a product of the histological differentiation of ectoderm and endoderm. In their monograph on the Actinians, published

272

a year later (1879) as the first of their definitive "Studies on the Germ-layer Theory," they continue their discussion, questioning the precise relationship of the two layers of the Coelenterates to the three of higher forms. On evidence that in some coelenterate groups germ-cells or musculature are derived from ectoderm and in others from endoderm, they conclude that "within particular animal groups the germ-layers have differentiated organologically inequivalently" (1879, p. 205). Furthermore they extend their generalizations, supporting themselves by evidence from other authors similar to that of Kölliker's outlined above, to include the other animal groups as well as the Coelenterates:

> The germ-layers are neither organological nor histological entities. It is not possible, if one knows the origin of an organ in one animal group, to carry over the result to all other animal groups. . . . Just as the capacity for transformation of individual cells, so is that of a germ-layer highly manifold, and it can express itself in the most different ways in the production of organs and tissues (1879, pp. 216, 217).

Here the Hertwigs have put their fingers on the whole solution of the germ-layer problem; but unfortunately they were not satisfied to stop here with a constructive contribution. Instead they chose to supplant the gastraea theory, which they had destroyed, with another theory which was not only unnecessary but even more far-fetched, if possible, than its predecessor.

This they achieved by continuing the discussion of the difficulty arising from the attempts to homologize similar tissues developing from different germ-layers in diploblastic and triploblastic forms, and to find any uniformity whatsoever in the mesoderm which originates and develops so widely divergently in the various animal forms. Instead of following out their original suggestion that the germ-layers have wider capacities for differentiation than is usually recognized, they preferred to force the widely differing behaviour of mesoderm in different forms into a common pattern by their coelome theory (1881). According to this, the mesoderm (the mesoderm is in this paper first subdivided into mesenchyme and mesoblast; the latter term had been in use to describe the whole middle layer for many years) necessarily always arises from the endoderm, enclosing within its two layers part of the alimentary cavity as the "coelome" (Haeckel's name for the pleuroperitoneal cavity of Remak). According to the Hertwigs (1881, p. 122):

> Ectoblast and entoblast are the primary germ-layers which originate by invagination of the blastula; they are therefore always the first formed and they can be referred back to a simple stem-form, the gastraea. . . . Parietal and visceral mesoblast, or the middle germ-layers, always originate later, and arise through a pouching or folding of the entoblast; . . . They bound a new cavity, the enterocoel, which may be considered a pinched-off diverticulum of the archenteron. As the two-layered animals are derivable from the gastraea, so are the four-layered from a coelome-form.

The whole theory, as an explanation of development, can probably never be better described than it has been by Braem (1895, p. 468) who wrote: "So the coelome theory, with all of its consequence, presents one of the most glaring inconsequences to which the morphological conception of the germ-layers can lead."

This nice statement of Braem's formed part of a series of papers published in 1895 and entitled "What is a Germ-layer?", in which the author scrutinized the whole germ-layer doctrine from many angles. He raised the same doubts as to its validity as had the other investigators whom we have quoted; the only solution of the problem that he could offer was that the germ-layer theory was based purely on topography, while the homologies, or rather the analogies, of the layers could be comprehended only on a physiological basis.

The Germ-Layers in Regeneration and Budding

To be sure, this particular period saw the beginnings of the first attempt since His's to deal with the problem from a physiological point of view, or at least from an experimental rather than a descriptive point of view. Perhaps the word *experimental* is dangerously used in this connection, since in one of the first important cases the experiment was performed by nature and simply observed and interpreted by the investigator. Hjort (1894a, b), in his study of bud-formation in the Ascidians, made the accurate and cogent observation that in *Botryllus* organs are not formed from the same germ-layers in egg-development and in budding. In development from the egg, for instance, the atrial chamber and the ganglion are each formed from the ectoderm in *Botryllus*; in the bud they are each derived not from the outer but from the inner layer. Hjort concluded that the layers of the bud are not germ-layers in the ordinary sense, but were composed of still indifferent material.

The import of this discovery was at once appreciated as jeopardizing the validity of the doctrine. Heider (1897), in a paper that like Braem's was entitled with a rhetorical question never answered, "Is the Germ-layer Doctrine Shattered?", insisted that findings like those of Hjort were irrelevant so far as the germ-layer doctrine in embryology was concerned. The doctrine, according to Heider, still holds for embryology, where it belongs, whether or not it holds true for the cases of budding and regeneration which are problems separate from those of embryology.

A more convincing argument, however, had been promulgated the year before by E. B. Wilson (1896) in a brilliant lecture at Woods Hole on "The Embryological Criterion of Homology." Wilson maintained that the conditions in budformation and regeneration were vitally significant for a comprehension of the processes in the embryo. He wrote (pp. 112-113):

It may be urged that in regeneration and agamogenesis development is condensed and abbreviated so as no longer to repeat the phyletic development, and this is no doubt true. This explanation contains, however, a fatal admission; for if secondary modification may go so far as completely to destroy the typical relationships between the germ-layers and the parts of the adult, then those relationships are not of an essential or necessary character, and we cannot assume that the germ-layers have any *fixed* morphological value, even in the gastrula.

First Experimental Attack on the Problem

While philosophically speaking it may have seemed difficult to their contemporaries to choose between the interpretations of Heider and Wilson, even before their papers had been published the first experiment had been performed along the lines of the later ones which were finally to throw the balance to the side of Wilson. During 1892-93 Herbst subjected echino-derm eggs to treatment with a large variety of salts. He found that lithium had a specific effect on their development, namely the production of exogastrulae and entogastrulae in which the amount of endoderm in the embryo is greatly increased at the expense of the ectoderm.

In figures 11, 6, 12-14, there thus occurs a gradual increase of endoderm, and hand in hand with it a successive reduction of ectoderm. In figure 13 the latter is present only as the small button labelled *ga,* and in figure 14 it is no longer present at all; here the whole blastula wall has been transformed to endoderm (1893, p. 144).

Herbst appreciated the implication of his results; not so did his contemporaries who did not wish to. Heider, for instance, in the paper referred to above, mentioned the lithium-embryos only as a possible explanation of how in the production of endoderm in Coelenterates the processes of multipolar migration and delamination might have been derived from polar migration.

The Pathologists and the Germ-Layer Doctrine

Indeed the main body of embryologists (cf. Sedgwick, 1910) went their way, promulgating the germ-layer doctrine and

276

attempting always to support and strengthen it. One other group of scientific investigators discussed the problem avidly: the pathologists, who were seeking panaceas to solve the atypical growth problem. Some of them, perhaps most notably Marchand (1899-1900), unsuccessfully sought the aid of the germ-layer doctrine. They contributed more to the embryologists, however, than they received from them, since they could furnish evidence both pro and con. Not the most influential, but perhaps one of the most interesting results of the cooperation between pathology and embryology, was the prophecy of the experiment, and its results, which have been most instrumental in abolishing the notion of the fixity of the layers. C. S. Minot in a paper on the embryological basis of pathology wrote, in 1901 (p. 485): "It seems quite probable to me that the cells of the germ-layers are at first quite indifferent, so that if it were possible to graft a young mesodermal cell on to the ectoderm or endoderm, it would become a true ectodermal or endodermal cell, as the case may be." A similar experiment, performed by Mangold a quarter of a century later, has been considered one of the crucial experiments in the demonstration of the non-specificity of the germ-layers.

MODERN EXPERIMENTAL WORK

1. Vertebrates

The turn of the century saw the embryologists change their method of attack from observation to actual operative manipulation. The capacity of the germ-layers for differentiation could now be tested as well as inferred. We may first discuss in this connection the results of the work on vertebrate embryos.

The interpretation of the experiments on the germ-layers of the Vertebrates was facilitated, in fact made possible, by the background work of Vogt (1925) who charted out on the amphibian blastula, by means of local vital staining, the precise locations of the areas later to become chorda, mesoderm, gut, epidermis and nervous system. Once the position of these cell-groups before gastrulation was known, their behavior in unusual positions, or in isolation, could be appreciated.

Perhaps the most far-reaching results on the activity of the germ-layers, established experimentally, were those which demonstrated the influence of the lower invaginated layers of the amphibian embryo on the differentiation of the overlying ectoderm. Spemann had, in 1918, as is well known, noted the power of transplanted dorsal lip of the blastopore of the amphibian gastrula to induce the formation of a new embryo from presumptive epidermis; in 1924, in an investigation carried out with the collaboration of Hilde Mangold, similar experiments were performed using hosts and donors of different species whose tissues were sharply distinguishable from each other in sectioned material. From the results of this experiment it became apparent that the medullary plate in the induced embryo was formed by the host, while the underlying gut, chorda and mesoderm were furnished in part by the grafted dorsal lip. This result, and others of Spemann's (1918) from experiments in which presumptive epidermis was exchanged with presumptive medullary plate, or in which areas of medullary plate and mesoderm of the neurula were rotated through 180° (1912), suggested that the lower layers were somehow responsible for the differentiation of the upper. This was crucially and definitely demonstrated by Marx, who found, in 1925, that a piece of already invaginated archenteron roof, implanted into the blastocoele cavity, induced the formation of medullary plate from presumptive epidermis. Subsequently Bautzmann (1926, '28) was able to show by similar transplantation experiments that both presumptive chorda and presumptive mesoderm display the power of inducing the overlying epidermis to differentiate medullary plate.

All of these transplantation experiments suggest immediately the interpretation that the underlying layers, particularly mesoderm and chorda, as the inducing system (to use a term later introduced), are somehow inherently different in their capacities than the responding system of the overlying ectoderm. This interpretation has been in one way borne out by results of explantation experiments, and by the production of amphibian exogastrulae. When amphibian embryos, especially axolotls, are treated with appropriate salt solutions, the mesoderm, endoderm and chorda roll outwards instead of inwards, with the result that the ectoderm remains simply an empty bag. In such exogastrulae, the mesoderm and endoderm and chorda self-differentiate to form somites, gut and notochord histologically quite typical of the normal embryo; the ectoderm, on the other hand, deprived of the proximity of these layers, forms only epidermis and never nervous system (Holtfreter, 1933).

Similarly in explantation experiments, in which isolated parts of the amphibian gastrula are cultured in salt solutions, as shown by Holtfreter's (1938 a, b) masterly work, isolated ectoderm fails to differentiate nervous tissue; it forms only epidermis when deprived of influence of cells of the other layers. The presumptive endoderm, whose rôle has been least clearly analyzed in the transplantation experiments, when isolated in salt solution self-differentiates only endodermal structures.

Cells of the presumptive chorda and mesoderm regions, in contrast to those of the other two germ-layers, readily overstep the classical bounds of the germ-layers, and when isolated in salt-solution can self-differentiate, or induce from their own cells, according to interpretation, medullary plate and epidermis on the one hand, and gut on the other, in addition to forming the usual mesodermal structures.

If the experiments are carried out, however, by placing the isolates *in vivo* rather than *in vitro*, the ectoderm and endoderm can accomplish far more than in salt solution. This has been demonstrated by Kusche (1929) and Bautzmann (1929), who placed the tissues into the empty orbital cavity of older larvae, and Holtfreter (1929) who implanted them into the abdominal cavity of amphibian larvae. In these cases, presumptive ectoderm formed not only medullary tube, but also notochord and muscle, and presumptive endoderm was able to differentiate notochord. Here where the cells were subjected to influences of highly complex organic nature, even ectoderm and endoderm were able to differentiate structures normally formed by the other germ-layers. The nature of these external influences and of their action is unknown. But their effect is sufficient to demonstrate that the differentiating cells themselves have a wider capacity for diversification than the other experiments had suggested.

These are by no means the only clear-cut experiments demonstrating the variety of potencies expressible by the cells of the amphibian gastrula. Mangold had in 1923 performed the experiment postulated twenty years before by Minot and thus dealt the germ-layer doctrine one of its most mortal blows. He found that presumptive ectoderm formed somites, chorda, pronephros, etc. when grafted into appropriate regions. Furthermore, Bruns (1935) showed that when large defects were made in the presumptive ectoderm of amphibian gastrulae, the medullary plate could be formed from presumptive mesoderm. Lopaschov (1935) also showed that when several explants of presumptive mesoderm fused they frequently produced medullary plate. Lehmann (1937) has shown that lithium has a specific mesodermizing effect on presumptive notochord material in the amphibian gastrula.

Similar demonstrations have been made on other forms than amphibians. Hunt (1937 a and b) has shown for the chick that after removal of the presumptive endoderm the mesoderm can form gut, and indeed that even normally it makes a large contribution to the formation of this structure. It also has been shown for the fishes (Oppenheimer, 1938) that presumptive mesoderm can differentiate nervous structures under certain conditions.

The perfectly valid objection can be raised that in all the cases enumerated the cells whose accomplishments are being studied have been observed acting under highly abnormal conditions, and though it does not necessarily invalidate the results of the experiments, this is to a large extent true. There are, however, some striking cases in vertebrate development where, even in the intact embryo, cells of one germ-layer form structures usually contributed by the others. One of these, touched on by Kölliker (1884), is in tail-formation in the Vertebrates. Kölliker had postulated that all the structures in the tail of a vertebrate embryo were formed from a blastema that was primarily mesodermal in origin. Such is not precisely the case in the amphibian embryo, but the actual conditions as they are support Kölliker's conclusion very strongly. The notochord of the amphibian embryo's tail is formed as a prolongation of that of the trunk. The tail somites, however, as demonstrated conclusively by the vital staining experiments of Bijtel (1931), are formed by the posterior portion of the medullary plate itself. Here is a clear-cut case in normal development where typically mesodermal structures are formed by cells ectodermal in origin.

Another such case is shown by the behavior of the cells of the neural crest. The history of the work on this problem has been fully reviewed by Harrison and therefore need only be summarily discussed here. [All references concerning the the neural crest cited here may be obtained from Harrison's (1938) paper.] The neural crest, as every one knows, is clearly an ectodermal derivative in the sense of the germ-layer doctrine. However, it was demonstrated even in the last century that it furnished mesenchyme (Kastschenko and Goronowitsch), and, in 1894, it was given, together with the branchial sensory placodes which make a similar contribution, the name of mesectoderm, by von Kupffer. In 1897 Miss Platt showed, on morphological grounds, that the branchial skeleton was derived from mesectoderm. The recent experimental evidence has demonstrated that the neural crest unquestionably forms the Schwann sheath-cells, the spinal ganglia, part of the cranial ganglia, the branchial skeleton, mesenchyme, melanophores and xanthophores, possibly the ganglia of the sympathetic nervous system, and probably the pia-arachnoid membranes.

2. *Invertebrates*

Such varied accomplishments of the germ-layers are characteristic not only of the Vertebrates, but of Invertebrates as well. Probably as many single isolated cases could be enumerated for the Invertebrates as have been for the Vertebrates, but here we shall confine our remarks to two groups.

One of the most clear-cut cases imaginable of the transformability of the germ-layers has been presented by Penners (1926, '37a and b, '38) in his beautiful studies of the development of *Tubifex*. The *Tubifex* egg, as described by Penners (1924), exhibits the spiral cleavage characteristic of the annelid egg. It is further characterized by the presence at its animal and ventral poles of a special "pole-plasm" which passes during cleavage into the cells 2d and 4d which give rise respectively to the ectodermal and mesodermal germ-bands of the embryo. If the pole-plasm is eliminated or divided the cells 2d and 4d and subsequently the germ-bands fail to form or are doubled, as the case may be. Penners (1926) showed that if 2d or 4d were excluded from development, ectodermal or mesodermal germ-bands respectively failed to form; each type of germ-band, however, could differentiate apparently normally in the absence of the other (i.e. when 2d was removed and 4d left intact or vice versa). Later (1937a) he performed similar experiments, allowing the worms to develop to late stages, and the results here were extraordinarily interesting. In the absence of the ectodermal germ-bands, the mesoderm can later form all the organs usually formed by the ectodermal —central nervous system, circular musculature, lateral line, and the ectodermal portion of the seta-sacs. If, however, the source of the mesodermal germ-bands is removed and the ectodermal left intact (Penners, 1937b) the organs normally formed by the mesoderm are not replaced. It is nevertheless extremely interesting and important that in a form characterized by a relatively highly mosaic development the organs formed normally by one germ-layer can be formed by another.

The modern work on the Echinoderms has shown that in this form also the germ-layers have great adaptability. This was first suggested by Herbst's (1892–93) chemical experiments; it has been demonstrated repeatedly in defect- and transplantation experiments. The Rünnstroms (1918–19) showed, for instance, that animal halves of a holothurian egg, containing only presumptive ectoderm, could differentiate the coelome which is normally formed by mesenchyme, and subsequently Hörstadius (1928) has shown that coelome may be formed in regeneration by ectoderm, endoderm or mesoderm. Recently the chemical and defect- and transplantation experiments have been extended, and they have been amplified and reinterpreted in the light of physiological studies on the developing egg and its parts in such a way that our picture of the developing echinoderm egg is as complete as any we have in embryology.

In the early defect-experiments, Driesch (1891–92, 1892–93, 1900) erroneously supposed all the parts of the developing echinoderm to be totipotent. This problem was clarified by Hörstadius (1928, '35) who showed that isolated animal halves of eggs, which contain only presumptive ectoderm, cannot gastrulate or form endoderm, while isolated vegetal halves can gastrulate and form plutei; sometimes the plutei have an overabundance of endoderm, and sometimes the isolated vegetal halves form exogastrulae with very large guts. The results of these experiments, and of similar ones involving smaller parts of the egg, gained significance with the publication of von Ubisch's (1933) paper which demonstrated on the basis of vital staining experiments the precise normal rôles of the various portions of the egg. The animal half of the egg, consisting at the 32-cell stage of a dorsal group of 8 cells (an^1) and a ventral group of 8 (an^2), forms the ectoderm of the dorsal surface of the pluteus. The vegetal half is divided at the 64-cell stage into a dorsal ring of 8 cells (veg^1) which forms aboral ectoderm, a more ventral ring of 8 cells (veg^2) which forms the endoderm, and at its most ventral pole the micromeres which form the mesenchyme. Driesch (1893) knew that the micromeres formed the mesenchyme, and all the workers previous to von Ubisch appreciated that the animal pole represented presumptive ectoderm. The main important point demonstrated by von Ubisch was that the upper part of the vegetal half also contained presumptive ectoderm.

The transformability of the germ-layers has been fully demonstrated by Hörstadius (1935) in his ingenious experiments of separating and recombining the cells whose normal behaviour is well known. He has shown, for instance, that when veg^2, which comprises the presumptive endoderm and normally forms gut, is eliminated from development, a normal pluteus results whose gut is formed by veg^1 which is composed of the presumptive ectoderm for the aboral surface. If both veg^1 and veg^2 are eliminated, again a normal pluteus forms whose gut is made by ectoderm of the animal half of the egg. In both of these cases the micromeres are considered to induce the ectoderm to become endoderm; but no matter what the mechanism, the result is that presumptive ectoderm forms endodermal structures. Similarly, micromeres implanted into the animal pole of whole eggs induce the formation of accessory gut from presumptive ectoderm. Endodermizing of presumptive ectodermal material occurs also when blastomeres are separated and recombined in such a way that the proportion of presumptive ectoderm to presumptive endoderm is far greater than usual; for instance, when a meridional half of an egg is combined with an animal half.

The transformability of the presumptive endodermal cells has also been shown by Hörstadius (1928). An isolated veg^2 group, for instance, is able to form ectoderm, though to be sure such ectoderm is slightly abnormal, as shown by the fact that it forms no stomodaeum nor ciliated band, and the skeleton, whose arrangement depends on an interaction between ectoderm and mesenchyme, is somewhat abnormal. Driesch (1893) had known that eggs deprived of their micromeres could form normal plutei. Hörstadius demonstrated that in such eggs the secondary mesenchyme, which is derived from veg^2, is formed earlier than normal and serves to form the skeleton.

Fortunately in the case of the echinoderm egg the physiological basis for the transformability of the germ-layers is being studied. Herbst (1892, '93) had shown that in whole eggs presumptive ectoderm could be caused to differentiate endoderm by the action of lithium. Von Ubisch (1929) showed that isolated animal halves, consisting only of presumptive ectoderm, which normally form no endoderm and fail to gastrulate, could accomplish both these tasks after treatment with lithium. Hörstadius (1936) has shown, by varying the length of treatment and by using parts of eggs isolated for varying lengths of time, that the action of the lithium on the presumptive ectoderm is strikingly similar to that of implanted micromeres.

This work, beautiful in itself, has gained considerably in significance through the work of Lindahl and his co-workers (Lindahl, 1936; Lindahl and Stordal, 1937; Lindahl and Öhman, 1938). Lindahl suggested originally that in the whole egg the animal half, the presumptive ectoderm, exhibits a higher respiratory rate than the vegetal. Similarly, eggs "animalized" by chemical treatment have a higher respiratory rate than isolated vegetal halves. The action of lithium inhibits respiration, so that the presumptive ectoderm which is made to form endoderm simultaneously decreases its respiratory rate. Conversely, the presence of NaSCN or the absence of sulphate ion stimulates respiration and ectodermalizes presumptive endoderm. There are probably two systems of respiration involved at the two poles of the egg which act in a way synergistically, and the system at the animal pole is probably concerned with carbohydrate metabolism.

Lindahl and Holter (1938, unpublished) have been unable to find confirmatory evidence of Lindahl's original statement that the respiratory rate is higher in the animal than in the vegetal portion of the egg. In any case, no matter what the precise nature of the respiratory systems, the transformation of ectoderm to endoderm, and vice versa, has been shown definitely to have a metabolic as well as a morphological basis.

CONCLUSIONS

The only conclusion that can be maintained, as a result of all the experiments that have been enumerated, is that the doctrine of the absolute specificity of the germ-layers as enunciated in the last century must be abandoned. There are no doubt countless cases where in a specific animal form, the cells of one germ-layer cannot alone perform the functions characteristic of another, as for instance is the case with the ectodermal germ-bands of *Tubifex* (Penners, 1937b). There are however so many contrary accomplishments that even in the classical cases the differentiation of the cells must be based on other factors than their derivation from a specific layer. The nature of such factors probably varies in every instance. In some cases, such as the *Tubifex* egg, the constitution of the cytoplasm before cleavage plays an important rôle. In other cases, as with the echinoderm egg, the special metabolism of parts of the egg is of decisive importance. The precise topographical position of the cells is often significant, as in the case of amphibian development. The interactions of various cells one with another are of vital importance in controlling their differentiation in the Vertebrates.

If so many factors other than the origin of the cells from particular germ-layers are of such vital importance, the question arises:—What is the significance of the germ-layers, if any? No matter what the precise factors involved, it seems certain that the precise location of a cell during gastrulation in many forms, or the precise origin of its cytoplasm from the egg in others, is in many cases correlated with the type of its later activity; therefore in a certain sense the germ-layers are of topographic significance, since the cells pass through them in their orderly progression of movements. In a teleological sense, formation of germ-layers seems to be the embryo's method of sorting out its constituent parts. The essential point is, however, that this method is not the only method that the embryo can call upon to attain a specific end, and here as in many other cases in development the embryo can, when necessary, modify or abandon one method in favor of another. This point, anticipated by Kölliker (1879), as we have already shown, has been well stated in the Brachet textbook (p. 296): "In reality, the germ-layers, like the blastomeres, have an actual potentiality and a total potentiality; the former is what they normally become; the latter what they are capable of forming in addition under diverse natural or experimental influences."

The task of the student of the germ-layers then must become more than an attempt to discern how the embryo sorts its cells into one layer or another; it must become an elucidation of how the wide potencies of the germ-layers become subject to limitation to their normal accomplishment. Pander, who was first to describe the germ-layers, was fortunate and wise in emphasizing the interactions of the layers with each other. We should do well to emulate him, for only when we can more appreciate the manner and mechanisms of such interactions shall we understand the true significance of the germ-layers themselves.

REFERENCES

Papers with comprehensive bibliographies on the germ-layer doctrine are marked with an asterisk.

ALLMAN, G. J. 1853. On the anatomy and physiology of *Cordylophora*: A contribution to our knowledge of Tubularian zoophytes. *Phil. Trans. Roy. Soc. London,* vol. 143, pp. 367–384.

VON BAER, K. E. 1828–37. Ueber Entwicklungsgeschichte der Thiere. Beobachtung und Reflexion. *Königsberg.*

BALFOUR, F. M. 1873. The development and growth of the layers of the blastoderm. *Quart. J. Micr. Sci.,* vol. 13, pp. 266–276.

BAUTZMANN, H. 1926. Experimentelle Untersuchungen zur Abgrenzung des Organisationszentrums bei *Triton taeniatus,* mit einem Anhang: Ueber Induktion durch Blastulamaterial. *Arch. f. Entw.-mech.,* Bd. 108, S. 283–321.

———. 1928. Experimentelle Untersuchungen über die Induktionsfähigkeit von Chorda und Mesoderm bei *Triton. Arch. f. Entw.-mech.,* Bd. 114, S. 177–225.

———. 1929. Ueber bedeutungsfremde Selbstdifferenzierung aus Teilstücken des Amphibienkeimes. *Naturwiss.,* Jahrg. 17, S. 818-827.

BIJTEL, J. 1931. Ueber die Entwicklung des Schwanzes bei Amphibien. *Arch. f. Entw.-mech.,* Bd. 125, S. 448–486.

BRACHET, A. 1935. Traité d'embryologie des vertébrés. Seconde édition revue et complétée par A. Dalcq et P. Gerard. *Paris.*

*BRAEM, F. 1895. Was ist ein Keimblatt? *Biol. Centralbl.,* Bd. 15, S. 427–443, 466–476, 491–506.

BRUNS, E. 1931. Experimente über das Regulationsvermögen der Blastula von *Triton taeniatus* und *Bombinator pachypus. Arch. f. Entw.-mech.,* Bd. 123, S. 682–718.

CUVIER, G. 1846. Leçons d'anatomie comparée. Tome huitième contenant les organes de la génération et des sécretions, avec une leçon complémentaire des organes de relations; par G. Cuvier et G.-L. Duvernoy. 2ième édition, corrigée et augmentée. *Paris.*

DRIESCH, H. 1891–92. Entwicklungsmechanische Studien. I. Der Werth der beiden ersten Furchungszellen in der Echinodermenentwicklung. Experimentelle Erzeugung von Theil- und Doppel-bildung. II. Ueber die Beziehungen des Lichtes zur ersten Etappe der thierischen Formbildung. *Zeit. wiss. Zool.*, Bd. 53, S. 160–189.

————. 1892-93. Entwicklungsmechanische Studien. III. Die Ver-minderung des Furchungsmaterials und ihre Folgen (Weiteres ueber Theilbildungen). IV. Experimentelle Veränderungen des Typus der Furchung und ihre Folgen (Wirkungen von Wärme-zufuhr und von Druck). V. Von der Furchung doppelbefruchteter Eier. VI. Ueber einige allgemeine Fragen der theoretischen Mor-phologie. *Zeit. wiss. Zool.*, Bd. 55, S. 1–62.

————. 1893. Entwicklungsmechanische Studien. VII. Exogastrula und Anenteria (über die Wirkung von Wärmezufuhr auf die Lar-venentwicklung der Echiniden). VIII. Ueber Variation der Mikro-merenbildung (Wirkung von Verdünnung des Meerwassers). IX. Ueber die Vertretbarkeit der "Anlagen" von Ektoderm und Ento-derm. X. Ueber allgemeine entwicklungsmechanische Ergebnisse. *Mitt. zool. Stat. Neapel,* Bd. 11, S. 221–254.

————. 1900. Die isolirten Blastomeren des Echinidenkeimes. Eine Nachprüfung und Erweiterung früherer Untersuchungen. *Arch. f. Entw.-mech.,* Bd. 10, S. 361–410.

HAECKEL, E. 1866. Generelle Morphologie. *Berlin.*

————. 1872. Die Kalkschwämme. Eine Monographie. *Berlin.*

*HARRISON, R. G. 1938. Die Neuralleiste. Erganzheft zum *Anat. Anz.,* Bd. 85, S. 3–30.

*HEIDER, K. 1897. Ist die Keimblattlehre erschüttert? *Schubergs Zool. Centralbl.,* Jahrg. 4, S. 725–737.

HERBST, C. 1892. Experimentelle Untersuchungen über den Ein-fluss der veränderten chemischen Zusammensetzung des umgehen-den Mediums auf die Entwicklung der Thiere. I. Theil. Versuche an Seeigeleiern. *Zeit. wiss. Zool.,* Bd. 55, S. 446–518.

————. 1893. Experimentelle Untersuchungen über den Einfluss der veränderten chemischen Zusammensetzung des umgebenden Mediums auf die Entwicklung der Thiere. II. Theil. Weiteres über die morphologische Wirkung der Lithiumsalze und ihre theo-retische Bedeutung. *Mitt. zool. Stat. Neapel,* Bd. 11, S. 136–220.

HERTWIG, O. 1881. Die Entwicklung des mittleren Keimblattes der Wirbelthiere. *Jena.*

*————. 1906. "Die Lehre von den Keimblättern." *In* O. HERTWIG: Handbuch der vergleichenden und experimentellen Entwickelungs-lehre der Wirbeltiere. Bd. I, Theil I, S. 699–967. *Jena.*

————, AND R. 1878. Der Organismus der Medusen und seine Stellung zur Keimblättertheorie. *Jena.*

————, AND ————. 1879. Studien zur Blättertheorie. Heft I. Die Aktinien anatomisch und histologisch mit besonderer Berücksichtigung des Nervenmuskelsystems untersucht. *Jena.*

————, AND ————. 1880. Studien zur Blättertheorie. Heft II. Die Chaetognäthen. Ihre Anatomie, Systematik und Entwickelungsgeschichte. *Jena.*

————, AND ————. 1881. Studien zur Blättertheorie. Heft IV. Die Coelomtheorie. Versuch einer Erklärung des mittleren Keimblattes. *Jena.*

HERTWIG, R. 1880. Studien zur Blättertheorie. Heft III. Ueber den Bau der Ctenophoren. *Jena.*

HIS, W. 1865. Die Häute und Höhlen des Körpers. *Basel.*

————. 1874. Unsere Körperform und das physiologische Problem ihrer Enstehung. *Leipzig.*

HJORT, J. 1893. Ueber den Entwicklungscyclus der zusammengesetzten Ascidien. *Mitt. zool. Stat. Neapel,* Bd. 10, S. 584–618.

————. 1895. Beitrag zur Keimblätterlehre und Entwickelungsmechanik der Ascidienknospung. *Anat. Anz.,* Bd. 10, S. 215–229.

HÖRSTADIUS, S. 1928. Ueber die Determination des Keimes bei Echinodermen. *Acta Zool.,* vol. 9, pp. 1–191.

————. 1935. Ueber die Determination im Verlaufe der Eiachse bei Seeigeln. *Pubbl. Staz. Zool. Nap.,* vol. 14, pp. 253-429.

————. 1936. Ueber die zeitliche Determination im Keim von *Paracentrotus lividus* Lk. *Arch. f. Entw.-mech.,* Bd. 135, S. 1–39.

HOLTFRETER, J. 1929. Ueber die Aufzucht isolierter Teile des Amphibienkeimes. I. Methode eine Gewebezüchtung in vivo. *Arch. f. Entw.-mech.,* Bd. 117, S. 421–510.

————. 1933. Die totale Exogastrulation, eine Selbstablösung des Ektoderms vom Entomesoderm. Entwicklung und funktionelles Verhalten nervenloser Organe. *Arch. f. Entw.-mech.,* Bd. 129, S. 670–793.

————. 1938a. Differenzierungspotenzen isolierter Teile der Urodelengastrula. *Arch. f. Entw.-mech.,* Bd. 138, S. 522–656.

————. 1938b. Differenzierungspotenzen isolierter Teile der Anurengastrula. *Arch. f. Entw.-mech.,* Bd. 138, S. 657–738.

HUNT, T. E. 1937a. The development of gut and its derivatives from the mesectoderm and mesentoderm of early chick blastoderms. *Anat. Rec.,* vol. 68, pp. 349–369.

————. 1937b. The origin of entodermal cells from the primitive streak of the chick embryo. *Anat. Rec.*, vol. 68, pp. 449–459.

HUXLEY, T. H. 1868–96. "The physical basis of life." *In* Method and Results, New York, 1896. (Lecture delivered in 1868.)

————. 1849. On the anatomy and affinities of the family of the Medusae. *Phil. Trans. Roy. Soc. London*, vol. 139, pp. 413–434.

————. 1869. An Introduction to the Classification of Animals. *London.*

————. 1871–72. A Manual of the Anatomy of Vertebrated Animals. *New York*, 1872 (*London*, 1871).

KLEINENBERG, N. 1872. Hydra. Eine Monographie. *Leipzig.*

————. 1886. Die Entstehung des Annelids aus der Larve von *Lopadorhyncus*. Nebst Bemerkungen über die Entwicklung anderer Polychaeten. *Leipzig.*

VON KÖLLIKER, A. 1879. Entwickelungsgeschichte des Menschen und der höheren Thiere. Zweite ganz umgearbeitete Auflage. *Leipzig.*

————. 1884. Die embryonalen Keimblätter und die Gewebe. *Zeit. wiss. Zool.*, Bd. 40, S. 179–213.

————. 1889. Handbuch der Gewebelehre des Menschen. 6. umgearbeitete Auflage. Erster Band: Die allgemeine Gewebelehre und die Systeme der Haut, Knochen und Muskeln. *Leipzig.*

KOWALEWSKI, A. 1867a. Entwickelungsgeschichte des *Amphioxus lanceolatus*. *Mém. de l'acad. de St. Pétersbourg*, VIIe Série, T. 11, No. 4.

————. 1867b. Beiträge zur Entwickelungsgeschichte der Holothurien. *Mém. de l'acad. de St. Pétersbourg*, VIIe Série, T. 11, No. 6.

————. 1869–71. Embryologische Studien an Würmern und Arthropoden. *Mém. de l'acad. de St. Pétersbourg*, VIIe Série, T. 16, No. 12.

KUSCHE, W. 1929. Interplantation umschriebener Zellbezirke aus der Blastula und Gastrula von Amphibien. *Arch. f. Entw.-mech.*, Bd. 120, S. 192–271.

LANKESTER, E. R. 1873. On the primitive cell-layers of the embryo as the basis of genealogical classification of animals, and on the origin of vascular and lymph systems. *Ann. and Mag. Nat. Hist.*, Series 4, vol. 11, pp. 321–338.

————. 1877. Notes on the embryology and classification of the animal kingdom: comprising a revision of speculations relative to the origin and significance of the germ-layers. *Quart. J. Micr. Sci.*, vol. 17, pp. 399–454.

LEHMANN, F. E. 1937. Mesodermisierung der präsumptiven Chorda-materials durch Einwirkung von Lithiumchlorid auf die Gastrula von *Triton alpestris. Arch. f. Entw.-mech.,* Bd. 136, S. 112–116.

LINDAHL, P. 1936. Zur Kenntnis der physiologischen Grundlagen der Determination im Seeigelkeim. *Acta Zool.,* vol. 17, pp. 79–365.

———, AND L. O. ÖHMANN. 1938. Weitere Studien über Stoffwech-sel und Determination im Seeigelkeim. *Biol. Zentralbl.,* Bd. 58, S. 179–228.

———, AND ÅKE STORDAL. 1937. Zur Kenntnis des vegetativen Stoff-wechsels im Seeigelei. *Arch. f. Entw.-mech.,* Bd. 136, S. 44–63.

LOPASCHOV, G. 1935. Die Entwicklungsleistungen des Gastrulameso-derms in Abhängigkeit von Veränderungen seiner Masse. *Biol. Zentralbl.,* Bd. 55, S. 606–615.

*MANGOLD, O. 1923. Transplantationsversuche zur Frage der Spezifi-tät und der Bildung der Keimblätter in der Entwicklung. *Arch. f. mikr. Anat. und Ent.-gesch.,* Bd. 100, S. 198–301.

MARCHAND, F. 1899. Ueber die Beziehungen der pathologischen Anatomie zur Entwickelungsgeschichte, besonders der Keimblatt-lehre. *Verh. d. deutsch. patholog. Gesellsch. München,* Jahrg. 2, S. 38–107.

MARX, A. 1925. Experimentelle Untersuchungen zur Frage der De-termination der Medullarplatte. *Arch. f. Entw.-mech.,* Bd. 105, S. 20–44.

MINOT, C. S. 1901. The embryological basis of pathology. Sci., N.S., vol. 13, pp. 481–498.

OPPENHEIMER, J. M. 1938. Potencies for differentiation in the tele-ostean germ-ring. *J. Exp. Zool.,* vol. 79, pp. 185–212.

PANDER, C. 1817a. Beyträge zur Entwickelungsgeschichte des Hühn-chens im Eye. *Würzburg.*

———. 1817b. Dissertatio inauguralis, sistens historiam metamor-phoseos, quam ovum incubatum prioribus quinque diebus subit. *Würzburg.*

PENNERS, A. 1924. Experimentelle Untersuchungen zum Determina-tions-problem am Keim von *Tubifex rivulorum* Lam. I. Die dupli-citas cruciata und organbildenden Substanzen. *Arch. f. mikr. Anat. u. Entw.-gesch.,* Bd. 102, S. 51–100.

———. 1926. Experimentelle Untersuchungen zum Determinations-problem am Keim von *Tubifex rivulorum* Lam. II. Die Entwick-lung teilweise abgetöteter Keime. *Zeit. wiss. Zool.,* Bd. 127, S. 1–140.

————. 1937a. Regulation am Keim von *Tubifex rivulorum* Lam. nach Ausschaltung des ektodermalen Keimstreifs. *Zeit. wiss. Zool.*, Bd. 149, S. 86–130.

————. 1937b. Abhängigkeit der Formbildung vom Mesoderm in Tubifex-Embryo. *Zeit. wiss. Zool.*, Bd. 150, S. 305–357.

RATHKE, M. H. 1825. Flusskrebs. *Isis von Oken,* Jahrg. 1825, Theil 2, S. 1093–1100.

————. 1829. Untersuchungen über die Bildung und Entwickelung des Flusskrebses. *Leipzig.*

REMAK, R. 1850–55. Untersuchungen über die Entwickelung der Wirbelthiere. *Berlin.*

RUNNSTRÖM, J., AND S. 1918–19. Ueber die Entwicklung von *Cucumaria frondosus* Gunnerus und *Psolus phantapus* Strussenfelt. *Bergens Mus. Aarbok. Naturv. Raekke,* 5; 9.

RUSSELL, E. S. 1916. Form and Function. A Contribution to the History of Animal Morphology. *London.*

SEDGWICK, A. 1910. "Embryology." *In* Encyclopedia Brittanica, 11th edition, vol. 9, pp. 314–329. *Cambridge.*

SPEMANN, H. 1912. Ueber die Entwicklung umgedrehter Hirnteile bei Amphibienembryonen. *Zool. Jahrb.*, Suppl. 15, pp. 1–48.

SPEMANN, H. 1918. Ueber die Determination der ersten Organanlagen des Amphibienembryo I–VI. *Arch. f. Entw.-mech.*, Bd. 43, S. 448–555.

————, AND H. MANGOLD. 1924. Ueber Induktion von Embryonalanlagen durch Implantation artfremder Organisatoren. *Arch f. mikr. Anat. und Entw.-gesch.*, Bd. 100, S. 599–638.

VON UBISCH, L. 1929. Ueber die Determination der larvalen Organe und der Imaginalanlage bei dem Seeigelkeim. *Arch. f. Entw.-mech.*, Bd. 117, S. 80–122.

————. 1933. Formbildungsanalyse an Seeigellarven. *Naturwiss.*, Jahrg. 21, S. 183–186.

VOGT, W. 1925. Gestaltungsanalyse am Amphibienkeim mit örtlicher Vitalfärbung. Vorwort über Wege und Ziele. I. Methode und Wirkungsweise der örtlichen Vitalfärbung mit Agar als Farbträger. *Arch. f. Entw.-mech.*, Bd. 106, S. 542–610.

WOLFF, C. F. 1759. Theoria generationis. *Halle.*

————. 1812. Ueber die Bildung des Darmkanals im bebrüteten Hühnchen. Uebersetzt und mit einer einleitenden Abhandlung und Anmerkungen von Johann Friedrich Meckel. *Halle.* Originally published by Wolff as follows: De formatione intestinorum praecipue, tum et de amnio spurio, aliisque partibus embryonis Gallinacei nondum visis. Novi Comment. Acad. Sci. Imp. Petropol. vols. 12 and 13, 1768–69.

WILSON, E. B.   1894–96.   The Embryological Criterion of Homology. Biological Lectures delivered at the Marine Biological Laboratory in the summer session of 1894. *Boston.*

K. E. von Baer's
Beginning Insights into
Causal-Analytical Relationships
during Development[*]

INTRODUCTION

IN 1958 Arthur O. Lovejoy wrote for a book on the *Fore-runners of Darwin* an essay on embryology and evolution, and in it he stated that "no biologist today (1958), I think, would accept von Baer's embryological doctrine as a whole, or even its most distinctive and essential theses" (Lovejoy, 1959, p. 442). By von Baer's doctrine Lovejoy seems to mean four italicized statements in the fifth Scholion (von Baer, 1828, I, 224), which devotes itself primarily to recapitulation.

Lovejoy is one of our most distinguished philosophers of science, and it would be presumptuous to enter into dispute with him on the history of philosophical concepts. It does seem, however, that the majority of working embryologists find little to quarrel with in the statements by von Baer to which Lovejoy refers, and particularly in the second of them: "From the most general in form-relationships the less general

* This article is an expansion of a lecture prepared at the Stazione Zoologica, Naples, and delivered at the University of Belgrade in 1960, during the tenure of National Science Foundation Senior Postdoctoral Fellowship No. 59002. The manuscript was completed in its present form at Brown University, to which I am very grateful for summer hospitality. Reprinted from *Developmental Biology*, Vol. VII, 1963, pp. 11–21. Academic Press, Inc., New York, N.Y.

develops, and so on, until finally the most special [das Spe-
ciellste] emerges" (von Baer, 1828, I, 224). Modern embryology, based as it is on epigenetic convictions, stands on the
concept that development proceeds from the general to the
special, or it falls. When doubts are raised as to the validity
of von Baer's concepts, it becomes desirable to re-examine
them in the light of our present beliefs, and when we do so
we find in them not merely all we expected, if we are admirers
of von Baer, but even more.

Historians of biology and of embryology customarily do full
justice to von Baer's most obvious contributions. They give
him ample recognition not only for his scientific discoveries
(the notochord, the mammalian and the human egg) but also
for his broad conceptual advances: for his generalization of
the germ layer concept; for his emphasis, already mentioned,
on development from the general to the special, from the
apparently homogeneous to the patently heterogeneous; for
his denial of the validity of the biogenetic law even before
Haeckel had overvalued it. It is fully acknowledged that by
demonstrating in terms of Pander's germ layers the true meaning of Wolff's concept of epigenesis, he transformed embryology into a systematic and comparative science.

What I believe has not been appreciated is how far beyond
his predecessors he went in his feeling for the dynamic qualities of the epigenetic process, and how closely his thought
sometimes approximated that of late nineteenth and early
twentieth century thinkers with respect to what Roux called
the *Causalnexus* of events, what we would call mechanisms of
development. It is this aspect of von Baer's reflections that will
be briefly examined here.

EVIDENCE

Mechanisms of Differentiation at the Embryological Level

Von Baer's concepts of developmental mechanisms start,
as do our own, from the premise that development proceeds

from the general to the special, and he makes the generalization, in his own final summary of Part I, that "in internal development special parts develop from more general ones, and their particularity grows" (von Baer, 1828, I, 263). The German word that I have translated as particularity is *Besonderheit*. It might almost have been translated specificity in our own sense. Von Baer's primary examples of what he means by it, repeated with variations in several portions of the text, are furnished by the development of the chick. Here we may combine portions of two of them:

The more special develops from a more general type. The development of the chick bears witness to this at every moment. In the beginning, when the back [der Rücken] closes, it is a vertebrate, and nothing more. When it constricts itself off from the yolk, and its gill clefts close and the allantois forms, it proves itself to be a vertebrate that cannot live in the water. Then later the two intestinal caeca form, a difference appears in the extremities, and the beak begins to appear; the lungs push upwards, the rudiments of the airsacs are apparent, and we no longer can doubt that we are looking at a bird. While the character of a bird becomes still more evident through further development of the wings and airsacs, through fusion of the carpals, and so forth, the web between the toes vanishes and we recognize a land bird. The beak and the feet proceed from a general shape to a particular [besondere] one, the crop develops, the stomach has already divided into two chambers, the nasal shield appears. The bird attains the character of a gallinaceous bird, and finally that of a domestic chicken (von Baer, 1828, I, 221). . . . Finally its individuality [Individualität] develops, and is complete only when the level of life outside the shell is attained. For, manifestly, newly hatched chicks resemble each other much more closely than do adult fowl (von Baer, 1828, I, 140).

When he speaks, elsewhere in his text, of the law that development proceeds from the general to the special, from the homogeneous to the heterogeneous, he states specifically that "some considerations may not be superfluous as to the *manner* [Weise] by which the process occurs" (von Baer, 1828, I, 153), and continues by saying that three kinds of differentiation take place (and *Differenzirung* is the word he used). Primary differentiation he considered to be the separation of the embryo into the heterogeneous layers, the germ layers; the other two types of differentiation are "histological" and "morphological segregation" (*ibid.*, 154–155).

"Morphological, like histological segregation," he writes, "is also the production of something special from something general, with the only difference that morphological differentiation depends on modified growth, and produces *relative* differences . . . while histological segregation produces *antagonistic* ones" (von Baer, 1828, I, 156–157). His use of the word antagonistic [antagonistische] justifies the translation of the word *Sonderung* as segregation. A number of authors who have translated excerpts from von Baer's book into English have translated *morphologische* and *histologische Sonderung* as morphological and histological differentiation. *Sonderung* has the same root as *Besonderheit* which von Baer used to signify particularity, but the verb *sondern* means to separate, to set asunder, and that von Baer may have had intimations of something like segregation in Lillie's sense, or canalization in Waddington's, is suggested by his more detailed analysis of histological segregation.

"All is transformation," he asserts, "nothing is development *de novo*. . . . If a part is formed by internal differentiation, there was not a hole there before. For instance when a nerve . . . is formed, there was not a hole but a common mass that separates itself into nerve and not-nerve" [Nerv und Nichtnerv] (von Baer, 1828, I, 156). And in contrasting histological with morphological segregation, he speaks of the former as "more plastic [plastische], evoking contrasts" (*loc. cit.*).

What did he mean by plastic? In Part I of his book he uses the word plastic to describe the lower layers of the embryo as opposed to the upper or animal layers, although in Part II he has usually shifted to the use of the word vegetative instead of plastic. But he sometimes does seem to use it in a more general sense (see von Baer, 1828, I, 193, for instance), and on occasion he suggests that he envisaged embryonic parts as modifiable in development, in the modern sense, and that he sensed the importance of causal relationships in modifying sequences of embryonic events. In fact, he says so, in so many words.

In Part II of his book, where he is discussing the fact that the development of various physiological functions of the embryo, its sensory life, its digestion, its respiration, its circulation, and so forth, can be divided into various periods, he says that "all such periods are not however absolutely distinct from one another, but pass one into another, and in one the preparation for the next is always recognizable" (von Baer, 1837, II, 153). In Part I, he says that "it is in itself clear that each step in development is made possible only by the immediately preceding state of the embryo" (von Baer, 1828, I, 147).

A number of examples that he contemplates from this point of view are scattered, rather sparsely, to be sure, through his writings, and in some of them it is even striking that he is wary of confusing cause with effect. In his small monograph on developmental duplicities, for instance, he has an appendix on malformations in chick embryos, and in this he writes that some of his observations on early anomalies have supported him in his conviction that "normal heart formation is caused by normal brain formation, or rather, that both are the result of the same condition, the normal curvature of the head of the embryo" (von Baer, 1845, p. 102). In Part II of his large book, he writes of the fact that "the blood vessel walls are not the cause but the result of blood circulation" (von Baer, 1837, II, 127). "The development of the ribs," he says too, "is not independent, but subordinate to the general growth of the embryo, as is shown by the fact that the younger the embryo the further forward are their abdominal ends directed" (von Baer, 1837, II, 99–100).

The objection might be raised that these examples, and

other similar ones (see for instance von Baer, 1828, I, 88, 174) show that von Baer couched his interpretations of causal relationships only in terms of gross mechanical influences (as though that alone were not enough, in his day), and fail to indicate any appreciation of what we might consider subtler tissue interactions. This too he may have had. "The eye," he writes, "seems to be an outgrowth of the nerve tube that protrudes through the muscle layer[1] as far as the skin layer,[1] and the outer parts of the eye are changes in the skin evoked as a result [dadurch hervorgerufene]" (von Baer, 1828, I, 155). By the outer parts of the eye, von Baer did not mean the lens, which he thought formed by an albuminous mass that forms also the vitreous body, nor yet the choroid and sclera, which he thought split off from the retina; and he knew that the cornea was part of the sclera. What he possibly meant were the eyelids and nictitating membrane, which he calls outer parts of the eye in the passage in Part II where he gives the clearest account of his views on development of the eye (von Baer, 1837, II, 113–116). That he did not happen to hit specifically on the optic cup-lens induction system that was to prove so important in later embryological history may be less significant than that he did state in no uncertain terms that the developing eye evokes the formation of other structures by the skin.

He even went one step farther back, and inquired into the factors responsible for the formation of the optic vesicle itself. "The eyes are thus lateral prominences on the posterior part of the first brain vesicle. I have not been able to find that this region is indicated or preformed in the head end of the dorsal plate; on the contrary I must believe that the eyes are pushed out [hervorgetrieben] from the inside of the brain vesicle, and

1 Von Baer considered that there are four germ layers, two upper or animal layers, the serous layer (which gives rise to the skin layer) and the muscle layer; and two lower plastic (Part I) or vegetative (Part II) layers, the vessel layer and the mucous layer. The serous and mucous layers would correspond to our ectoderm and endoderm, respectively; the muscle layer and vessel layer, to our mesoderm.

only their outer thin curved surface represents the original wall of the front of the plate" (von Baer, 1828, I, 24).

"But what," inquires von Baer next, "is the agent that pushes them out [das Hervortreibende]?" (*loc. cit.*). He answered in terms that would not be very meaningful to us, but nonetheless the question drives the inquiry into causal relationships in development yet one step farther toward basic mechanisms.

Interpretations of Developmental Phenomena in Chemical and Physical Terms

No doubt many who have never read the full text of von Baer's treatise are familiar with the passages, often quoted, in which he mused about relating developmental processes to truly cosmic forces. "I should be satisfied," he wrote in the preface to Part I, "if it were considered my contribution to have shown that the type of organization determines the manner of development. Other people to come will be honored for their accomplishments. But victory will go to that fortunate man who relates the formative forces of the animal body to the common energy or the life destiny of the Universe. The tree from which his cradle will be hewn has not yet germinated!" (von Baer, 1828, I, xxii). At the very end of Part I, he expresses the same idea in a passage at once more figurative yet more definite with respect to embryological events: "There is *one* basic thought that runs through all forms and stages of animal development and dominates all their individual relationships. It is the same thought that in the wide space of the Universe gathered separate masses into spheres and combined them into solar systems; the same thought that caused the weathered dust on the surface of our planet to grow into the forms of life. But this thought is nothing but life itself, and the words and syllables in which it expresses itself are the various forms of life" (von Baer, 1828, I, 263–264).

Remarks in the main body of his text confirm that these lyrical passages at beginning and end of Part I expressed more than idle or hopeful dreams. Von Baer spoke somewhat critically of the concept of the ladder of nature as a way of arranging phenomena "from monad to man" (von Baer, 1828, I, 207), and he was doing more than echoing its terminology. And though philosophically he tended toward distinctly vitalistic beliefs, he nonetheless, at least occasionally, looked for strictly physical explanations of embryological phenomena that interested or puzzled him.

He was concerned, for instance, with asymmetry in the developing chick, as we still are today, and, although cumbersomely, he attempted to relate it to what was a modern physical discovery in his day:

The process that is effective along the axis of the egg results in the fact that the embryo that lies along the axis collects its newly accrued material along a broader surface and in deeper volume on the left than on the right, where the shapes taper more to a point. This was already true when the blastoderm was still pear-shaped; it is true in the primitive streak, and holds in general for all its parts. These conditions, accordingly, might be related to electromagnetism (von Baer, 1828, I, 13).

And even when at his closest to Naturphilosophie, in his typological considerations of adult organization based on polarity and symmetry, he compared certain relationships to those in a series of galvanic cells (von Baer, 1828, I, 210).

He saw, further, that embryonic phenomena at the subvisible level might be the subject not only of speculation and analogy, but that they might be open to actual physical explanation:

The heterogeneous substances that lie one behind each other along the axis of the egg, when stimulated by heat, cause a dynamic process that proceeds along the axis of the egg and that might perhaps be more closely defined by exact physical investigation (von Baer, 1828, I, 12–13).

Whether or not he himself performed exact physical investigations on developing embryos, he took advantage, in compiling his text and his lectures, of those that had been made by others. He reports fully, in Part II, the available chemical data on the chemical constitution of the shell of the hen's egg (von Baer, 1837, II, 11–12), of the albumen (*ibid.*, pp. 13–14), and of the yolk (*ibid.*, pp. 20–21). He was interested in the change of weight of unincubated and incubated eggs (*ibid.*, pp. 36–37), and devotes several pages (*ibid.*, pp. 38–40, also pp. 39–41 fn.) to a discussion of Ermann's studies on the development of eggs in irrespirable gases. Knowing the study by Bischoff on the quantity of oxygen in the egg, he went so far as to ask his colleague Dr. Dulk in Königsberg to measure the change in oxygen and carbon dioxide content of the egg during successive stages of development. "The result of this investigation," wrote von Baer, "is so important for embryology and for all of physiology that I consider it my duty to make known here, in an appendix, what he has so kindly communicated to me about it" (*ibid.*, p. 37 fn.). Part II of von Baer's work was never completed, and the appendix never added, but Dulk's results are duly reported in the literature, in a section on organic chemistry in a journal of physics and chemistry (Dulk, 1830). Von Baer was interested too in the passage of chemical substances from the albumen and yolk to the embryo. He comments that phosphorus gradually decreases in the albumen, increases in the yolk, and finally accumulates, together with calcium, as phosphoric acid in the bones; he remarks also on the increase of iron during incubation (von Baer, 1837, II, 42–43).

In sum, von Baer, whose great contribution to embryology was a vast synthetic scheme, was aware also of the value of analysis in developmental study.

DISCUSSION

Von Baer's primary interest, as he said for himself in a passage already quoted, concentrated on organization of type as determinative of developmental pattern. And he himself stated that his considerations of sequential events were secondary to this. "Although it is in itself clear that each step forward in development is made possible only by the preceding state of the embryo, nevertheless the total development is governed and directed by the whole essence [Wesenheit] of the animal that-is-to-be. And thus conditions at any moment are not alone absolutely determining for the future" (von Baer, 1828, I, 147; a very similar statement is found also on the following page).

Although von Baer did comment, as we have seen, on sequences of events and conditions of the moment, he did not organize or arrange his remarks on them. When the excerpts quoted above are assembled out of context, as here, and placed in order, they suggest that von Baer had intimations of many important later concepts. But the reader must be warned to remember that such remarks are rare in the long volumes, not collected into a single chapter, and none were mentioned by von Baer in his summaries; they seem to have the quality of *obiter dicta*. The comment about the importance of Dulk's work is found in a footnote, not the text, and so is the remark that the eye evokes changes in the overlying skin. In fact, the latter is incorporated in a paragraph introduced principally to emphasize that the eye grows *through* the muscle layer, the ear *into* it, and the nose *up to* it (von Baer's italics).

It is hardly surprising that von Baer should have indulged in speculations that one thing leads to another. Beyond the fact that it is hard to escape such an interpretation when observing living embryos, von Baer, who had wide interests in other fields of science besides embryology, lived at a time when exciting new philosophies described the universe in what we might call epigenetic terms. "We must envisage," wrote Laplace, "the present state of the universe as the effect of its previous state and as the cause of that which will follow" (Laplace, 1820, p. ii). And Leibniz: "The present always holds the future in its womb" (cited from Dolch, 1959, p. 150). What a short step it must have been for von Baer, whose mind was permeated with thoughts of the wholeness of things, to transfer such concepts from the total universe to the total embryo he considered such an integral part of it!

How von Baer's ideas on these and other subjects originated, how they emancipated themselves, at least to some degree, from Naturphilosophie and developed in his own imagination, are important questions that have received some attention and deserve more, but they will not be discussed here. The more immediate question, from the point of view of modern embryology, is whether von Baer's ideas were of significance in influencing the ideas of the investigators who began at the end of the nineteenth century the experimental program that validated for once and all the dynamic interpretations of epigenesis. It is unthinkable that Germans becoming educated and specializing in embryology during the latter part of the nineteenth century,[2] particularly those who made the significant contributions, would not have read von Baer's treatise, and it would probably not be too difficult to prove from the record that they did. Driesch dedicated to von Baer's memory (and that of Albert Wigand) his wonderful little *Analytische Theorie der organischen Entwicklung,* written before he had abandoned the hope that he could "analyze into their final elements the processes of morphogenesis of organisms" (Driesch, 1894, p. v). And Roux, as early as 1888, when speaking of developmental mechanics as a new science, said: "But the greatest of us all in the past, the present, and the

[2] It was read even by American graduate students during the 1890's. Ross Harrison's copy, bought from a reputable bookdealer, has Alexander Agassiz' bookplate in it. Harrison wrote to G. H. Parker to inquire about its history, and Parker replied that H. H. Field had borrowed it to use when writing his dissertation in the winter 1890–1891 and had lost it in a valise on the Fall River boat (letter of December 17, 1936, G. H. Parker to R. G. Harrison, now, together with the Agassiz-Harrison copy of the book, in my possession).

far future, Carl Ernst von Baer, has already predetermined its goal, and has at the same time provided the directions for the foundation and the plan of its structure" (Roux, 1895, II, 25). Thus, it would seem, Roux and Driesch acknowledged the fulness of their debt.

SUMMARY

A number of comments scattered throughout the text of von Baer's *Ueber Entwickelungsgeschichte der Thiere* suggest that von Baer had considerable insight into the dynamics of epigenesis, and that he was aware of causal relationships in development.

In postulating the manner in which development proceeds from the general to the special, he considered that there are three kinds of differentiation: differentiation into germ layers, and histological and morphological segregation. He emphasized the dichotomous nature of histological segregation, stating that it evokes contrasts, and for one example stated that, when a nerve is formed, there was not nothing there before but a common mass that separates itself into nerve and not-nerve.

He speaks of histological segregation as plastic, and there is evidence that he envisaged differentiating tissues as modifiable in their development. He stated specifically that "each step in development is made possible by the immediately preceding state of the embryo." He stated, for an example, that "the eye seems to be an outgrowth of the nerve tube that protrudes through the muscle layer as far as the skin layer, and the outer parts of the eye are changes in the skin evoked as a result." By the outer parts of the eye he probably meant the eyelids and nictitating membrane, but it is interesting that he believed the optic rudiment to evoke the formation of other structures by the skin. Von Baer also attempted to explain selected embryological phenomena in physical terms (electromagnetism,

306

galvanism) and believed that some of them might be open to exact physical investigation.

It may well be that such passages exerted an influence on the development of the ideas of later nineteenth and early twentieth century investigators who, in Germany at least, must certainly have read them, and they may thus have played their part in leading toward our modern dynamic concepts of epigenesis.

REFERENCES

VON BAER, K. E. (1828, 1837). "Ueber Entwickelungsgeschichte der Thiere. Beobachtung und Reflexion." I. Theil, 1828; II. Theil, 1837. Bornträger, Königsberg.

VON BAER, K. E. (1845). "Ueber doppelleibige Missgeburten oder organische Verdoppelungen in Wirbelthieren." Buchdruckerei der kaiserlichen Akademie der Wissenschaften, St. Petersburg.

DOLCH, H. (1959). Ueber die Einwirkung philosophischer Gedankengänge bei der Formung der naturwissenschaftlichen Entwicklungstheorie. *In* Naturwissenschaft und Theologie, Heft 2, pp. 138–156. Max Hueber, Munich.

DRIESCH, H. (1894). "Analytische Theorie der organischen Entwicklung." Wilhelm Engelmann, Leipzig.

DULK [no initial given]. (1830). Untersuchungen über die in den Hühner-Eiern enthaltene Luft. *J. Chem. u. Physik* 58, 363–369.

LAPLACE, P. S., Marquis de. (1820). "Théorie analytique des probabilités," 3d ed. Mme. Ve Courcier, Paris.

LOVEJOY, A. O. (1959). Recent criticism of the Darwinian theory of recapitulation: its grounds and its initiator. *In* "Forerunners of Darwin: 1745–1859" (B. Glass, O. Temkin, and W. L. Straus, Jr., eds.), pp. 438–458. The Johns Hopkins Press, Baltimore, Maryland.

ROUX, W. (1895). Die Entwickelungsmechanik der Organismen, eine anatomische Wissenschaft der Zukunft. *In* W. Roux, "Gesammelte Abhandlungen über Entwickelungsmechanik der Organismen," Vol. II, pp. 24–54. Wilhelm Engelmann, Leipzig.

John and William Hunter
and Some Eighteenth Century
Scientific Moods*

I AM especially happy to have the privilege of speaking to your Section on Medical History, because I am so deeply obligated to the College of Physicians for its repeated kindnesses, which have been a primary factor enabling me to carry out whatever work I have attempted on the Hunters. But there is more involved than the excellence of the collections and the helpfulness of the staff.

William Hunter, who already then had a strong interest in obstetrics, made a trip to Leyden in the spring of 1748 and visited Albinus. In July 1748 John Redman, your first President, was awarded the degree of Doctor of Medicine at Leyden, having worked with Albinus and having written his thesis on an obstetrical topic. I do not happen to know whether William Hunter and John Redman met in Leyden in 1748 or in London the next year when Redman was at Guy's, but it is at least a possibility. In any case, we do know that three of the twenty-four Founders of this College, John Morgan, William

* Presented before the Section on Medical History of the College of Physicians of Philadelphia, 4 December 1956. This meeting celebrated the recent restoration of the Hunter homestead, at Long Calderwood, Scotland, as a memorial to John and William Hunter. Reprinted from *Transactions & Studies of the College of Physicians of Philadelphia*, 4 Ser., Vol. XXV, 1957, pp. 97–102.

Shippen Jr. and Benjamin Rush were students of the Hunters. John and William Hunter are neither of them very far from us here.

It is in part because they had so many connections, as teachers and friends, with people of personal consequence to us that the Hunters continue to be a source of interest. We derive some of our ideas from them; we value them because of their ideas; and what I wish to do is raise a few questions about the type of ideas they had.

Much of what is known of them[1] contributes to the delineation of their differences of character. William seems to us highly polished and elegant, erudite and constrained. John, in contrast, looms up a less scholarly figure. He is rougher and blunter, expressing his frank and original opinions not only more freely but more crudely. His primary attribute seems an abundance of physical and intellectual energy, of warmth and vitality, that spills over into a flood of creative effort rarely paralleled in the history of biology and medicine. "My mind is like a bee-hive," he said to John Abernethy, and Abernethy, one of the most distinguished of his students and followers, adds, "The simile struck me, on account of its correctness. For, in the midst of buz [sic] and apparent confusion, there was great order; regularity of structure; and abundant food, collected with incessant industry, from the choicest stores of nature."[2]

A contrast between the Hunters becomes clear however not

[1] Simmons, S. F.: *An Account of the life and writings of the late William Hunter*, J. Johnson, London, 1783, is the only report of William by a contemporary. Ottley, D.: "The Life of John Hunter" in *The Works of John Hunter*, edited by J. F. Palmer, 5 volumes, Longman, Rees, Orme, Brown, Green, and Longman, London, 1835–1837, is the most useful near-contemporary biography of John; Ottley's sources are discussed in Oppenheimer, J. M.: *New Aspects of John and William Hunter*, Henry Schuman, New York, 1946, pp. 23–24. The fullest and most reliable information concerning both brothers is found in Peachey, G. C.: *A Memoir of William and John Hunter*, printed for the author by William Brendon and Son Ltd., Plymouth (Eng.), 1924.

[2] Abernethy, J.: *The Hunterian oration, for the year 1819*, Longman, Hurst, Rees, Orme, and Brown, London, 1819, p. 48.

only from consideration of the anecdotes handed down about their lives,[3] but also from examination of the quantity and variety of their published works.

We might begin with an evaluation of those of the elder brother.[4] Three books by William Hunter have been published. The posthumous *Two introductory lectures*,[5] while of great interest for the light it casts on William's character and on the quality of his teaching, is not especially relevant for our discussion here. His important book was the great folio *Anatomy of the human gravid uterus*.[6] This was in course of careful preparation for over 30 years. In the styles of its writing, its illustration, its printing it was nothing short of magnificent, and the subject-matter was deserving of the format. I would wish some one in this audience closer than myself to William's profession to comment on present opinions as to the quality of its contents; but surely it remains one of the truly great anatomical monographs of history.

The first of his books to have been published during his lifetime, the *Medical commentaries*,[7] did not purport to be unified in content and covered a number of separate subjects, many of them specifically related to his various scientific controversies which do not concern us here. The *Medical commentaries*, however, also included a small number of essays relating to his anatomical discoveries that might just as appropriately have been published in periodicals and which can be considered together with his articles of the latter type. His actual publications in periodicals numbered about 18. If we

3 See especially the biographies by Simmons and Ottley mentioned in fn. 1.

4 I do not know of any list of the writings of William Hunter that can be considered complete in the sense of modern bibliography. A list useful within limits is to be found in Mather, G. R.: *Two great Scotsmen, the brothers William and John Hunter,* James Maclehose and Sons, Glasgow, 1893, pp. 240–241.

5 Hunter, W.: *Two introductory lectures,* J. Johnson, London, 1784.

6 Hunter, W.: *Anatomia uteri humani gravidi,* J. Baskerville, Birmingham, 1774. This was the only medical publication ever issued by the famous Baskerville Press.

7 Hunter, W.: *Medical commentaries, Part I,* A. Millar, London, 1762; *Supplement,* A. Hamilton, London, 1764.

consider the subjects covered in these and in the relevant comparable essays in the *Medical commentaries*, we find that we can categorize them without too much difficulty. Seven of the essays or articles dealt with one or another aspect of the circulatory system (including the lymphatics), the same number with the skeleton (including one on tendons). Four related to the reproductive system, the subject of his big monograph. The rest dealt with a few miscellaneous other subjects: emphysema, the cellular membrane, the pupillary membrane; signs of murder; a disorder of the stomach; the lacrymal ducts; an autopsy report; a description of an animal from India. Clearly there is some breadth of range here, but it is a limited one.

The accomplishments of John were very different indeed. He published three books in his lifetime: *The Natural history of the human teeth, A Treatise on the venereal disease,* and *Observations on certain parts of the animal oeconomy*.[8] The *Animal oeconomy,* like William's *Medical commentaries,* consisted of a group of separate short essays, some of which had been and the rest of which might have been, so far as their character was concerned, published in the *Philosophical Transactions of the Royal Society.* John's fourth book, *A Treatise on the blood, inflammation and gun-shot wounds,* virtually ready to go to press when he died, appeared the year after his death.[9] Like William Hunter's monograph, this too

---

[8] Hunter, J.: *The Natural history of the human teeth,* J. Johnson, London, 1771; *A Treatise on the venereal disease,* sold at No. 13 Castle Street, Leicester Square, London, 1786; *Observations on certain parts of the animal oeconomy,* sold at 13 Castle Street, Leicester Square, London, 1786. A second edition of the *Animal oeconomy* was published by Hunter in 1792. Le Fanu, W. R.: *John Hunter A List of his books,* University Press, Cambridge (Printed for the Royal College of Surgeons of England), 1946, gives a complete bibliographical description of John's books, but no such accurate list has been compiled for his articles. Le Fanu (p. 5) gives references to such lists of the latter as are available.

[9] Hunter, J.: *A Treatise on the blood, inflammation and gun-shot wounds,* John Richardson for George Nicol, 1794. Le Fanu (*op. cit.*) lists various other posthumous publications, only one or two of which will concern us; these will be described below in the appropriate references.

was in preparation for over 30 years. It lacked the felicity of William's style, and its single-mindedness. But it was crammed full of observations and ideas, and had John written nothing else in his whole lifetime it would easily have made his fame.

John's short papers are extraordinarily difficult to count and to classify, even more so than William's. Some of his articles, like the six Croonian Lectures delivered at the Royal Society, were not published in his lifetime but were later included by Owen in his edition of the *Animal oeconomy* which forms volume 4 of the posthumous collected *Works*. Some articles were during John's lifetime and with his authorization written and prepared by his brother-in-law Everard Home; in these cases Home's name is published as author, but the titles specify that the materials were furnished by Hunter. John also published several anatomical notes in John White's *Journal of a voyage to New South Wales* and in Alexander Russell's *Natural history of Aleppo*,[10] all of which might appropriately have found their way into periodicals under other circumstances. In any case, the number of short articles that can be ascribed to John (including those in the *Animal oeconomy* and in the books by White and Russell) is over 50, thus well over twice the number of William's short articles.

Comparison, however, of the number of published articles of the two brothers is limited in value by the fact that a great bulk of John's materials was still unpublished at his death. It is commonly believed that Sir Everard Home, one of his executors, who burned the majority of the manuscripts, based many of his own articles[11] on Hunter's manuscript materials; however some of the latter, copied by William Clift before the originals were burned, have been published either in the

10 White, J.: *Journal of a voyage to New South Wales,* printed for J. Debrett, London, 1790; Russell, A.: *Natural history of Aleppo,* 2d edition, G. G. and J. Robinson, London, 1794.

11 A rough list of Home's publications is found in Oppenheimer, J. M.: *New aspects of John and William Hunter, op. cit.,* pp. 91–105.

catalogues of the museum collections, or in the *Essays and observations on natural history, anatomy, physiology, psychology and geology* which Richard Owen edited and published in 1861.[12]

It is not, however, through sheer force of quantity, but rather by virtue of the bewildering variety of topics covered, that the work of John differs from that of William. The subjects of William's interests, you will remember, fell into a small number of natural groupings. John's completely defy classification: even the published articles, which probably represent only a minority of his fields of investigation, cover topics as diverse for instance as postmortem digestion of the stomach (1772), airsacs in birds (1774), production of heat by animals and vegetables (1775), apparent transmission of smallpox from mother to fetus (1780), organs of hearing in fishes (1782), descent of the testis (1786), structure of the placenta (1786), secretion by the crop of the breeding pigeon (1786), olfactory nerves (1786), extirpation of one ovary (1787), comparative observations on wolf, jackal and dog (1787), structure and oeconomy of whales (1787), introsusception (1789), horny excrescences of the human body (1791), bees (1792), fossil bones presented to the Royal Society (1794), etcetera etcetera.

Small wonder that John's literary style fell below his brother's; he occupied his time with experiments and observations, accurate to a high degree, rather than in perfecting his prose. If William, however, concentrated on more circumscribed subjects than John[13] and approached them with a higher degree of perfectionism; and if John expended his energies on far more diversified aspects of natural history,

12 Hunter, J.: *Essays and observations on natural history, anatomy, physiology, psychology, and geology*, 2 volumes, edited by R. Owen, John van Voorst, London, 1861.

13 William had, by the way, far wider interests outside of his profession than did John; see Oppenheimer, J. M.: *New Aspects of John and William Hunter*, op. cit., and "John and William Hunter and some contemporaries in literature and art," *Bull. Hist. Med.* XXIII, 21–47 (1949).

morphology, physiology and pathology, in his efforts to place surgery on the broadest possible biological basis, yet still there were some features common to their modes and moods of work.

For instance we have been thinking of both of them, simply because it comes natural to do so, as scientists, though William was strictly a medical man, and John technically a surgical one. In both cases, their contributions went beyond those of sound practitioners and inspiring teachers, and popular and successful though they became in these phases of their callings, their great gifts were as investigators. They made scientific discoveries, and important ones. Even when the subjects of their writings were frankly medical or surgical in content, they were not mere case reports; their intent was always implicitly investigative in the broadest sense of the word.

Furthermore, whether they dealt with materials from their practice or from the field of natural history or whatever, they both exhibited in common the characteristic that as scientists they particularly excelled as investigators of the concrete. They observed; and they preserved; and what is perhaps most noteworthy in their writings is that they refrained completely from the construction of elaborate theories designed to encompass every observed fact in a single synthetic system.

This is perhaps the more remarkable in the case of John, who had a strong speculative cast to his mind, as is demonstrated, for only one instance (there are many more), by his development in the *Treatise on the blood, inflammation and gun-shot wounds* of the theme that the blood is alive. He thought often in terms of general principles: "In the works of Nature, where we see a similarity in principle, or effects produced from similar causes, it is reasonable to suppose that they [those works] are similar in their great principles, and therefore may arise from one cause."[14] But his especial talent

14 Hunter, J.: *Essays and observations, op. cit.,* I, 113. See also Buckle, H. T.: *History of civilization in England,* from the 2nd London edition, D. Appleton and

was for the marshalling of facts, and as one of the Hunterian Orators has so well said, "His hypotheses . . . never diminished his zeal for facts."[15]

Anatomy in general in Great Britain at the time of the Hunters was a science based principally on observation, which is particularly noteworthy only because it stands in such sharp contrast to conditions elsewhere. In Germany in particular a strong movement was developing towards what is often called transcendental anatomy, which relied on the concept of Unity of Type. This held not only that each organism (or organ) presents its own modifications of one ideal Type or Archetype, but also that the variations are significant only insofar as they are subservient to the Type. The anatomist who clings to this doctrine sees his primary task as inferring from the observable modifications what the theoretical Archetype might be. He thus becomes almost more a philosopher than a scientist; and on the Continent *Naturphilosophie* became the predominant, if not the exclusive, mood of many of the most influential minds.[16]

Naturphilosophie prided itself on subjectivity, not objectivity, resting to a far greater proportion than science proper on intuitive rather than observational phenomena. Hence it has sometimes been called romantic philosophy, and the biology which it fostered was in a sense romantic biology, just as the history which grew out of it was romantic history, and the literature romantic literature. Now to what degree, and this is the primary question which I wish to leave uppermost in your minds, were the Hunters involved in the fact that when the romantic movement was to flourish in England, it

Company, New York, 1890, II, 432–453, for an excellent discussion of John's speculative tendencies and accomplishments.

15 Paget, Sir J.: *The Hunterian oration, 1877,* Longmans, Green, & Co., London, 1877, p. 20.

16 Rádl, E.: *Geschichte der biologischen Theorien,* Teil I, 1905, Teil II, 1909, Wilhelm Engelmann, Leipzig; and Russell, E. S.: *Form and function,* John Murray, London, 1916, give full discussions of the ideas implicit in the concept of Unity of Type.

became largely a literary movement and did not grow into a scientific one also, as abroad?

We have been speaking this evening of connections; and the specific connections between the Hunters and the romantic movement were not so remote as might seem on first thought. On the literary side, John and William's sister Dorothea was the mother not only of Matthew Baillie the pathologist, but also of Joanna Baillie, the distinguished poetess and dramatist who was for a half century the close friend of Sir Walter Scott (himself, by the way, the grandson of a distinguished Scottish physician). William Hunter seems to have been a friend of Allan Ramsay the younger, whose father, like the Hunters born in Lanarkshire, was one of the heralds of the literary romantic movement in England. Robert Burns was an admirer of poems written by Mrs. John Hunter; and in fact, some of her own poems ("My mother bids me bind my hair," and "The Spirit song," for instance) were themselves lyrics with a strong romantic undertone.

On the scientific side, John's significance for the fate of transcendental anatomy in England could hardly have been more direct, since the one English anatomist who was most influenced by *Naturphilosophie* and who spoke up most strongly for it was none other than Richard Owen, who, though his life failed to overlap in years that of John, yet derived his intellectual descent almost immediately from him.

Owen's first position in London, as a youth of 20 or 21, was as prosector at Bart's to John's former student John Abernethy. He became two years later (1827) assistant to the curator of Hunter's museum, William Clift, who had been Hunter's protégé and amanuensis at the time of his death. In 1835 he married Clift's daughter, and in 1842 became Joint Conservator of the Museum with his father-in-law, and Conservator shortly later when Clift retired. The preparation of the great catalogues of John Hunter's collections was largely his. Furthermore, from 1836 to 1856 he was the first Hunterian Professor of comparative anatomy and physiology at the Royal College of Surgeons, with duties to present 24 lectures per annum illustrated by specimens from the collections. And he lived with the collections not only figuratively but literally, from 1835 until 1852 actually residing in apartments prepared for his use at the College of Surgeons.

It was within the period of the lectureship and of his residence at the College that he is said to have been influenced by the writings of Oken, one of the more extreme of the German *Naturphilosophen;* it was certainly during this period that he published his own principal theoretical views, in a book *On the archetype and homologies of the vertebrate skeleton*[17] which labors the concept that the vertebrate skeleton consists of a series of comparable segments, each of which is a modified vertebra. It might seem now that he was holding a fanciful view in maintaining for instance that the maxillary bone represents the haemapophysis of the nasal vertebra, or the keel of a bird's sternum that of a thoracic one. But these were far less *outré* than many of the opinions expressed by Oken, who for example considered the whole animal kingdom to represent a single organism.

Owen's transcendentalism was short-lived in England; in 1858, just ten years after the publication of Owen's book *On the archetype,* Huxley completely demolished in his Croonian Lecture[18] the vertebral theory of the skull, for once and for all. But Owen's speculations on the archetype of the veterbrate skeleton were in no way his sole preoccupation, and after the delivery of Huxley's Croonian Lecture as well as before Owen devoted his primary efforts to the study of hard anatomy, anatomy which dealt with hard bones, hard teeth, hard shells, hard fossils, not ideas. Even Huxley, who distrusted him as a

17 Owen, R.: *On the archetype and homologies of the vertebrate skeleton,* John van Voorst, London, 1848.
18 Huxley, T. H.: "On the theory of the vertebrate skull," *Proc. Roy. Soc.* IX, 381–457 (1857–59; Croonian Lecture delivered 17 June 1858).

person as heartily as he disapproved of him as a transcendentalist, gave full credit to the value of his anatomical research: "The historian of comparative anatomy and palaeontology will always assign to Owen a place next to, and hardly lower than that of Cuvier. . . . It was not uncommon to hear our countryman called 'the British Cuvier,' and so far, in my judgment, the collocation was justified, high as the praise it implies";[19] then after some disparagement of Owen's "philosophical anatomy," Huxley concludes that "whatever view is taken of Sir Richard Owen's speculations . . . his claims to a high place among those who have made great and permanently valuable contributions to knowledge remain unassailable."[20]

I submit that Owen succumbed to seduction by transcendentalism in only one or two books, instead of becoming immersed in abstraction to the exclusion of all factual anatomy, in large part because of his training in the Hunterian tradition, of his experience in the Hunterian museum, of his work with the Hunterian specimens in his hands and his eyes and his mind. Romanticism often includes an element of otherworldliness; Hunter's specimens could hardly have been more exclusively of this world, and their substantiality and Hunter's solid treatment of them affected not only Owen but those who gave ear to Owen. While Owen's book *On the archetype* surely exerted some influence in England it was far less than the effect of comparable writings in *Naturphilosophie* on the Continent. This, as so much else, we owe to the Hunters, whose type of contribution assured that British anatomy escaped the perversion and adulteration it might otherwise have suffered.

[19] Huxley, T. H.: "Owen's position in the history of anatomical science," in Owen, R.: *The Life of Richard Owen*, John Murray, London, 1894, II, 312. Huxley was a little less mellow 36 years before when he wrote to Hooker: "What a capital title that is they give him of the *British* Cuvier. He stands in exactly the same relation to the French as British brandy to cognac" (Huxley, L.: *Life and letters of Thomas Henry Huxley*, D. Appleton and Company, New York, I, 172).

[20] Huxley, T. H.: "Owen's position in the history of anatomical science," in Owen, R.: *The Life of Richard Owen, op. cit.*, II, 332.

It is not to the Hunters alone that this good fortune of British anatomy is to be attributed; of course the philosophical conditions were favorable in Britain for their kind of work and for that of their successors. But this in no wise minimizes their accomplishment; it was they, and not Locke and Berkeley and Hume[21] who enlarged the horizons of human and comparative anatomy and physiology. We started this evening by saying that we derive some of our ideas from them. Surely we inherit from them some of our modes of work as scientists; and if their voices speak to us clearly across two centuries, undistorted by pseudoscientific aberrations, this we owe to the vigor and the strength and the intellectual power with which they thought and worked.

21 Mrs. John Hunter was a cousin of David Hume's, see Hume, D.: *The Letters of David Hume,* Clarendon Press, Oxford, 1932, II, 324.

John Hunter, Sir Thomas Browne and the Experimental Method*

> Let thy Studies be free as thy Thoughts and Contemplations, but fly not only upon the wings of Imagination; joyn Sense unto Reason, and Experiment unto Speculation, and so give life unto Embryon Truths, and Verities yet in their Chaos.[1]

Probably the greatest interest that John Hunter holds for posterity is related to the fact of his own preoccupation with the experimental method: its application by him to the widest variety of biological problems signalized the beginning of modern experimental medicine as it is familiar to the twentieth century. The experimental method, in its purest form, had been introduced into medicine by William Harvey during the early seventeenth century: *De Motu Cordis* was published in 1628. John Hunter, who was the first investigator in Great Britain to prove the applicability of the method more generally to medicine, surgery, comparative anatomy and comparative physiology in their broadest aspects, was born exactly 100 years later, in 1728. The problem which we propose to examine tonight is why the time-lag between Harvey and Hunter was of so great duration as a century.

* Based on an address delivered at the Johns Hopkins Medical History Club, Baltimore, Md., Monday, January 27, 1947. Reprinted from *Bulletin of the History of Medicine*, Vol. XXI, 1947, pp. 17–32. The Johns Hopkins Press, Baltimore, Md.

1 *The Works of Sir Thomas Browne*, edited in six volumes by Geoffrey Keynes, Faber & Gwyer, Faber & Faber, London, 1928-1931, I, 123.

I shall take the liberty of trying to answer the question as to why John Hunter succeeded, by examining the attempts of another famous British natural historian and physician, closer to Harvey chronologically, who failed; namely, Sir Thomas Browne. I shall talk perhaps more about Sir Thomas than about Hunter, for which an apology is due to an audience who came presumably to hear about Hunter first and foremost. But here, as in history and in science, Hunter's influence is everywhere pervasive, whether explicitly obvious or no, and as ever he will emerge at the end as hero.

Familiar as Sir Thomas is to many, I should like to lay stress on some aspects of his scientific outlook that may bear emphasis, especially, his attitude toward the experimental method. Sir Thomas Browne seems a quaint figure to modern physicians, and much of the great interest in his work has been in the past primarily literary or perhaps philosophical. As a fortunate result of his popularity on these planes, there has been preserved a large number of his writings, correspondence, miscellany and notebooks as well as his published books, and these furnish much pertinent information on the particular point in which we are interested.

His appreciation of the scientific method was often clearly expressed: — in his praise in the *Pseudodoxia* of "the definitive confirmator and test of things uncertain, that is, the sense of man";[2] in his admonition to the reader of the *Christian Morals*, quoted above as a rubric, and lastly in his comments on Harvey himself, "that ocular Philosopher, and singular discloser of truth,"[3] as he called him. "You may gett one in English and read it often," he wrote to his son Edward of the treatise *De Generatione Animalium*, "for it is an excellent peece and full of observations,"[4] and in the *Pseudodoxia* he spoke of the same work as "that excellent discourse . . . So

2 *Ibid.,* II, 219.
3 *Ibid.,* II, 304.
4 *Ibid.,* VI, 68.

strongly erected upon the two great pillars of truth, experience and solid reason."[5]

What was the intellectual background of this man, that, classicist as he was, he could be so quick to appreciate the implications of Harvey's contribution? His education was an interesting one. Winchester School, familiar still as one of the great public schools of England, and Broadgates Hall, Oxford, later to become Pembroke College and Samuel Johnson's alma mater, first nurtured him. He found his way next to Montpellier, where a few generations previously Rondelet,[6] as a contemporary of Vesalius and like him and Servetus a student of Günther's, had carved out his dissections with his own hands and had induced Henri II to erect there the first anatomical amphitheatre for France. Browne may well have felt at Montpellier a strong breath of the intellectual Renaissance; and it may have been from a former Chancellor of Montpellier that he had his first inspiration for the *Pseudodoxia,* though he, to be sure, denied it:

Dr. Primrose hath made a learned Discourse of vulgar Errors in Physick. . . . Laurentius Joubertus by the same Title led our expectation into thoughts of great relief; whereby notwithstanding we reaped no advantage, it answering scarce at all the promise of the inscription.[7]

From Montpellier he travelled to Padua, where Harvey — that stem of the rod of Vesalius and Fallopius and Fabricius — had learned before him; and thence to Leyden, where to took his degree of Doctor of Medicine. A respectable education, indeed, at its inception, compared to that of John Hunter, whose training derived almost solely from "the great volume

---

5 *Ibid.,* II, 304.

6 Rondelet suffered the same posthumous fate as John Hunter, in that the bulk of his writings were lost to posterity. They were left to Laurent Joubert, his successor as Chancellor of Montpellier, for editing and publication, and were not heard of after.

7 *Ibid.,* II, 5.

of nature,"[8] and at the end one that could not fail to stimulate a fertile mind.

That Browne profited directly from the teachings of the prophets of the new learning is manifest in a multitude of remarks in which he preached explicitly the doctrine that "sight is the best judge."[9] We shall quote here only those relating to anatomy and animal biology, as more directly in John Hunter's field, though Browne worked as well in many other areas of natural history.

The first shall be of the Elephant, whereof there generally passeth an opinion it hath no joints; and this absurdity is seconded with another, that being unable to lie down, it sleepeth against a Tree; which the Hunters observing, do saw it almost asunder; whereon the Beast relying, by the fall of the Tree, falls also down it self, and is able to rise no more. . . .

They forget or consult not experience, whereof not many years past, we have had the advantage in England, by an Elephant shewn in many parts thereof, not only in the posture of standing, but kneeling and lying down. . . . If . . . any shall affirm the joints of Elephants are differently framed from most of other quadrupeds . . . he doth herein no injury unto truth. But if . . . he affirmeth also they have no articulations at all, he incurs the controulment of reason, and cannot avoid the contradiction also of sense.[10]

That he made his own independent observations, as well as pleading with others to do so, is also abundantly clear from his writings. "When it first came into my garden," he wrote of an ostrich procured by his son Edward, presumably one of those brought by the "Embassadour of the King of Fez & Morocco"[11] to the King, and probably, as Sir Thomas said,

8 W. Wadd, *Nugae chirurgicae; or, a biographical miscellany, illustrative of a collection of professional portraits*, Nichols, London, 1824, p. 232. To the benefit of John Hunter, of whose manners such harsh words have been spoken, let it be emphasized that there is no line in his works that I should not happily read to this or any other audience. Not so for Sir Thomas: there are various obscenities in his writings.

9 Browne, *op. cit.*, V, 316.

10 *Ibid.*, II, 179-183.

11 *Ibid.*, VI, 235.

"the first oestridge dissected in England, at least to any purpose":[12]

it soone eat up all the gilliflowers, Tulip leaves, & fed greedily upon what was green. . . .

When it tooke downe a large onyon it stuck awhile in the *Gula* & did not descend directly, butt wound backward behind the neck whereby I might perceave that the Gullett turned much, butt this is not peculiar unto the oestridge, butt the same hath been observed in the stork[13] when it swallowes downe froggs & prettie bigge bitts.

It made sometimes a strange noyse, had a very odde note especially in the morning & perhaps when hungry.

According to Aldrovandus, some hold that there is an antipathie between it an[d] a horse which an oestridge will not endure to see or bee neere, butt while I kept it I could not confirme this opinion, which might perhaps bee raysed because a common way of hunting & taking them is by swift horses.[14]

One of his letters to Edward about the ostrich was accompanied by a delightful sketch of the head of an ostrich, copied

[12] *Ibid.*, VI, 242.

[13] Browne's observations, in the *Natural History of Norfolk,* on "a kind of stork . . . shott in the wing by the sea neere Hasburrowe," were followed by the remark: "I could not butt take notice of the conceit of some who looked upon it as an ill omen, saying if storks come over into England, pray God a commonwealth do not come after" (*ibid.,* V, 394), a comment which he repeated in a letter to Edward (*ibid.,* VI, 173), and one of which Hunter no doubt would have approved. It is illuminating that both Browne and Hunter, although advanced in their intellectual attitude towards science, were loyal subjects of the King — indeed Browne was knighted for his Royalist sympathies during the Civil War — and conservative in their political thinking. Cf. Hunter's remarks about Burke: "Mr. Burke's speeches put one in mind of a shrub full of flowers, which is pretty while viewed; but, strip it of its flowers, and it will hardly be taken notice of" (John Hunter, *Essays and observations on natural history, anatomy, physiology, psychology, and geology,* 2 volumes, van Voorst, London, 1861, I, 280), and about Fox: "Accusing Mr. Fox of having debauched the minds of most of the young men of fashion in this kingdom, I was answered, that he was liked by them all: I made reply, that they were similar in that respect to the women; for they could not help having a fondness for the man that had seduced them" (*loc. cit.*). Hunter himself seemed to have had a certain fondness for him too, if we can consider as genuine the peculiar inscription "Left to my friend Charles James Fox, M. P., 1793" which is reported to be written on the back of the gold watch which had been presented to Hunter by the staff of St. George's Hospital (Geoffrey Spry Leverton, "Life and Works of John Hunter," *St. Bart.'s Hosp.* J., 1944, XLVIII, 71).

[14] Browne, *op. cit.,* V, 324.

from a cut by Ray in Willughby's *Ornithologia* either by Sir Thomas or his daughter Frances.[15] It is pertinent to our discussion of Browne's scientific contributions to add that Ray accepted his aid when preparing his own volume on birds. "When Mr Ray was to print his Ornithologie, or discription of birds," wrote Sir Thomas to his son Edward in 1682, "I lent him many draughts of birds in colours, which I had caused at times to bee drawne."[16]

Browne did not confine his observations to exotic beasts, however, casually available in England,[17] but extended them to a host of familiar forms surrounding him. For instance:

That Moles are blind and have no eyes, though a common opinion, is received with much variety; some affirming only they have no sight; . . . some that they have eyes, but no sight; . . . some neither eyes nor sight; . . . some both eyes and sight. . . . That they have eyes in their head is manifest unto any, that wants them not in his own; and are discoverable, not only in old ones, but as we have observed in young and naked conceptions, taken out of the belly of the Dam.[18]

The experience of observation of "young and naked conceptions, taken out of the belly of the Dam," was one of his favourites:

That a Bear brings forth her young informous and unshapen, which she fashioneth after by licking them over, is an opinion not only vulgar, and common with us at present: but hath been of old delivered by ancient Writers. . . . In the Valley of Anania about Trent, in a Bear which the Hunters eventerated or opened, I beheld the young ones with all their parts distinct: and not without shape, as many conceive: giving more credit unto Aristotle and Pliny, then experience and their proper senses.[19]

15 Reproduced *ibid.*, VI, 239. "I have enclosed these 2 heads of an ostridge which Franck suddenly drewe out" (*ibid.*, VI, 238).

16 *Ibid.*, VI, 250.

17 Those who exclaim at the unconventionality of John Hunter's menagerie at Earl's Court, and his buffaloes in harness, might wonder equally at the ostrich, and the stork, and the bittern, and the shearwater which Sir Thomas maintained in his garden for observation.

18 *Ibid.*, II, 250-251.

19 *Ibid.*, II, 196-197.

He was ready to dissect as well as to make more superficial observations:

The . . . Assertion, that an Horse hath no gall, is very general, nor only swallowed by the people, and common Farriers, but also received by good Veterinarians, and some who have laudably discoursed upon Horses. . . .

It is again controllable by experience, for we have made some search and enquiry herein. . . . In the particular enquiry into that part, in the concave or simous part of the Liver, whereabout the Gall is usually seated in quadrupedes, I discover an hollow, long, and membranous substance, of a pale colour without, and lined with Choler and Gall within; which part is by branches diffused into the lobes and several parcels of the Liver; from whence receiving the fiery superfluity, or cholerick remainder, by a manifest and open passage, it conveyeth it into the *duodenum* or upper gut, thence into the lower bowels; which is the manner of its derivation in Man and other Animals. And therefore although there be no eminent and circular follicle, no round bag or vesicle which long containeth this humour: yet is there a manifest receptacle and passage of choler from the Liver into the Guts.[20]

Not only was he happy to confute the statements of the authorities, but, more important, he admitted evidence at variance with his own generalizations: for instance, in the *Garden of Cyrus,* where he was everywhere seeking patterns to conform to the quincunx, he wrote:

As for those Rhomboidal Figures made by the Cartilagineous parts of the Wezon, in the Lungs of great Fishes, and other animals, as Rondeletius discovered, we have not found them so to answer our Figures as to be drawn into illustration; Something we expected in the more discernible texture of the lungs of frogs, which notwithstanding being but two curious bladders not weighing above a grain, we found interwoven with veins, not observing any just order. More orderly situated are those cretaceous and chalky concretions found sometimes in the bignesse of a small fetch on either side their spine; which being not agreeable unto our order, nor yet observed by any, we shall not here discourse on.[21]

20 *Ibid.,* II, 184-185.
21 *Ibid.,* IV, 100.

And who can doubt that he spoke out of his own experience and delight when he wrote in the *Pseudodoxia*:

Whoever observeth the first progression of the seed before motion, or shall take notice of the strange indistinction of parts in the Tadpole, even when it moveth about, and how successively the inward parts do seem to discover themselves, until their last perfection; may easily discern the high curiosity of Nature in these inferiour animals, and what a long line is run to make a Frog.[22]

That he added "Experiment unto Speculation" as well as "Sense unto Reason" is also clearly evident from his writings. Some of his "experiments," to be sure, were admittedly naive in their motivation:

That a King-fisher hanged by the bill, sheweth in what quarter the wind is by an occult and secret propriety, converting the breast to that point of the Horizon from whence the wind doth blow, is a received opinion, and very strange; introducing natural Weather-cocks, and extending Magnetical positions as far as Animal Natures. A conceit supported chiefly by present practice, yet not made out by Reason or Experience. . . .
As for experiment, we cannot make it out by any we have attempted; for if a single King-fisher be hanged up with untwisted silk in an open room, and where the air is free, it observes not a constant respect unto the mouth of the wind, but variously converting, doth seldom breast it right. If two be suspended in the same room, they will not regularly conform their breasts, but oft times respect the opposite points of Heaven.[23]

That the young Vipers force their way through the bowels of their Dam, or that the female Viper in the act of generation bites off the head of the male, in revenge whereof the young ones eat through the womb and belly of the female, is a very ancient tradition. . . .
As for the experiment, although we have thrice attempted it, it hath not well succeeded; for though we fed them with Milk, Bran, Cheese, &c. the females always died before the young ones were mature for this eruption.[24]

22 *Ibid.*, II, 230.
23 *Ibid.*, II, 213-214.
24 *Ibid.*, II, 237-238.

Others of his own experiments were however less credulous; some of these follow:

It is generally conceived, an Ear-wig hath no Wings, and is reckoned amongst impennous insects by many; but he that shall narrowly observe them, or shall with a needle put a side the short and sheathy cases on their back, may extend and draw forth two wings of a proportionable length for flight, and larger then in many flies. The experiment of Pennius is yet more perfect, who with a Rush or Bristle so pricked them as to make them flie.[25]

That Worms are exanguious Animals, and such as have no bloud at all, is the determination of Phylosophy . . . We refer it unto the discernment of others what to determine of that red and sanguineous humor, found more plentifully about the Torquis or carneous Circle of great Worms in the Spring, affording in Linnen or Paper an indiscernable tincture from bloud. Or wherein that differeth from a vein, which in an apparent blew runneth along the body, and if dexterously pricked with a lancet, emitteth a red drop, which pricked on either side it will not readily afford.[26]

There is found in the Summer a kind of Spider called a Tainct; . . . this by Country people is accounted a deadly poison unto Cows and Horses; who, if they suddenly die, and swell thereon, ascribe their death hereto, and will commonly say, they have licked a Tainct. Now to satisfie the doubts of men we have called this tradition unto experiment; we have given hereof unto Dogs, Chickens, Calves and Horses, and not in the singular number; yet never could find the least disturbance ensue.[27]

Even these experiments, however, were more primitive perhaps than some he performed, which bore the stamp of a somewhat maturer mind:

And because many affirm, and some deliver, that in regard it hath lungs and breatheth, a Frog may be easily drowned; though the reason be probable, I find not the experiment answerable; for fastning one about a span under water, it lived almost six days. Nor is it only hard to destroy one in water, but difficult also at land: for it will live long after

25 *Ibid.*, II, 297.
26 *Loc. cit.*
27 *Ibid.*, II, 298-299.

the lungs and heart be out; how long it will live in the seed, or whether the spawn of this year being preserved, will not arise into Frogs in the next, might also be enquired: and we are prepared to trie.[28]

The windpipe of hernes & bitterns cutt, they live & goe about after & make a noyse:—butt if you tye the lower part of the weazon they gaspe & dye sooner.[29]

Digestion is delivered to bee made in the lower part of the stomack: evidenced in pickerells, a voracious animal, whoe swallowe fishes, & gradually digest them at the lower extreme, the upper remaining un-altered, though the lower part seemes of hardest mutation, they swal-lowing the head formost; & their mawes are long, not round & short.
One kept in a cesterne lived 6 dayes, the roach in the mawe not half digested.[30]

A ginnie pigge castrated grew bigger.
A monkey of twelve years old guelded.
A rabbet of a yeare old the same time, March XII. 1649. The ejacula-tory vessels cutt close to the parastatoe, the seminall veynes about 2 inches upward bled litle; dogs bleed more, horses for prevention of the effusion are seared.
The different magnitude of testicles & how in the same animals they agrandise about the time of coition in the spring is very remarkable.[31]

These quoted fragments represent only a smattering of examples of his interest in natural history of animals; further examples from the *Pseudodoxia,* from his *Miscellany Tracts,* from his *Notes on the Natural History of Norfolk,* from his *Observations in Anatomy,* from his letters to his son Edward, from his common-place books and from other miscellaneous writings, could be added in sufficient numbers to fill a copious volume. Since these are available to any who care to savour the delights of dipping into his published works, further enumeration of them will be omitted here. What remains for us here, rather, is the attempt to discover why he made no

28 *Ibid.,* II, 230.
29 *Ibid.,* V, 341.
30 *Ibid.,* V, 338.
31 *Ibid.,* V, 336.

more of himself as a scientist, so that we may compare him later with John Hunter.

There are those who believe that Browne did not fail for not making the attempt. Edmund Gosse, his best biographer, but still a limited one and no scientist, believed he nourished a strong desire to become elected to the Royal Society, and quoted excerpts from his letters to Henry Oldenburg to suggest the petulance of his hopes.[32] The letters, however, need not be so interpreted, and clearly Browne's relationships with the Royal Society were cordial: Browne, who, like the Hunters, was an avid collector, made liberal contributions to the Royal Society's Museum, as is apparent from Grew's *Catalogue,* and frequently advised his son Edward, in his letters to him, quite without bitterness, how to proceed in his own relationships with the Royal Society. These, indeed, were so successful that the Society elected Edward, far less skillful a scientist than his father, to its Fellowship. I believe it may be safely assumed that its failure so to honour Sir Thomas was due not so much to a deliberate snub to his scientific efforts, as to the Society's antagonism to the form in which his contributions were described. The Society at its origin expressed itself clearly as standing against pomposity and lack of simplicity in contemporary scientific thought and expression, exacting, in the words of Sprat, "from all its members a close, naked, natural way of speaking . . . bringing all things as near the mathematical plainness as they can."[33] Surely Sir Thomas, had he coveted the Fellowship, could have abandoned his verbosity had he desired; he preferred his art to the honour.

There is another point, too. He was surely a doting father, if ever a father doted: and much of his work in natural history and anatomy he turned over to his son. Indeed, a large proportion of his letters to Edward is made up of information that

[32] Edmund Gosse, *Sir Thomas Browne,* Macmillan, London, 1905, pp. 157-158.
[33] Quoted by C. H. Herford in the introduction to Sir Thomas Browne, *Religio Medici and other writings,* Dent, London [1937], p. xv.

Sir Thomas gave him to use for his own. Many of the letters to Edward are in content in a way reminiscent, though very different from them in style, of Hunter's letters to his intellectual son Jenner:

Examine the spine of fishes & how the spinall marrowe is ordered in them. . . . Mr Antonie Myngay intends for London on Monday next; by him I intend to send the cranium of a swan of this yeare. You may consider the eare bones [*word missing*] 2 slender long bones of the upper jawe & how the skull hath some litle places not turnd into bone &c.[34]

I sent unto you the scull of a poulcats head by yong Mr Whitefoot. . . . I gave a Badgers skull unto Dr Clark & if you meet with an opportunity keep one: the lower jawe of that wch I had, needed no tying to the upper, butt would move and hold to the upper jawe without any tye.[35]

If you intend the next time to read of the Larynx and the voyce, you may do well to gett the Larynx of severall animals & looke into Casserius & Aquapendente, which you had from hence, which will bee the fittest to keepe drye, & in the same site & order as they are in the animal, nor only the Larynx, butt the *Aspera Arteria* within, as of a horse, an Asse, a beare, a catt, & to find out the way of the purring of a catt, grunting of [a] hogge, hoarse voyce of a beare, Lyon, &c., why a bull hath a lesse acute voyce then an ox or cowe, since the voyce in other masles is deeper & in castrated men more shrill, feminine & acute. . . . And also why in Asthmaticall persons the wheasing & piping is made at the expiration not the inspiration, or at least farre more, & the like which meditation & thoughts may hint.[36]

I hope you receaved the paper I sent concerning the fistula of a dolphin & the proper place thereof. It may bee brought in when you speake *de pulm.* or *de respiratione,* & I would not have you omitt it; & if you did not keepe the skull of the dolphin you cutt up, I will God willing send you one. . . . When you see the elephant observe whether hee bendeth his knees before & behind foreward differently from other Quadrupeds, as Aristotle observeth, & whether his belly bee the softest & smoothest part; the testes are not exterior & outward butt inwardly in the body, as Aristotle. Perhaps the booke hath the dissection of a

34 Browne, *Works,* ed. Keynes, VI, 101.
35 *Ibid.,* VI, 217-218.
36 *Ibid.,* VI, 114.

camell; it were good to observe of what that bunch in the back con-
sisteth, whether the backbone or spine ariseth up into it, or it bee a
lump of flesh upon it & the spine notwithstanding bee as in others.
I thought good to give these hints, because probably they would not
come into your mind. My hedghogge being putt into my garden gott
away with 2 yong ones & I never look to find them agayne; observe the
teeth because you speake of them, *de dentibus.* God blesse you all.[37]

Not only were the letters full of hints and casual observations, but they often included long passages for Edward to use
verbatim; and indeed, there is good evidence that the whole
of Edward Browne's Harveian Oration was written by his
father.[38] That Sir Thomas contributed so liberally to his son
may account in part for his own lack of recognition as a
scientist. But that he was so generous can hardly be attributed
to his own weakness of scientific interest: after all, John
Hunter, to posterity's dismay, turned over the major portion
of his own writings to his son-in-law.

One of Sir Thomas's literary critics has analyzed Browne's
failure to attain scientific success as follows: "Browne was
scientific just up to the point where the examination of detail
ends, and its coordination begins. . . . Such inquiries are the
stuff of which great scientific theories are made. Browne,
however, used his love of details for another purpose: he
co-ordinated them, not into a scientific theory, but into a work
of art."[39] I, for one, am not convinced that this is the whole
story; there is some possibility that Browne was thinking,
when he wrote the *Garden of Cyrus,* with a logic, or lack
of it, akin to that of the investigators who promulgated the
doctrine of the Unity of Type.

Sir Thomas himself was perhaps better able to diagnose his
own case:

Although in this long journey we miss the intended end, yet are there

37 *Ibid.,* VI, 77-78.
38 *Ibid.,* VI, 194, f. n. 2.
39 Lytton Strachey, *Books and Characters, French and English,* Harcourt, Brace,
New York, 1922, pp. 43-44.

many things of truth disclosed by the way; and the collaterall verity may unto reasonable speculations some what requite the capital indiscovery.[40]

Here may be one clue to the ultimate difference between Sir Thomas and John Hunter. Hunter was never even momentarily distracted by the collateral verities, let alone "requited for the capital indiscovery"; he never could allow his scientific observations to be diluted by material not immediately germane to the subject under observation.

Compare their outlooks on some of the problems they examined in common. Sir Thomas's notes on castration were some of them cited above; a paragraph follows them which may be appended here:

To castrate a peacock, what alteration it produceth in their plumage, might it cause it in their flesh wch is white & tender, more probably it may better the flesh of Bustards.[41]

John Hunter's notes on castration were at a higher level than those of a gastronome:

In the dissection of a spayed sow the vagina was very small, was thin in its coats, and pale. The rugae were very faint, became smaller and smaller upwards, and at last terminated in a blind point. This shows that in spaying they cut off the horns of the uterus, or rather the whole of the uterus.[42]

Hunter's greater attention to what we consider scientific detail is expressed, too, in his description of an experiment which we know Sir Thomas performed: "Aristotle sayth," wrote Browne, "that the tayle of a snake cutt of will growe agayne. I have observ'd the same in a green lizard";[43] and this is the full citation. Compare Hunter's paragraph dealing with the same phenomenon:

[40] Browne, *op. cit.*, III, 255.
[41] *Ibid.*, V, 336.
[42] Hunter, *op. cit.*, I, 237.
[43] Browne, *op. cit.*, V, 306.

The tails of lizards are so tender as to be easily pulled off by the strength of the animal when held by the tail; but this tenderness is only confined to the part of the tail beyond the bed of the penis, for there the tail is very strong. The reason why the tail should be so brittle, is perhaps to allow the animal to make its escape when caught by the tail, for it is generally broken in that way.[44]

Compare, too, their comments on the anatomy of bees; "he that would exactly discern the shape of a Bee's mouth," wrote Browne,

needs observing eyes, and good augmenting glasses, wherein is discoverable one of the neatest peeces in nature; and must have a more piercing eye then mine, who findes out the shape of buls' heads, in the guts of drones pressed out behind, according to the experiment of Gomesius; wherein notwithstanding there seemeth somewhat which might incline a pliant fancy to credulity of similitude.[45]

There are no "pliant fancies to credulity of similitude" in Hunter's account of the animals he loved so dearly ("I amuse myself with bees,"[46] he used to say):

All this tribe of insects have pincers or forceps at their mouths; which, in the bee, serve as a weapon of offence and defence, for holding anything they want to move from place to place; as also to model their wax in the making of their cells. The blades of the forceps cross one another, but it is not always the same that overlaps.[47]

And he wrote of a "small Bee which I caught on the St. John's Wort, collecting Farina":

I caught four or five of this species in the month of July, collecting farina: they were all females. They are longer than the small common fly, but not thicker. They have two pincers [mandibles] and a proboscis. The proboscis is attached under the head: it first passes a little back under the head, and then folds immediately on itself, passing forwards to the anterior part of the head between the two pincers, lying there as in a groove; and, when it opens or unfolds for use, it falls back and

[44] Hunter, *op. cit.*, II, 364.
[45] Browne, *op. cit.*, IV, 97.
[46] Sir James Paget, *Hunterian Oration*, Longmans, London, 1877, p. 10.
[47] Hunter, *op. cit.*, II, 447.

down. The first fold or joint consists of two horny parts [maxillae], passing nearly parallel to each other, having a joint at the head; the last fold consists of three parts, also horny and passing parallel to each other: the middle one is the broadest, and is an additional one just between the outer ones. There is a soft springy part, I believe feathered, as also with a horny process which is moveable, or has a joint. This is just the contrary way to the situation of the fixing and unfolding of the proboscis of the humble-bee or common bee.[48]

But the most expressive pointing up of their difference is accomplished by their remarks on the metamorphoses of the silkworms. "The silk-moth" wrote Hunter,

like all of this class of insects, is first an egg, then a caterpillar, chrysalis, and moth. The caterpillar is a long body, consisting of a head, body, and tail with appendages. . . .

While in the caterpillar-state they spin silk threads from their mouth by way of attachment. If the head is first removed from the object to which the animal may be attached, it then holds fast by its two holders at the tail; and, when these are got the better of, it has no hold: but, if the tail be removed first, it fixes its head by its silk, and it is held by that means, and will allow of being pulled to any length from its hold, just as a spider is by means of its silk. If it be made to hang by its silk, it winds or coils up this silk thread round its fore-feet; therefore it has the same power with the spider.[49]

And Sir Thomas, in the *Religio*:

Those strange and mystical transmigrations that I have observed in Silk-worms, turned my Philosophy into Divinity. There is in these works of nature, which seem to puzzle reason, something Divine, and hath more in it then the eye of a common spectator doth discover.[50]

And earlier, too, in the *Religio,* he made a similar confession: "Where I cannot satisfy my reason, I love to humour my fancy."[51] Here is the salient point: Hunter was incapable of humouring his fancy where he could not satisfy his reason. "Why think?" he had written Jenner; "why not try the ex-

48 *Ibid.,* II, 455.
49 *Ibid.,* II, 466-467.
50 Browne, *op. cit.,* I, 50.
51 *Ibid.,* I, 14.

periment?"[52] Hunter could never have included among his queries that revealing note from Sir Thomas's common-place book: "Whether possession bee not often mistaken for wich-craft, and many thought to bee bewiched which are indeed possessed?"[53] The question would have been as utterly without meaning for him as it is for us.

This, indeed, is the crux of the whole matter: the manner of the framing of the question. "Quaere in your Aristotle,"[54] Browne wrote to his son Edward in a letter dealing with shedding and regeneration of the cuticle, and this is a revelation, too. Not only in the *Pseudodoxia*, whose explicit purpose was to make "Enquiries into very many received tenents and commonly presumed truths,"[55] but in all of his thinking, Browne proceeded from the question for the question's sake; Hunter proceeded primarily from the organism and from his consuming interest in the organism as such. No one who has read a word of his writing can have the slightest doubt of it, just as no one familiar with Browne can attribute to him this trait of mind.

But what does this tell of the two men themselves? Was Hunter's more modern way of looking at biological problems something that was related only to his own innate qualities of mind, or was it conditioned within him by the fact that he was living in an England which had become familiarized, since Browne's day, with the ideas of Bacon, and Descartes, and Leibniz, and Newton?

Browne, of course, who read more than most, had read Descartes[56] and probably Bacon, and his thinking was almost certainly thereby affected. Hunter, who claimed to have read nothing, had almost certainly no first-hand acquaintance of

[52] Stephen Paget, *John Hunter, man of science and surgeon (1728-1793)*, Longmans, London, 1897, p. 107.
[53] Browne, *op. cit.*, V, 254.
[54] *Ibid.*, VI, 80.
[55] *Ibid.*, II, 1.
[56] *Ibid.*, II, 113, 136; VI, 283.

them; yet they probably influenced him more, indirectly, than they had Sir Thomas directly. For that intervening century had surely ripened in England a growing appreciation of the experiment as a method, and of an animal as a mechanism; and to this extent Hunter enjoyed benefits not available to Browne. The definition of science had altered; a language of science had developed; the systematization of zoology had meantime been effected.

The exploitation of these later advantages was not however a necessary prerequisite for the application of the experimental method to biology. Harvey accomplished it without them, as did Robert Boyle, and Stephen Hales. There was something in the spirit of the times that encouraged the fruition of Hunter's labours; but there was something in the man and the mind that motivated his endeavour — something akin to what had been in the minds of Harvey, and Boyle, and Hales — something alien to the mind of Sir Thomas Browne.

Browne's deliberate and studied calling to account of the statements of the classical "authorities," the gullibility of his experimental approach, and indeed, his heavy verbosity, all mark him as a thinker characteristic of his period, which he lacked the intellectual power to escape. Hunter's declared and manifest disregard for the literature of science in favour of its practice, the single-mindedness, the force and the originality of his scientific achievement, the simplicity — self-conscious and inarticulate though it sometimes seems — of his literary expression, all distinguish him as an investigator great in any age, and a prophet who by sheer power of intellect transcended his own. The factors in his intellectual environment which influenced him cannot be ignored, but surely he rose high above the level of contemporary thought to point the way into the thinking of the future, and for this the credit is owing to him and to him alone.

337

William Harvey
and Historical Change*

RECENTLY I received a letter from a lawyer in Washington asking me for a specific example of a situation where particular knowledge of scientific history had been a critical determining factor in bringing about a new scientific discovery. How would you respond to such a request? Science, like life itself, indeed like history itself, is a historical phenomenon. It can build itself only out of its past. The values of historical studies in science do not differ from those of history in any other intellectual or artistic endeavor. Too many people before me have spoken for history for it to require any defense from me. But an evaluation of a great idea, or of a great man, or of a great movement, is always in order, just as is that of a great work of art. We are moved; our minds and emotions, if moved, are not the same as they were before their exposure to what moved them. But what in their greatness moves us? and how? Let us ask William Harvey.

To introduce William Harvey by saying that he discovered the circulation of the blood is tantamount to saying that Christopher Columbus discovered America. Very many of our

* A lecture broadcast under the title "Historical Studies" over the Voice of America in 1961 in the Forum Series on the Biological Sciences, a presentation on "Arts and Sciences in Mid-Century America." Reprinted from *Frontiers of Biology. Twenty Lectures Originally Broadcast over the Voice of America,* coordinated by Gairdner Moment, Houghton Mifflin Company, Boston, Mass., 1962, pp. 9-17.

elementary textbooks in biology or physiology mention his name; even the most anti-historicist of our pedagogues deign to speak of him to their students. He opened up not only new continents but new dimensions of thought. It is probably safe to say that no other single discovery in biological and medical history has had such consequence as his. (His rival in this respect might be said to be Darwin, of whom so much has been made of late. But Harvey could, and did, precede Darwin; and Darwin took for granted much about organisms that could be learned only as a sequel to Harvey's theories.)

William Harvey was, to date him, Physician Extraordinary to King James I of England, and Physician in Ordinary to his son, Charles I. Born in 1578, he died in 1657; the tercentenary of his death is thus just four years behind us.

We have said that his name appears in many elementary books. What interests us here, however, is the frequency with which, after 300 years, he figures in the more technical literature of the learned periodicals and in specialized biographies. The tercentenary year, of course, temporarily increased it. But even in the off years, no year is really off for Harvey in the medico-historical literature; his thought continues to remain a source of fresh investigation, and each year sees the publication of new studies of it. His ideas on the circulation are said to have been first expressed publicly in 1616; his treatise on them was published in 1628. Why, after three and a quarter centuries, are they still of such burning interest to scholars, and thus, by indirection, to their students, and their students' students? What does Harvey say to us across the centuries, that we cannot let him rest?

Before turning to his scientific contributions, we may inquire into him as a man. He has been depicted, fortunately, in one of the most vivid thumbnail sketches in all of English literature, by his friend John Aubrey. Let us quote a few extracts from it here to remind ourselves of the man behind the thought.

"William Harvey, was always very contemplative, and the first that I heare of that was curious in Anatomie in England. I remember I have heard him say he wrote a booke *De Insectis,* which he had been many yeares about, and had made dissections of Frogges, Toades, and a number of other Animals, and had made curious Observations on them, which papers, together with his goods, in his Lodgings at Whitehall, were plundered at the beginning of the Rebellion, he being for the King, and with him at Oxon; but he often sayd, That of all the losses he sustained, no griefe was so crucifying to him as the losse of these papers, which for love or money he could never retrive or obtaine.

"When Charles I by reason of the Tumults left London, he attended him, and was at the fight of Edge-hill with him; and during the fight, the Prince and Duke of Yorke were committed to his care. He told me that he withdrew with them under a hedge, and tooke out of his pockett a booke and read; but he had not read very long before a Bullet of a great Gun grazed on the ground neare him, which made him remove his station. . . .

"I had not the honour to be acquainted with him till 1651. . . . I was at that time bound for Italy. . . . He was very communicative, and willing to instruct any that were modest and respectfull to him. And in order to my Journey, gave me, i.e. dictated to me, what to see, what company to keepe, what Bookes to read, how to manage my Studies: in short, he bid me goe to the Fountain head, and read Aristotle, Cicero, Avicenna. . . .

"He did delight to be in the darke, and told me he could then best contemplate. He had a house heretofore at Combe, in Surrey, a good aire and prospect, where he had Caves made in the Earth, in which in Summer time he delighted to meditate.

"Ah! my old Friend Dr. Harvey — I knew him right well. He made me sitt by him 2 or 3 hours together in his meditating apartment discoursing. Why, had he been stiffe, starcht, and retired, as other formall Doctors are, he had known no more than they. From the meanest person, in some way, or other, the learnedst man may learn something. Pride has been one of the greatest stoppers of the Advancement of Learning.

"He was far from Bigotry.

"He was wont to say that man was but a great, mischievous Baboon. . . .

"I have heard him say, that after his Booke of the *Circulation of the Blood* came-out, that he fell mightily in his Practize, and that 'twas beleeved by the vulgar that he was crackbrained; and all the Physitians were gainst his Opinion, and envyed him; many wrote against him. With much adoe at last, in about 20 or 30 yeares time, it was recieved in all the Universities in the world; and, as Mr. Hobbes sayes in his book *De Corpore, he is the only man, perhaps, that ever lived to see his owne Doctrine established in his life-time.* . . .

"He was hott-headed, and his thoughts working would many times keepe him from sleepinge; he told me then that his way was to rise out of his Bed and walke about his Chamber . . . till he was pretty coole . . . and then returne to bed, and sleepe very comfortably.

"He was not tall; but of the lowest stature, round faced, olivaster complexion; little Eie, round, very black, full of spirit; his haire was black as a Raven, but quite white 20 yeares before he dyed."[1]

Harvey wrote other treatises besides that on the circulation and the lost one on insects. A rough draft of a treatise on the physiology of animal movement seems to have escaped destruction by the Parliamentary soldiers; this was first published, with an English translation, in 1959. A long analysis of generation, published late in Harvey's own lifetime, was of inestimable influence on embryology. It confirms that the part

[1] *Aubrey's Brief Lives,* edited . . . by Oliver Lawson Dick, The University of Michigan Press, Ann Arbor, 1957, p. 128, pp. 129-130, pp. 131-132.

of the hen's egg that develops into the chick is what we call the blastoderm, not the chalazae, the conspicuous spirals of albumen we see whenever we open an egg into a dish. This was a service of incalculable importance; clearly, we cannot study development until we know what develops.

But his most important contribution was his theory concerning the circulation of the blood. The theory was, simply, that the blood moves through the body in a circle — a hypothesis whose enormity can be measured only against the background of earlier beliefs, which included no such concept of continuous repeated use of the same blood. For one thing, Harvey's predecessors and contemporaries believed the blood to be continually formed anew from the digested food, to be dissipated and used up in what we would call the tissues. For another thing, at most a very few others before Harvey (their number is moot, and a subject of dispute among medical historians) recognized that in mammals the blood circulates between the heart and the lungs. Finally, to Harvey the heart was a muscle, its action that of a pump, a sort of machine in nature — he likened it to a water-bellows; Harvey's predecessors considered its primary function the production of heat, then thought to be an entity in its own right.

Now the significance of these discoveries is manifest, and does not need to be spelled out in too great detail here. The importance of the blood for life has probably been appreciated ever since man attained sufficient intelligence to recognize that life ebbed when too much blood spilled. But all that we know of the metabolism of organisms, of organs, of tissues and cells, depends directly on our knowledge of the transit of the blood and its course through the vascular system and respiratory organs. This body of knowledge, so essential to our understanding of the life processes in health and disease, could never — and did never — develop out of the erroneous pre-Harveian notions as to the movements of the blood.

No less important than the content of his hypotheses were

the methods by which Harvey arrived at them and established their validity.

First, he built upon history. He never ceased to be an Aristotelian — remember his advice to Aubrey. "[The] motion [of the blood] may be called circular in the way that Aristotle says air and rain follow the circular motion of the stars,"[2] he wrote, years after the great astronomers had disproved the theory of the circular movement of the stars. In fact, in a sense Harvey even drew his inspiration to doubt from Aristotle; he quotes in his book on generation a wonderful passage from Aristotle admonishing us to appeal to nature direct:

"Give me leave therefore to whisper this to thee (friendly Reader)," wrote Harvey, "that thou be sure to weigh all that I deliver in these *Exercitations, touching the Generation of living Creatures,* in the steady scale of experiment; and give no longer credit to it, then thou perceivest it to be securely bottomed, by the faithful testimony of thy own eyes. This very thing did *Aristotle* perswade us to; who, when he has discoursed much of *Bees,* added at last: *That the Generation of Bees is after this manner, appears by reason, and by those things which are seen to come to pass after the maner of Bees. Yet we have not a sufficient discovery of what may fall out. Therefore when the discovery shall be compleated, then is Sense more to be trusted to, then Reason. For so far onely is Reason to be relied upon, as those things which are demonstrated agree with those things which are perceived by sense.*"[3]

Furthermore, Harvey was taught not only by ancient, but also by more immediate history. Fabricius, his teacher and friend in Padua, had rediscovered the valves in the veins, demonstrating them publicly in 1579, publishing his treatise

[2] William Harvey, *Exercitatio Anatomica De Motu Cordis et Sanguinis in Animalibus,* An English Translation . . . by Chauncey D. Leake, Charles C Thomas, Springfield, Illinois and Baltimore, Maryland, 1931, p. 70.

[3] William Harvey, *Anatomical exercitations concerning the generation of living creatures* translated by M. Llewellyn, Octavian Pulleyn, London, 1653, preface, ¶ 5 a–b.

on them in 1603. Harvey went beyond Fabricius to show the significance of the valves as directing, not damming, agents, and they thus provided him with one of his principal points of departure.

Next, Harvey built not only on history, but also on comparisons: he studied the hearts not only of various fishes, amphibians, reptiles, birds, and mammals, but also those of "snails, slugs, crabs, shrimps . . . wasps, hornets, and flies."[4] But most important, he not only compared these, he manipulated them — and in living as well as dead animals. Manipulation itself, in our modern fashion, was introduced into biology, into physiology and medicine, by Harvey. Manipulation was what taught him that the heart is a muscle. "Grasping the heart in the hand," he wrote, "it feels harder when it moves. This hardness is due to tension, as when one grasps the forearm and feels its tendons become knotty when the fingers are moved.[5] . . . The motion of the heart consists of a tightening all over, both contraction along the fibers, and constriction everywhere. In its movement it becomes erect, hard, and smaller. The motion is just the same as that of muscles when contracting along their tendons and fibers."[6]

But he did not content himself with holding the living heart in his hand; he performed experiments on it and on the blood vessels. He isolated parts of the heart; he ligated and divided arteries; he exerted pressure on veins on either side of the valves. His experiments were all simple, but in spite of — or perhaps because of — their simplicity, they were *crucial* experiments.

One of the extraordinary things about Harvey is that he seems to have taken experimentation for granted. He never feels obligated to defend or justify it; in the first two sentences of his introduction he puts it exactly in its proper place. "In

4 Harvey, *De Motu Cordis*, pp. 44–45.
5 *Ibid.*, p. 29.
6 *Ibid.*, p. 30.

344

discussing the movements and functions of the heart and arteries, we should first consider what others have said on these matters, and what the common and traditional viewpoint is. Then by anatomical study, repeated experiment, and careful observation, we may confirm what is correctly stated, but what is false make right."[7] He speaks frequently of one or another "experiment of Galen";[8] one could never guess, from his text alone, how many centuries had to pass before Galen's experimental method was again to be exploited.

Finally, in an age which in spite of Galileo's accomplishments in mechanics still explained physiological phenomena in terms of qualities, Harvey derived his ideas from quantitative considerations. He calculated the amount of blood that passes through the heart of a man in a half hour, knew it was greater than the amount contained in the whole body, and understood it could not be replenished rapidly enough to meet the requirements of the old theories. He sums it up for us himself. "What remains to be said on the quantity and source of [the] transferred blood, is, even if carefully reflected upon, so strange and undreamed of, that not only do I fear danger to myself from the malice of a few, but I dread lest I have all men as enemies, so much does habit or doctrine once absorbed, driving deeply its roots, become second nature, and so much does reverence for antiquity influence all men. But now the die is cast; my hope is in the love of truth and in the integrity of intelligence.

"First I seriously considered in many investigations how much blood might be lost from cutting the arteries in animal experiments. Then I reflected on the symmetry and size of the vessels entering and leaving the ventricles of the heart, for Nature, making nothing in vain, would not have given these vessels such relative greatness uselessly. Then I thought of the arrangement and structure of the valves and the rest of the

7 *Ibid.,* p. 7.
8 *Ibid.,* p. 11, p. 14, p. 19.

heart. On these and other such matters I pondered often and deeply. For a long time I turned over in my mind such questions as, how much blood is transmitted, and how short a time does its passage take. Not deeming it possible for the digested food mass to furnish such an abundance of blood, without totally draining the veins or rupturing the arteries, unless it somehow got back to the veins from the arteries and returned to the right ventricle of the heart, I began to think there was a sort of motion as in a circle."[9]

Now, as important as were the consequences of his new hypotheses and his new methods for the physiology that was to follow him, perhaps even more significant was their philosophical implication. Harvey himself was uncertain what this might be. "Whether or not the heart," he wrote in one passage, "besides transferring, distributing and giving motion to the blood, adds anything else to it, as heat, spirits, or perfection, may be discussed later and determined on other grounds."[10] "The heart is the center of life," he said in another chapter, "the sun of the Microcosm, as the sun itself might be called the heart of the world."[11] He may have spoken of the heart poetically still in Aristotelian terms, but he proved it to be a muscular pump, and in so doing, he opened the way to the consideration of the whole body as a machine. Thus he not only made possible a new and different kind of investigation of physiological processes, but he fixed for ever since man's place in nature.

The questions we ask ourselves about Harvey are the same ones that we ask concerning any great discovery, in any field, that changes all subsequent human thinking. How could Harvey, bound as he was to the Aristotelian concepts he never abandoned — and in fact by his own admission stimulated by them — free himself from the past sufficiently to make an in-

9 *Ibid.*, pp. 69–70.
10 *Ibid.*, p. 49.
11 *Ibid.*, p. 71.

tellectual leap not only away from the past, but far out of his own times? More specifically, why had it occurred to no one before him to count up the number of drams of blood passing through the heart in a half hour? and the crucial question, why *did* it occur to him? Why was it he, and not some one else before or after, who returned to physiology the Galenic habit of manipulation and experimentation which has been its principal spur to progress ever since? How can we presume to answer these questions? In fact, we cannot, though let us not forget that Aubrey, in his character sketch, emphasized that Harvey was a humble man, as all great biologists must be.

Let us put it another way. If we cannot answer these questions, what does it avail us to ask them, and why, after more than three centuries, do we keep returning to them over and over again, not as mere hero-worshippers (though we all are that when it comes to Harvey), but also as scholars and teachers? Knowing about Harvey does not make us his peers; what does it then do for us as scientists?

We never of course, as scientists or otherwise, really know him. That is, no matter how much we think, or read, or write about him, we cannot fathom his depths, understand him really. We do not understand our contemporaries whom we see every day; we do not understand ourselves; how can we then understand Harvey? We do not yet know the workings even of pedestrian minds, let alone those that are imaginative. Imagination has so far defied our analysis — whether in art, in literature, or in statesmanship.

But if we cannot understand the imagination, we can admire it; we can appreciate it in science, as we appreciate it in art and music. Those who teach the appreciation of art and music in our schools do not consider appreciation as a substitute for understanding; but surely it is an adjunct to it. It facilitates in our minds what understanding we can make of the creative process, whether art, music, literature, or science be the medium of creation.

347

There is another point, too. What is distinctive about the creative imagination is that it sees or hears or thinks something new. How can an idea be recognized as new except in contrast to the old? And more important, how can it develop as new if not out of the old that was its source? Harvey was not the first to study the movement of the blood; it was only because schooled in the concepts of Aristotle and Galen that he even thought about it. His great victory was that in thinking about it, he freed himself from their thought. Freedom is the essence — is it not? — of imaginative thinking in any realm. In every great scientific advance, and in many of the lesser ones that make up the everyday course of science, new freedom is gained from old ideas.

But there is one main thing about freedom. We are never simply free, suspended in isolation from our environment, intellectual or otherwise, past or present. We are free, if we are free at all, of something. If we make imaginative scientific advances, we become free of earlier scientific ideas. How can we become free of them if we do not know what they are?

We began by asking what moves us when we consider greatness. The important and moving element of greatness in the kind of science we are speaking of is just this ability to become free of the past although still related to it. Harvey exemplifies it. Harvey himself with all of his reverence for antiquity, expressed in the passages we have quoted, and in many others, too — Harvey provides an object lesson in the virtues of historical knowledge and appreciation. He does not, and cannot, tell us how, for all he revered his predecessors, he also emancipated himself from them. This is where we can only admire.

Knowing the ideas from which we must free ourselves, and their past, from which they became free, cannot alone make us into new latter-day Harveys. But we cannot even be minor physiologists, or scientists of any kind, and build further on our past, unless we know on what we build. In this sense,

348

freedom has its origins in the past as well as its hopes in the future; and the minds that construct the bridges through and across the present take their impetus for freedom from the minds that have stimulated their own. It is in order to enhance this impetus, thus for practical as well as esthetic reasons, that America sees values in historical studies in biology. America's hope, like that of Harvey, lies in "the love of truth and in the integrity of intelligence."

William Gilbert:
Plant Grafting and the
Grand Analogy[*]

I T is the present technique in intellectual history to attempt
to trace the influence of an idea or of a pattern of ideas
on the development of subsequent thought, and in science to
assess the rôle of particular discoveries in contributing to the
growth of those that succeed them. But what of the discovery
made centuries before its time, forgotten for centuries if
ever remembered, which had no immediate effect in stimu-
lating further progress in an experimental program it might
well have initiated, yet which in a subtle and elusive way may
have colored the whole fabric of thought for its originator
whose great contribution lay within a completely different
spectrum? A case in point is a highly modern experiment in
plant grafting performed some time before 1600 by William
Gilbert.

It could be a temptation to begin in the hackneyed way by
introducing Gilbert as "familiar to a modern audience" for

* Written at the Osborn Zoological Laboratory, Yale University, during the tenure
of a John Simon Guggenheim Memorial Foundation Fellowship. I am grateful to
the Historical Library of the Yale Medical Library for the use of its excellent collections, and to Mr. John Spurbeck of the Department of Biology, The Johns Hopkins University, for assistance in the preparation of the illustrations. Reprinted from
Journal of the History of Medicine and Allied Sciences, Vol. VIII, 1953, pp. 165-176.

his early work on electricity and magnetism, specifically for his analogy between the earth and a magnet,[1] an analogy at which he arrived as the outcome of a series of investigations which provided perhaps the first and certainly one of the purest examples of all time of the New Philosophy based on induction and experiment. Gilbert is probably, however, unfamiliar except to the professional historian or the professional physicist; he is certainly less well known than he deserves so far as the general informed public is concerned. To raise him to the position of eminence which the perspective of history assigns him is not, however, the function of the present communication. Rather this is to describe and discuss a particular experiment performed by Gilbert which seems to have escaped the notice of some of the authors who have recently reviewed the history of their subject, namely, the demonstration of plant polarity by comparing the development of grafts inserted in original and in reversed orientation.

The description and analysis of the experiment constitute an essential part of Chapter VI, Book III of *De Magnete*. The chapter is entitled "What seems to be a contrary movement of magnetic bodies is the regular tendence of union," and in its brevity (thirty lines in the original)[2] it is worthy of being reproduced in its entirety here:

IN magnetic bodies nature ever tends to union — not merely to confluence and agglomeration, but to agreement, so that the force that causes rotation and bearing toward the poles may not be disordered,

1 Gilbert, W. *De magnete, magnetisque corporibus, et de magno magnete tellure; physiologia noua, plurimis & argumentis, & experimentis demonstrata*. London, Peter Short, 1600. In the present communication, page references will be given both to the *editio princeps* and to P. Fleury Mottelay's translation, *On the loadstone and magnetic bodies, and on the great magnet the earth. A new physiology, demonstrated with many arguments and experiments*. New York and London, 1893. A translation superior to this with excellent notations by Sylvanus P. Thompson was issued by the Chiswick Press for the Gilbert Club in 1900, but only 250 copies of this were printed; therefore the references are given to the more readily available translation, which is on the whole reasonably satisfactory.

2 Gilbert, *op. cit.*, 1600, 130-131; 1893, 198-200.

as is shown in various ways in the following example. Let *CD* be an unbroken magnetic body, with *C* looking toward *B,* the earth's north,

B [*sic*] and *D* toward *A,* the earth's south. Now cut it in two in the middle, in the equator, and then *E* will tend to *A* and *F* to *B*. For, as in the whole, so in the divided stone, nature seeks to have these bodies united; hence the end *E* properly and eagerly comes together again with *F,* and the two combine, but *E* is never joined to *D* nor *F* to *C,* for, in that case, *C* would have to turn, in opposition, to nature, to *A,* the south, or *D* to *B,* the north — which were abnormal and incongruous. Separate the halves of the stone and turn *D* toward *C:* they come together nicely and combine. For *D* tends to the south, as before, and *C* to the north; *E* and *F,* which in the mine [in minera] were connate parts, are now greatly at variance, for they do not come together on account of material affinity, but take movement and tendence from the form. Hence the ends, whether they be conjoined or separate, tend in the same way, in accordance with magnetic law, toward the earth's poles in the first figure of the stone, whether broken or divided in the second figure; and *FE* of the second figure, when the two parts come together and form one body, is as perfect a magnetic mass as was *CD* when first produced in the mine [in sua venâ genitum]; and *FE,* placed on a float, turn to the earth's poles, and conform thereto in the same way as the unbroken stone.

This agreement of the magnetic form is seen in the shapes of plants.

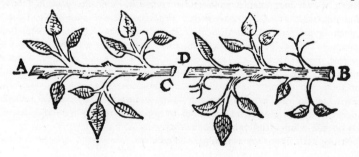

Let *AB* be a branch of ozier or other tree that sprouts readily; and let *A* be the upper part of the branch and *B* [*sic*] the part rootward. Divide the branch at *CD*. Now, the extremity *CD* [*sic*], if skilfully grafted again on *D*, begins to grow, just as *B* and *A*, when united, become consolidated and germinate. But if *D* be grafted in *A*, or *C* on *B*, they are at variance and grow not at all, but one of them dies because of the preposterous and unsuitable apposition, the vegetative force, which tends in a fixed direction, being now forced into a contrary one.

Gilbert's attribution of the results to the tendency of the vegetative force (*vis vegetiua*) in a fixed direction is a metaphysical interpretation; yet no more valid explanation of comparable phenomena on a physical basis has yet been proved. Granted that in some biological materials electrical forces may have their play, the modern postulate of molecular orientation[3] as the basis of polarity in the organism still remains to be verified. Our very word "polarity"[4] is borrowed from the concept of the poles of the earth to describe phenomena in the egg and the organism that we cannot yet otherwise define or explain.

Historical influence in science as in other fields is notoriously insusceptible to measurement, but the complete absence of reference to this experiment of Gilbert's by two such interesting and interested investigators of the historical aspects of the study of plant polarity as Vöchting[5] and Bloch[4] is suffi-

3 Harrison, R. G. "Relations of symmetry in the developing embryo." *Trans. Conn. Acad. Arts Sci.*, 1945, *36*, 277-330.

4 R. Bloch, in his excellent review, "Polarity in Plants" (*Botanical Rev.*, 1943, *9*, 261-310), claims that the extensive use of the word *polarity* in animal embryology and plant morphology ensued upon its introduction into the literature concerning animal regeneration by G. J. Allman (in: "Report of the present state of our knowledge of the reproductive system in the Hydroidea," *Brit. Ass. Adv. Sci.*, Rept. 33d meeting in . . . 1863 [London 1864], 351-426). It may be appropriate to remind the reader that it was Allman who also introduced the use of the terms *ectoderm* and *endoderm* into the literature as names for the external and internal layers of the coelenterates.

Whether or not the word for polarity was common between 1600 and 1863, the concept was a ruling idea in biological thinking, particularly through the mediation of the German "romantic" biologists, i.e., Goethe and Oken.

5 Vöchting, H. *Ueber Organbildung im Pflanzenreich. Physiologische Untersuchun-*

cient proof that performance of this experiment by Gilbert hardly altered the course of subsequent botanical experimentation. The question remains, however, as to how actively the execution of the experiment may have influenced Gilbert in his own thinking, and in the circumstances this is a question sufficiently impelling to warrant some further consideration.[6]

Before attempting to evaluate the significance of his experiment with reference to the development of Gilbert's thought, it may, however, first be appropriate to examine the possible influences which led him to perform it in the first place. Gilbert was by no means the first to have experimentally investigated functional polarity in plants. The planting of shoots in reverse orientation was known at least as early as the time of Theophrastus:[7]

> To return to the other trees: — in propagating them they set the cuttings upside down, as with vine-shoots. Some however say that that makes no difference, and least of all in propagating the vine; while others contend that the pomegranate thus propagated has a bushier growth and shades the fruit the better, and also that it is then less apt to shed the flower. This occurs also, they say, with the fig; when it is set upside down, it does not shed its fruit, and it makes a more accessible tree; and it does not shed its fruit, even if one breaks off the top as it begins to grow.

Pliny, while he did not specify the effect of planting cut-

---

gen über Wachstumsursachen und Lebenseinheiten. Erster Theil. Bonn, 1878. Also, *Ueber Transplantation am Pflanzenkörper. Untersuchungen zur Physiologie und Pathologie.* Tübingen, 1892. Bloch, *op. cit.*

[6] It was Gilbert's custom in *De magnete* to weight his experiments, designating them with "larger and smaller asterisks according to their importance and their subtility" (*op. cit.*, 1600, ij verso; 1893, xlix). Three experiments in Chapter VI of Book III are ornamented by the author's small asterisks: the division of the magnet, its refloating after the parts are reunited with the poles in their normal orientation, and the experiment on plant grafting.

[7] Theophrastus. *Enquiry into plants and minor works on odours and weather signs.* With an English translation by Sir Arthur Hort (Loeb Classical Library), London, 1916, I, 145 (*Enquiry into plants*, II, vi, 12). Referred to by Vöchting, 1878, *op. cit.*, 198. Vöchting also makes reference to Columella for a similar experiment, and to the warning of Palladius Rutilius, "Curandum, ne virgula inversa deponas."

tings in reversed orientation, warned that this was a procedure to be avoided:[8]

We must now speak of the planting of cuttings. In this care must be taken above all that the cuttings are made from trees that bear well, that they are not bent in shape nor scabbed or forked, that they are thick enough to fill the hand and not less than a foot long, that they are planted without injury to the bark and always with the cut end and the part that was nearest the root downward.

In an earlier chapter of the same book of the *Natural History*, however, he indicated that the reversal of orientation was not limited by the ancients only to ordinary planting, but that it was extended to actual grafting:[9] "But grafts are also inserted the other way round [inversi] when the intention is for them not to grow so long but to spread out."

Whether Gilbert knew the descriptions of these experiments by Pliny and Theophrastus must remain uncertain. If he was indeed aware of them, it might be considered curious that he did not mention that his own results seemed at variance with what had previously been reported. He made no specific citations of them, but his lack of frequent direct references to the ancients, in fact to any "authorities," is one of the most modern of the characteristics of Gilbert's monograph, in con-

---

[8] Pliny, *Natural history*. With an English translation . . . by H. Rackham (Loeb Classical Library), Cambridge (Massachusetts), 1950, V, 87 (*Natural history*, XVII, xxviii, 124).

Vöchting (1878, *op. cit.*, 199) writes with reference to the passage by Theophrastus: "Auch bei Plinius findet sich eine Aufgabe, deren Inhalt im Wesentlichen mit der eben angeführten Aussage von Theophrast übereinstimmt, und die dem letztern jedenfalls entnommen ist," and refers in his footnote to the source of this as *Natural history*, "XVII.11." I have been unable to locate such a statement by Pliny regarding reversed cuttings in Book XVII, chapter xi, or anywhere else in Book XVII, even in the particular edition of Pliny (Detlefsen, Berlin, 1866) cited by Vöchting. Possible explanation of Vöchting's error is to be found in footnote 14 below.

[9] Pliny, *op. cit.*, V, 75 (*Natural history*, XVII, xxiv, 106). Vöchting (1892, *op. cit.*, 58) refers to this correctly so far as book and chapter are concerned, but in the text of the same page he erroneously describes the experiment as one involving planting, not grafting: "Wie im historischen Abschnitt bemerkt, setzte man schon im Altertum Reiser in verkehrter Richtung zu dem Zweck ein, dass die Bäume mehr in die Breite als in die Höhe wüchsen."

trast to many books of the sixteenth century. But occasional references to writings both by Theophrastus and Pliny on the loadstone are found in *De Magnete,* and it is more than reasonable to assume that Gilbert, who was in turn Bachelor of Arts, Fellow, Master of Arts, Mathematical Examiner, Doctor of Medicine, and finally Senior Fellow of Saint John's College at Cambridge, was thoroughly well grounded in the classics.

It is, however, probably more to the point to emphasize that an experiment comparable to Pliny's inverse orientation of grafts was reported also by a contemporary of Gilbert's, Giovanni Battista della Porta of Naples, who in 1592 described his attempt as follows:[10]

> But the method of putting the graft [furculum] upside down according to Pliny in order that the tree should not grow upward, we have found false, to be sure we tried it with vine and with plum tree but they reached the same height as the rest.

Whether Gilbert knew this experiment, or even this particular publication of Porta's, there is no way to be certain. Though this passage, like those of Theophrastus and Pliny, was not cited, it is not impossible that Porta's failure to confirm the classical writers may have first attracted Gilbert to his new repetition of the experiment.

Porta wrote also, however, on the properties of the magnet, and this Gilbert knew very well; there are, in fact, more references to the work of Porta in *De Magnete* than there are to any other author. The work of the Neapolitan which Gilbert cited was the second edition of *Magiae Naturalis,*[11] a treatise

[10] Porta, G. B. della. *Libri XII* in quibus . . . plantarum cultus . . . et . . . ad frugum, vini ad fructuum multiplicationem experimenta . . . exhibentur. Frankfurt, 1592, 215 (L. IV, c. xxiv): "Sed modum inuersum furculum ferendi a Plinio appositum, ne arbor in altu excrescat, nos falsum reperimus, quippe in vite, & pruno experti, ad reliquarum altitudinem peruenerunt."

[11] Porta, G. B. della. *Magiae naturalis libri XX.* Naples, 1589; the first edition, in four books only, published in Naples in 1558, was written when the author was very young, only fifteen years old according to his own testimony which has, however, been questioned as to accuracy.

which touched on subjects ranging from distillation and "statick" and "pneumatick" experiments through magnetism, the generation of animals, horticulture and tempering steel to invisible writing, counterfeiting gold and beautifying women; it was of course particularly the discussions on the loadstone that Gilbert took up in *De Magnete*:[12]

Very recently Baptista Porta, a philosopher of no ordinary note, makes the 7th book of his *Magia Naturalis* [*sic*] a very storehouse and repertory of magnetic wonders; but he knows little about the movements of the loadstone, and has never seen much of them; much of what he has learned about its obvious properties, either from Messer Paolo, the Venetian, or through his own studies, is not very accurately noted and observed; the book is full of most erroneous experiments, as will appear in fitting place; still I hold him worthy of praise for that he essayed so great a task (even as he has essayed many another task, and successfully too, and with no inconsiderable results), and that he has given occasion for further researches.

The fact that Gilbert knew Porta's work on the loadstone

12 Gilbert, *op. cit.*, 1600, 6; 1893, 11. "Messer Paolo, the Venetian," incorrectly indexed by Mottelay as Marco Polo, who had been mentioned in a previous chapter, is in reality Fra Paolo Sarpi. Porta acknowledged his debt to Fra Paolo Sarpi in the Proem to his Book VII: "I knew at Venice R. M. Paulus, the Venetian, that was busied in the same study . . . from whom I not onely confess, that I gained something, but I glory in it, because of all the men I ever saw, I never knew any man more learned, or more ingenious, having obtained the whole body of learning; and is not onely the Splendor and Ornament of Venice or Italy, but of the whole world" (*Natural magick . . . in twenty books*. London, 1658, 190. This is an anonymous translation of the second edition).

Fra Paolo knew the work of Gilbert and both he and Porta corresponded with Gilbert and discussed him in correspondence with others. Fra Paolo considered Gilbert one of the two independent thinkers of his times: "Non hò veduto in questo secolo huomo, quale habbia scritto cosa sua propria, salvo Vieta in Francia & Gilberti i Inghilterra" (*Lettere Italiane di Fra Paolo Sarpi* . . . , Verona, 1673, 29-30). Gilbert is supposed to have visited Fra Paolo in Venice; the problem of the relationships between them has been considerably discussed, but has been highly disputed and is still controversial. For a well-documented treatment of the relationships between Porta, Gilbert, and Sarpi, which are not everywhere so critically evaluated, see the excellent discussion by Park Benjamin, *The intellectual rise in electricity, a history*, London, 1895, 224-344. Benjamin discusses only the problems of electricity and magnetism, not plant grafting; Sarpi is said, however, to have been an excellent botanist and it may be permissible at least to wonder about his possible connection with the plant grafting experiment.

hardly represents assurance that he knew Porta's experiment on the reversed orientation of plant grafts. This latter experiment is not discussed by Porta in the second edition of *Magiae Naturalis* which we know by the numbering of the books to be the one read by Gilbert; indeed, in setting down in this volume his rules for grafting, Porta, though echoing Pliny in many other respects, does not even repeat Pliny's warning for cuttings that they had best be set right side up:[13]

But now, as we did in our tract of the commixtion of divers kinds of living Creatures; so here also it is meet to prescribe certain rules, whereby we may cause those divers plants which we would intermingle, to join more easily, and to agree better together, for the producing of new and compounded fruits. First therefore, we must see that either of the Trees have their bark of one and the same nature: and both of them must have the same time of growing and shooting out of their sprigs; as was required of living creatures, that both of them should have the same time of breeding their young ones: for if the graffe have a hard or a dry bark, and the stock have a moist or soft bark, or that they be any way contrary to each other, we shall labour in vain. Then we must see that the ingraffing be made in the purest and soundest piece of the stock, so that it neither have any tumors or knobs, or any scars, neither yet hath been blasted. Again, it is very material, that the young graffes or shoots be fetcht from the most convenient place or part of the Trees; namely, from those boughs that grow toward the East, where the Sun is wont to rise in the Summer-time.[14] Again, they

13 Porta, 1658, *op. cit.,* 63.

14 The orientation of plants with reference to the cardinal points of the earth was an important concern for the ancients; see for instance Pliny, *Natural history, op. cit.,* V, 59 (XVII, xvi, 83-84): "The same authority [Cato] would not have omitted, if it were important, to recommend making a mark in the bark on the south side, so that when trees were transplanted they might be set in the same directions as regards the seasons as those to which they were accustomed, to prevent their north sides from being split if set facing the midday sun and their south sides from being nipped if facing the north wind. Some people also follow the contrary plan in the case of a vine or a fig, replanting them turned the other way round, from the view that this makes them grow thicker foliage and afford better shelter to their fruit and be less liable to lose it, and that a fig-tree so treated also becomes strong enough to be climbed." This, too, represents in a sense an experiment in plant polarity!

Can it be possible that this is the passage that Vöchting (see footnote 8 above) considered as adapted from Theophrastus and that he made the mistake of referring to it as XVII.11 instead of XVII.16? The editor of the Loeb edition of Theophrastus,

must be of a fruitful kind, and be taken off from young plants, such as never bare fruit before. They must also be taken in their prime, when they are beginning first to bud, and such as are of two years growth, and likely to bear fruit in their second year. And the stocks into which they are to be engraffed, must likewise be as young as may be graffed into; for if they be old, their hardnesse will scarce give any entertainment to strange shoots to be planted upon them. And many such observations must be diligently looked into, as we have shewed in our book of Husbandry.

But if the question must remain open as to whether Gilbert knew of Porta's 1592 publication in addition to the *Magiae Naturalis,* and hence as to whether he was cognizant of Porta's botanical experiment before he performed his own, there is a more interesting point that bears discussion, namely, what such knowledge might have contributed to him had his mind actually been exposed to it. This is a question that is answerable in a sense so far as the loadstone, if not the willow branch, is concerned. In the case of the loadstone, their analyses of their data can be contrasted, and from the difference between their interpretations a clue may be derived to elucidate the qualities of Gilbert's own intellectual power, and the clue is one which interestingly enough points back to the willow experiment as representative of something fundamentally central in his thinking.

Gilbert's great contribution was the inference from the behaviour of a spherical loadstone that the earth is a magnet. Porta, like Gilbert (and indeed like Peregrinus before them both), knew the spherical loadstone:[15]

---

in connection with a word from the passage from Theophrastus in question, gives a cross reference to this passage of Pliny, which might put him of the same mind as Vöchting. The wording of the second sentence of this Pliny passage, *out of its context,* might permit of this interpretation: "quod e diverso adfectant etiam quidam in vite ficoque, permutantes in contrariam; densiores enim folio ita fieri magisque protegere fructum et minus amittere, ficumque sic etiam scansilem fiere," but the context itself would certainly seem to suggest otherwise and to indicate that *in contrariam* refers to north and south rather than to rootward and skyward.

15 Porta, 1658, *op. cit.,* 207.

Let the Loadstone be turned round, by the wheel of the Jewellers, and polished. Then make a slender iron, as long as the axeltre of that round ball, and lay that upon the stone: for it will turn it self upon that line, that points just north and south. Mark the line upon the stone, with some delible paint: do the same on the other-side of the stone; and where it rests upon the ball, draw the same line: do the same the third and fourth time, upon the middle of it: and where those lines cross one the other and meet, those are the polar points. We may also find it out thus: Break a small needle, and put the smallest piece upon the same ball, and stir it; for when it comes to the just northern point, the needle will stand upright, that will make standers by admire, and will stand perpendicularly upon it: and till it do rise thus, be not weary of moving it up or down; for when you have found it, you will be glad of it.

Where lay the difference between Porta's exposition of the experiment and Gilbert's? Here may rest the explanation of their minds' likeness or unlikeness. Porta had no interpretation; he turned away at the end to a frivolity, "that will make standers by admire," and this was characteristic of his thinking. Gilbert drew from his little sphere the grand analogy; he considered the little sphere a little earth, the great earth like the small one a magnet; and by so doing, he established one of the fundamental truths on which all science has subsequently builded.

But the foundation for Gilbert's analogy lay deeper than a superficial resemblance in form or in action between a spherical earth and a spherical loadstone. Sphericity, like opposition, in itself could present no challenge to one so steeped as was Gilbert in Aristotelian physics and metaphysics. His analogy between earth and loadstone was intimately related in his own mind to what he considered to be an identity of the earth with a living organism, and here is the significance of the experiment with the willow. As he fitted the small and the large earth into a single scheme, he fitted them both into the same pattern with the willow, and on the same experimental basis.

Analogy is a knife that cuts two ways, and Gilbert trimmed both edges sharp. He argued his analogy not only from load-stone to plant, but also in the reverse direction from organism to earth:[16]

Therefore Aristotle is partly in the right when he says that the ex-halation which condenses in the earth's veins is the prime matter of metals: for exhalations are condensed in situations less warm than the place of their origin, and owing to the structure of lands and moun-tains, they are in due time condensed, as it were, in wombs, and changed into metals. But they do not of themselves alone constitute the veins of ore; only they flow into and coalesce with solider matter and form metals. When, therefore, this concreted matter has settled in more temperate cavities, in these moderately warm places it takes shape, just as in the warm uterus the seed or the embryo grows. . . . But that there is gold, or silver, or copper, or that any other metals exist, does not happen from any *quantitas* or proportion of matter nor by any specific virtues of matter, as the chemists fondly imagine; but it happens when, earth cavities and the conformation of the ground concurring with the fit matter, those metals take from universal nature the forms by which they are perfected, just as in the case of all other minerals, all plants and all animals.

It is not without significance that his own designation for his new philosophy, *physiologia,* has remained our term for the study of living function. The word was first used in our modern sense, according to Sherrington, by Jean Fernel in 1542; he used it again twelve years later as a title for the seven books constituting Part I of his *Medicina.* Jacob Sylvius used it in Paris in 1555; "A. M." used it in 1597 in an English translation of Guillemeau's *Surgery.*[17] Again a question arises which, again, remains incompletely answered, this time as to whether Gilbert knew the work of Fernel. There is a single reference to him in *De Magnete,* "Fernel, in his book *De Abditis Rerum Causis,* says that in the loadstone is a hidden

16 Gilbert, *op. cit.,* 1600, 20; 1893, 35–36.
17 Sir Charles Sherrington, *The endeavour of Jean Fernel, with a list of the edi-tions of his writings.* Cambridge (England), 1946.

and abstruse cause."[18] If Gilbert knew by 1600 this rather mystical volume, first published in 1544, it would seem most probable that as a physician he knew either the 1542 *De Naturali Parte Medicinae* in which the word first appeared in its present usage, or the re-issue of this volume in 1554, entitled *Physiologia,* forming part of the more inclusive *Medicina.* By 1600 the latter had appeared in over a dozen editions, some of which contained both the *Physiologia* and the *De Abditis Rerum Causis* between the same covers. Fernel was not so obscure a figure in his own age as he seems in ours; Gilbert was a cosmopolitan rather than a provincial figure in a cosmopolitan intellectual world. Gilbert's expansion of Fernel's term from its narrower to a wider cosmic sense offers further evidence of his preoccupation with the community of living and non-living matter in a unified universe.

But if Gilbert's obligations to Fernel, as those to Theophrastus and Pliny and Porta, can only be surmised, the greatest of his debts to the past he betrays by the whole fibre of his thought, namely, that to Aristotle, who in all actuality dominated the science of what is so often misrepresented as an anti-Aristotelian age. Gilbert's talk of opposition and contraries, of agreement, above all of *form* (the ends of the magnet "take movement and tendence from the form," remember he said, and "the metals take from universal nature the forms by which they are perfected") — that is what is old, not new, in *De Magnete,* and it grew, like so much of the Renaissance, out of Aristotle. Without Aristotle for background, Gilbert's thought would be unintelligible; in the light of Greek thought, the Elizabethan reflects lucidity — this was the glow of the times.

Harvey focuses it, too — he who left the vital spirits in the blood, unawakened to the meaning of his own discovery that the heart can be conceived of as a machine. Harvey, as a matter of fact, is in many ways a counterpart of Gilbert as an

18 Gilbert, *op. cit.,* 1600, 4; 1893, 8.

innovator in the new philosophy; out of the Aristotelian in his thought he, too, developed the method of induction and experiment. Harvey does not stand alone as herald of the new biology, nor Gilbert as the prophet of the new physics — together as intellectual companions they create the new world. It is no mere coincidence that Harvey and Gilbert both began as medical practitioners; the very conservatism of medical lore may have been what preserved for them a knowledge of Aristotle in humours, in coctions, in opposites. It kept it for them, furthermore, not only in dry, scholastic doctrine but in an armamentarium of living, working knowledge that they carried to the side of every patient. And in transmitting to them what was traditional in the physician's knowledge, it brought to them also, in spite of itself, Aristotle's idea of form dynamic as part of matter — an idea which made his biological concepts as alive and dynamic as the Renaissance was to prove them to be. Harvey abstracted from this heritage the concept of dynamism, Gilbert that of form; it was the analogy between the underlying "forms" of the mineral and vegetable kingdoms that Gilbert believed he demonstrated in his experiments with plant grafting.

Nature, animate and inanimate, for Gilbert the physician was one, and it was only out of the depth of this conviction that he could work his comparison between the earth and the magnet. "The magnetic force is animate, or imitates a soul," he wrote for the title to Chapter XII, Book V; "in many respects it surpasses the human soul while that is united to an organic body,"[19] and the chapter begins:[20] "Wonderful is the loadstone shown in many experiments to be, and, as it were, animate. And this one eminent property is the same which the ancients held to be a soul in the heavens, in the globes, and in the stars, in sun and moon."

The whole chapter continues as an elaboration on this

[19] Gilbert, *op. cit.*, 1600, 208; 1893, 308.
[20] *Loc. cit.*

theme, and it concludes:[21] "Wherefore, not without reason, Thales, as Aristotle reports in his book *De Anima*, declares the loadstone to be animate, a part of the ultimate mother earth and her beloved offspring."

If an interesting and important experiment that has apparently been forgotten by posterity has borne no direct impact on the later performance of comparable experiments, it may yet have exerted an indirect effect on the minds of all who have worked in science since 1600. It was the only experiment on living material that Gilbert either reported or performed to fortify his analogy between the living and the non-living. His great contribution to science was to bring the old relationships between microcosm and macrocosm open to the new experimental method which he initiated, and by his single experiment on the willow he accomplished just this. He may have argued or speculated about metals and embryos, but he experimented with the graft in inverse orientation. "Let whosoever would make the same experiments," he wrote of his whole programme in the Author's Preface to *De Magnete,* "handle the bodies carefully, skilfully and deftly, not heedlessly and bunglingly; when an experiment fails, let him not in ignorance condemn our discoveries, for there is naught in these Books that has not been investigated and again and again done and repeated under our eyes."[22]

Whether or not his analogy between the animate and the inanimate was valid is for the moment irrelevant. It was fruitful, in that it lay at the heart of his interest, and was thus bound up with the development of an investigation whose outcome has led not only to the dominant material characteristics of our present civilization, but also to the foundation of all of our subsequent scientific conceptions. For whether we concede to the universe, to the earth, to the magnet, or the organism a soul, we cannot escape the necessity of in-

21 Gilbert, *op. cit.,* 1600, 210; 1893, 312.
22 Gilbert, *op. cit.,* 1600, ij verso; 1893, xlix.

voking, as involved in all the known phenomena of animate or inanimate nature, electrical forces of one sort or another, and it was Gilbert who introduced these as inevitable material for experiment.

Postscript:
Additional References

Readers of these essays may wish to know of a number of books and articles not yet in print when the essays were first published.

Howard Adelmann's *Marcello Malpighi and the Evolution of Embryology* (5 vols., 2475 pp., Cornell University Press, Ithaca, N.Y., 1966) presents the fullest treatment available of the history of embryology, from antiquity through to the nineteenth century. Jacques Roger's *Les Sciences de la Vie dans la Pensée française du XVIIIe Siècle. La Génération des Animaux de Descartes à l'Encyclopédie* (842 pp., Armand Colin, Paris, 1963) is also a remarkably thorough and enlightening book. My reference lists refer only to the first edition of Joseph Needham's *History of Embryology;* a second edition, revised with the assistance of Arthur Hughes, was published by Abelard-Schuman, New York, in 1959.

Supplementary to my essay on the non-specificity of the germ-layers is the following: G. R. de Beer, "The differentiation of neural crest cells into visceral cartilages and odontoblasts in Amblystoma, and a re-examination of the germ-layer theory," *Proc. Roy. Soc. London,* Series B, **134** (1946): 377–398.

Georg Uschmann's *Geschichte der Zoologie und der zoologischen Anstalten in Jena 1779–1919* (Gustav Fischer, Jena, 1959) provides a wealth of fascinating information about Haeckel. Uschmann and Ilse Jahn have published an exchange of 39 letters between Haeckel and T. H. Huxley: "Die Briefwechsel zwischen Thomas Henry Huxley und Ernst Haeckel. Ein Beitrag zum Darwin-Jahr," *Wiss. Zeitschr. Friedrich-Schiller-Univ. Jena, Math.–naturwiss. Reihe, Jahrg.* **9** (1959–1960): 7–33.

Uschmann has also written a short biography of *Caspar Friedrich Wolff. Ein Pionier der modernen Embryologie* (Urania-Verlag, Leipzig/

POSTSCRIPT

Jena, 1955). A facsimile edition of Wolff's *Theorie von der Generation in zwei Abhandlungen erklärt und bewiesen* and *Theoria Generationis,* edited by Robert Herrlinger, has recently been published (Georg Olms, Hildesheim, 1966). Herrlinger's essay "C. F. Wolff's 'Theoria generationis' (1759). Die Geschichte einer epochemachenden Dissertation," *Zeitschr. Anat. u. Entw.-gesch.,* 121 (1959): 245–270, and B. E. Rajkov's "Caspar Friedrich Wolff," *Zool. Jb. Syst.,* 91 (1964): 555–626 are interesting and important. Rajkov includes a bibliography of Wolff's published and unpublished works.

I commented in my essay on John and William Hunter that no bibliography of William Hunter's publications had been published. One has subsequently appeared: W. R. Le Fanu's "The writings of William Hunter F.R.S.," *The Biblioteck,* 1 (1958): 3–14.

William Gilbert's *De Magnete,* as translated by P. Fleury Mottelay, is now available in paperback (Dover, New York, 1958). Allen J. Debus, in "Robert Fludd and the use of Gilbert's *De Magnete* in the weapon-salve controversy," *J. Hist. Med. & Allied Sci.,* 14 (1964): 389–417, has discussed Gilbert's influence on seventeenth century medicine.

Index

Lightface numerals indicate pages where the work of particular individuals is mentioned more or less in passing. Boldface numerals designate whole essays, or substantial portions of essays, dealing with the work of a particular person. Italics designate pages where references are to be found, either in footnotes or in reference lists according to the customs of the books or journals where the essays were first published. Text citations of my own work are indexed only in the case of experimental or historical articles not reproduced in this collection.

INDEX

Wilson, James Walter, 30, 31, *61*

Wolff, Christian, 135

Wolff, Caspar Friedrich, 3, 4, 9, 63, 65, 69, 132–136, 141, 165, 166, *172*, 174, 177, 215, 257–258, *293–294*, 296, 366–367, *367*

Wright, Sewall, 37, *61*

Yamada, Tuneo, 24, 26, *61*

Ziegler, H. E., 23

Ziller, Tuisken, 153

374